GEOMORPHOLOGICAL MODELS

Frank Ahnert (Editor)

GEOMORPHOLOGICAL MODELS

Theoretical and Empirical Aspects

CATENA SUPPLEMENT 10

CATENA – A Cooperating Journal of the International Society of Soil Science

ISSS-AISS-IBG

Cover photo by Frank Ahnert:

The system of weathering, slope denudation and streamwork near Nigel Pass, Western Canada (view reversed).

CIP-Titelaufnahme der Deutschen Bibliothek

Geomorphological models: theoret. and empir. aspects/Frank Ahnert (ed.). – Cremlingen-Destedt: Catena, 1987
(Catena: Supplement; 10) ISBN 3-923381-10-7, NE: Ahnert, Frank [Hrsg.]; Catena/Supplement

ISSN 0722–0723 / ISBN 3–923381–10–7

CONTENTS

PREFACE

In April of 1986 an International Workshop on Theoretical Geomorphological Models was held in Aachen, Germany. Its thirty-five participants came from eleven countries. The purpose of this meeting was to encourage discussion between empirical and theoretical geomorphologists. Neither group can advance its research effectively without the other. Empirical geomorphology provides the observational evidence from which theoretical considerations may be developed; in addition, it serves to confirm or reject the validity of theoretical concepts. Theoretical geomorphology, on the other hand, combines the available empirical knowledge with the application of general physical principles to arrive, by a process of generalization and abstraction, at the formulation of theories which in turn can suggest goals for further empirical research. Thus there is a need to communicate on both sides; accordingly, participants of the Aachen workshop came from both groups.

All but one of the eighteen papers in this volume were presented and discussed at the workshop; the one exception is the paper by TROFIMOV who had been unable to attend. Some of the manuscripts have been substantially modified after the workshop as a result of the discussion there. The papers are arranged under four major themes.

Six papers deal with slope processes and slope form. A model study by KIRKBY analyses the relative importance of wash processes and landslides for the growth of slope hollows. TORRI discusses soil detachability in theoretical terms, while AI & MIAO present a model of landslides resulting from neotectonic stresses. AHNERT tests the applicability of a single model program to the simulation of process response systems at different scales; in an investigation of landforms on the Colorado Plateau, SCHMIDT points out structural and lithological factors that require special attention in model designs. DE PLOEY & POESEN raise some critical questions about the validity of model assumptions in slope development research.

Channel processes and channel form are the topic of the following four papers. SCHICK, HASSAN & LEKACH lead off this group with a probabilistic model approach to the burial and exposure of pebbles in the channel fill during downstream transport; ERGENZINGER shows the underlying order in the development of seemingly disorderly braided channel patterns. BAND investigates the lateral migration and change of the junction angle during the development of tributary streams, and WIECZOREK presents a general function for the geometry of meander bends.

The next group of papers, dealing with questions related to water and sediment yields, is led off by YAIR & ENZEL with a comparison of these variables in the arid and the semi-arid parts of the Negev. ICHIM & RADOANE have made a multivariate investigation of ninety-nine small catchments in Romania, and RAWAT discusses the present state of modelling knowledge related to water and sediment. More abstract is MILLERs methodological assessment of the theoretically important 'latent' variables that underlie the indicator variables which we observe in water and sediment studies.

As the concluding section there are four papers on general theoretical considerations. Based on the mass continuity equation, HARDISTY describes the local rate of surface lowering as a transport response function which may serve to characterise the stability of the system involved. HAIGH urges that all investigation of natural systems should include recognition of their hierarchical structure, and TROFIMOV offers an appraisal of geomorphological prediction. In the last paper, SCHEIDEGGER seeks to condense the factors and interactions that affect the evolution of landforms into a set of five 'fundamental principles'.

The papers span a wide range of topics. Their contents may also reflect, to some extent, the various stages of methodological advancement and the various directions of geomorphological research that exist in different parts of the world today. However, common to all papers is the aim to contribute to the strengthening of the ties between theoretical and empirical geomorphology. This found expression also in the long, intensive and lively discussion which followed the presentation of virtually every paper at the meeting in Aachen.

The International Workshop on Theoretical Geomorphological Models took place within the framework of the IGU Commission on Measurement, Theory and Application in Geomorphology. It was made possible by financial assistance from the Deutsche Forschungsgemeinschaft, the Land Nordrhein-Westfalen, the Environmental Branch of the US Army Research Office (London), the International Geographical Union and the RWTH (University of Technology) Aachen. The participants are grateful for this support.

In addition, the editor thanks especially R.B. BRYAN, N.J. COX, J. DE PLOEY, W.E. DIETRICH, T. DUNNE, P. ERGENZINGER, M.J. KIRKBY, E. PAULISSEN, K.-H. SCHMIDT and J. THORNES for their valuable contribution as reviewers of the manuscripts that were submitted for this volume.

Department of Geography,
RWTH Aachen, July 1987

Frank Ahnert

CATENA SUPPLEMENT 10   p.1–14   Braunschweig 1987

MODELLING SOME INFLUENCES OF SOIL EROSION, LANDSLIDES AND VALLEY GRADIENT ON DRAINAGE DENSITY AND HOLLOW DEVELOPMENT

M.J. **Kirkby**, Leeds

SUMMARY

Landscape evolution has been simulated by a two dimensional model over a rhomboidal 32×32 grid. The overland flow contribution at any point is calculated in terms of the locally derived saturation deficit, which is summed along drainage paths to give total overland flow discharges. Sediment removal is modelled as being transport-limited; with a creep/splash term proportional to gradient added to a wash term which is proportional to overland flow power (i.e. flow × gradient) squared. The simulation results and the sediment equations have been analyzed in terms of the stability criterion for hollow growth. For the sediment transport law used, semi-arid climates with insignificant subsurface flow show increasing drainage density with increasing valley gradients; whereas humid climates with substantial sub-surface flow show weak decreases in drainage density with gradient. A comparison is made with the stability criteria for hollow enlargement by landslides, for which drainage density always increases with valley gradient.

ISSN 0722-0723
ISBN 3-923381-10-7
©1987 by CATENA VERLAG,
D–3302 Cremlingen-Destedt, W. Germany
3-923381-10-7/87/5011851/US$ 2.00 + 0.25

1 INTRODUCTION

This paper pursues the consequences of analysing whether hollows are unstable in the context of gully formation by either wash processes or landslides. Each of these groups of processes is assumed to act in combination with creep or splash processes which are dominant near divides. Instability is examined in the sense of the SMITH & BRETHERTON (1972) criterion that a proto-hollow, considered as a small perturbation in the surface, will grow with an initially positive feed-back, into a macroscopic feature which would be identified on the ground as a valley head. The criterion for unstable hollow growth in this sense is that where flows of water and sediment converge, the combined water flow drives a sediment transport greater than the sum of the sediment inflows, so that there is excess transporting capacity which is able to enlarge the hollow. In other words, instability occurs if sediment transport in the neighbourhood of the proto–hollow increases more than linearly with catchment area. This qualitative argument may be formalized to give the mathematical condition that small pertubations will grow unstably if and only if:

$$a\partial S/\partial a > S \tag{1}$$

where
S = the sediment transport across unit contour length, and
a = the 'unit area', or the area draining to unit contour length (a generalisation of distance from the divide to allow for contour plan curvature).

The differentiation should be performed keeping gradient constant. This criterion was derived by SMITH & BRETHERTON (1972). They also showed that the same criterion is a necessary and sufficient condition for slope forms to be concave up in profile under conditions of equilibrium with a constant rate of uplift.

The stability criterion is applied below to two cases: first to potential hollow enlargement by soil erosion due to overland flow; and second to hollow enlargement by landslides along the valley axis. In each case, hollows tend to be infilled by the splash or creep processes. Possible conditions for hollow enlargement are obtained by analysis of simplified process rate equations. In the case of wash, the analytical forecasts are compared with a two dimensional simulation model which illustrates both the course of slope evolution and the strength of the tendency to hollow enlargement.

2 TWO DIMENSIONAL SIMULATION MODEL

The slope evolution model used here is a development of the one described in KIRKBY (1986). Flow, sediment transport and erosion are simulated over a grid of equilateral triangles, with boundaries as shown in fig.2, forming a rhombus of 32×32 cells. The upper edge of the grid is treated as a divide, and the lower edge as a base level. The two sides are considered to roll onto one another in order to minimise edge effects. Flow of water and sediment from each point in the grid is assigned to the lowest of the six neighbouring cells, forcing the flow into a series of dendritic networks. Sediment removal is assumed to be transport limited, and erosion or deposition are derived from a mass continuity equation applied to each grid cell. Significant differences from the previous model formulation lie in the procedure for estimating overland flow, and in the sediment transport law used.

Overland flow is now formulated, to take account of sub-surface saturation and thus of partial contributing areas, whereas previously overland flow was assumed to be generated uniformly over the area by Hortonian overland flow. It is recognised that other possibilities, notably macropore bypassing and/or pipeflow are not covered by this analysis. The formulation is similar to that used in KIRKBY (1976, 1980). Saturation deficits at the start of a storm are estimated as in equilibrium with an average net rainfall i, on the assumption of an exponential soil store (BEVEN & KIRKBY 1979). For unit area a, the discharge per unit contour width q may be written for the steady state assumption:

$$q = ia,$$

and as the outflow from the exponential store:

$$q = q_o g \exp(-D/M),$$

where
M = a soil parameter having the dimensions of length.

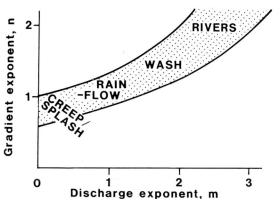

Fig. 1: *The trend of empirial expressions for sediment transport by creep, splash and wash; of the form Sediment Transport proportional to (Discharge)^m × (Gradient)^n.*

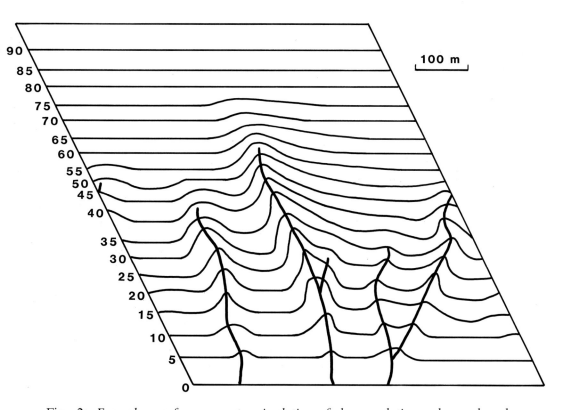

Fig. 2: *Example run from computer simulation of slope evolution under wash and splash/creep.*

Parameter values are: $\beta = M/r_0 = 2$: Creep rate $k = 10^{-3}m^2y^{-1}$: Wash rate $\alpha = 10^{-5}m^2y^{-1}$: 2.35 m erosion after 1000 iterations, representing 0.73 My elapsed from initial pertubed uniform gradient.

Equating these expressions, the soil moisture deficit D is given by:

$$D = M \ln[q_o g/(ia)] = M \ln(q_o/i) - M \ln(\theta),$$

where
$\theta = a/g$

In particular, saturation (zero deficit) occurs at $\theta_c = \ln(q_o/i)$, a position which depends on both soil and rainfall variables. Substituting to eliminate q_o:

$$D = M \ln(\theta_c/\theta) \qquad (2)$$

when this expression is positive, and zero otherwise. The parameter M may be interpreted as showing the rate of decrease of saturated hydraulic conductivity with depth in the soil. At a depth corresponding to deficit D, the hydraulic conductivity

$$K_{SAT} = \frac{\epsilon q_o}{M} \exp(-D/M)$$

where
ϵ = the water-filled porosity at the relevant depth.

Overland flow production is estimated on the basis of daily rainfall totals. The production per unit area on a day with rainfall r is estimated as:

$$\Delta Q = p(r - D) \qquad (3)$$

when this expression is positive, and zero otherwise; where p is a fixed proportion related to soil properties. This expression assumes that all overland flow is generated by saturation excess or return flow mechanisms. Sediment transport by wash is estimated from annual totals of overland flow. These totals are obtained by summing local production rates over an assumed exponential distribution of daily rainfall amounts. Combining equations (1) and (2) above and summing over the distribution:

$$\Delta Q = pR\exp(-D/r_0) = p(\theta/\theta_c)^{M/r_0} \qquad (4)$$

where
R = the mean annual rainfall,
r_0 = the mean rainfall per rain day

and other symbols are as previously defined. This local mean annual production rate is then summed downslope along all flow lines. The case previously modelled was equivalent to an 'arid' situation with $M/r_0 \to 0$, associated with a constant rate of overland flow production and no significant antecedent moisture (KIRKBY 1986).

Fig.1 shows a generalization of empirical relationships in the literature, in which rates of sediment transport have been expressed as proportional to distance, area or discharge to the power of m, multiplied by gradient to the power of n. This includes the classic research into soil erosion rates by MUSGRAVE (1947) and others. The previous two dimensional model used exponents $m = 0, n = 1$ for creep and splash; and $m = 2, n = 1$ for wash. In the present version of the model, the gradient exponent for wash has been raised to $n = 2$, which is more in keeping with previous empirical values, and this exponent has been used to estimate wash sediment transport.

Fig.2 illustrates a realization of the revised model for conditions with appreciable sub-surface flow, starting from a fractally perturbed uniform initial slope. It can be seen that a well developed valley system has become established in the lower part of the area, while initial irregularities near the divide have been eliminated, leaving a smooth general convexity. The stable and unstable zones are thus clearly present. Fig.3 shows long profiles down the initial surface, and down the main divide and valley of the final form shown in fig.2. Although

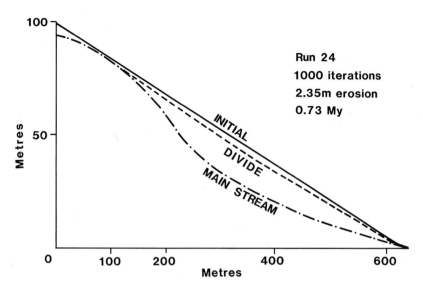

Fig. 3: *Long profiles for the simulation run shown in fig.2. Profiles shown for initial gradient, and final gradients along main divide and main valley axis.*

the condition of constant downcutting is not met, the zones of profile convexity and concavity can be seen to be approximately associated with the zones of stability and instability respectively.

The streams marked in fig.2 are not explicit in the model, since sediment transport rates are everywhere defined only in terms of overland flow discharge and gradient. Streams have instead been defined in a way which reflects the stability criterion as closely as possible. At each cross-profile of the modelled slope, measured parallel to the upper and lower boundaries of the grid, the initial relief due to the perturbations has been compared with the relief after an average lowering of approximately one metre. Fig.4 shows the ratios of final to initial relief at successive cross-profiles around the possible stream head positions. Points have been joined to show the downslope sequence. On the basis of the stability criterion, instability should

be associated with a ratio greater than unity; and stability with lesser ratios. It may be seen that there is a zone where the criterion is in doubt, and the critical point has been taken from the heavy curve drawn through the lower values of the ratio at each unit area. Along each valley axis, this criterion has been used to define the stream head position in terms of demonstrable hollow growth, and the streams in fig.2 are drawn from this analysis. This method provides a refinement of the basic notion of a contour crenulation to distinguish those which are actively being enlarged.

Fig.5 shows the relationship obtained from a series of model runs, in the form of a relationship between critical unit catchment area, defined as just described, and the catchment gradient. Runs have been grouped by the exponent M/r_0 which appears in equation (3) above, which is an indicator of the importance of sub-surface flow rising from near-zero

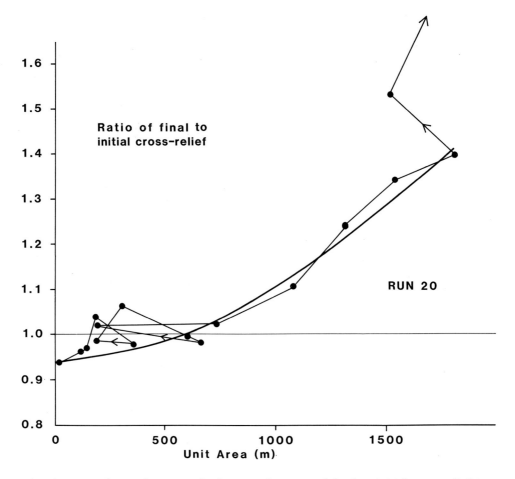

Fig. 4: *Example simulation result showing the ratio of final to initial cross-relief in terms of unit area at successive points downslope, joined by solid line. Heavy line shows best fit curve fitted to lower ratios, to establish effective detection threshold for hollow enlargement.*

for the arid case to a value of 2–3 for a humid climate like that of Britain. The slopes of the lines drawn through these points are not obtained as a best fit, but are derived from analysis of the stability criterion, which is described in the next section. It may be seen that critical unit area decreases as catchments steepen for the arid case, but where sub-surface flow is more important, the direction of this relationship is reversed.

3   ANALYSIS OF STABILITY FOR WASH PROCESS

The criterion of Equation (1) may be applied to erosion under the influence of a particular process law to define the theoretical bounds of unstable hollow growth, for an assumed topography. To examine the initiation of channels under circumstances comparable to the model runs, the topography has been assumed

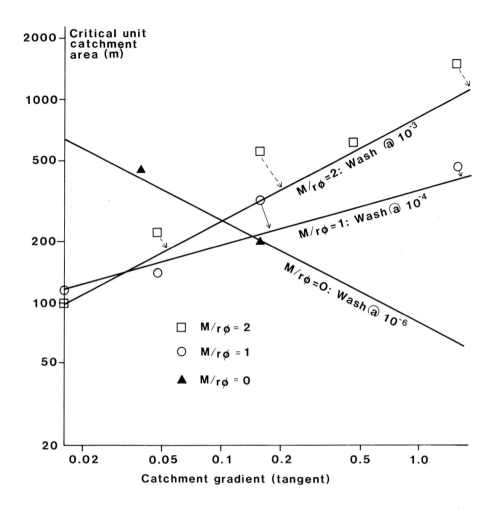

Fig. 5: *Critical unit area for hollow enlargement plotted against catchment gradient.*

Points are from computer simulations. Lines are calculated as 2.5 × critical areas obtained from equation (7) with gradient exponent $n = 2$.

to be a uniformly sloping plane, of gradient g. For this surface $\theta = a/g$, and equation (4) may be integrated downslope to give the overland flow:

$$Q = pa(\theta/\theta_c)^{M/r_o}/(M/r_0 + 1) \qquad (5)$$

This expression may be substituted into the sediment transport law, which is here taken in the slightly more general form:

$$S = kg + \alpha Q^2 g^n \qquad (6)$$

where

k, α = rate constants for creep/splash and wash and

n = the gradient exponent which, in model runs, has had the value of 2.0.

Differentiating equation (6) with respect to a, keeping gradient constant, applying the stability criterion (equation (1)), the critical area for instability is:

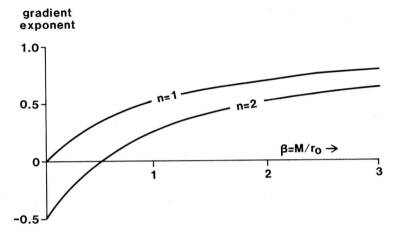

Fig. 6: *Gradient exponent from equation (7) for critical wash unit area as a power of catchment gradient; expressed in terms of wash gradient exponent n (in equation 6) and importance of sub-surface flow (β = M /r0).*

$$a_c =$$

$$\frac{k(1 + \beta)^2}{\alpha(2\beta + 1)} \theta_c^{2\beta}(pR)^{-2^{1/[2(1+\beta)]}}$$

$$g^{[(2\beta+1-n)/2(\beta+1)]} \quad (7)$$

where
$\beta = M/r_0$ and other terms are as previously defined.

The relationship between critical unit area and gradient is contained in the final term of this expression, and the gradient exponent is shown in fig.6 as $\beta = M/r_0$ and the exponent n are varied. Where the gradient exponents for creep and wash are the same (i.e. $n = 1$), the exponent is never negative, although in the arid case ($\beta = 0$) the exponent falls to zero and critical ara is completely independent of gradient (as in th former version of the two dimensional model). For the $n = 2$ case now being modelled, the reversal of gradient dependence shown in fig.5 is clearly predicted. This change in direction may be best understood by considering the two components of gradient dependence involved. In the absence of sub-surface flow ($\beta = 0$), higher gradients produce greater dominance by wash erosion over creep/splash for a given unit area. A smaller area is therefore required to sustain hollow growth from a steeper catchment. Where however, sub-surface flow is significant, soil water levels are closer to saturation on gentle than on steep slopes, so that overland flow is increased: this effect is able to outweigh the direct influence of gradient, and so produce the reversal in trend.

The gradient exponents prdicted by equation (7) have been used to draw the lines in fig.5, but the absolute values for critical area are consistently underestimated by the equation. The reason probably lies in the strength of hollow enlargement near the theoretical threshold. At the threshold, the rate of hollow enlargement is zero, and rates of enlargement are directly related to differences from the threshold value. Thus observable enlargement can only occur some distance downslope from the threshold.

To give best agreement with model runs, the lines shown in fig.5 are drawn for critical areas of $2.5 \times$ the predicted threshold value from equation (7).

4 THE STABILITY CRITERION FOR LANDSLIDE HOLLOWS

There is considerable evidence that many valley head hollows are extended and perhaps formed by landslides during heavy rainstorms and/or in association with earthquakes (e.g. SIMONETT 1967, DIETRICH & DUNNE 1978, CROZIER et al. 1980). There is evidence, for sites in California and Oregon, of an inverse relationship between the area needed to support a stream head and valley gradient (DIETRICH et al. 1986). This relationship has been supported by an analysis of the dependence of critical slope angle on regolith thickness, which is partly derived from IIDA & OKUNISHI (1983). Here the landslide process is instead analysed in the context of the SMITH & BRETHERTON criterion for unstable hollow growth, which refers to 'stability' in a different sense to that used in geotechnical stability analyses.

Removal by landslides in combination with creep or splash is modelled here in terms of the continuity equation:

$$-\partial z/\partial t = \partial S/\partial x \qquad (8)$$

where the rate of lowering is the sum of that from creep/splash and that from slides.

As above in equation (6), creep and/or splash removal is assumed to be transport limited, at a rate defined by the simplest diffusive process law:

$$S = kg \qquad (9)$$

For landslides, removal is assumed to be erosion limited, that is to say that lowering is assumed to occur at a rate proportional to the surplus transporting capacity, or the excess of capacity over actual transport rate. This concept has been explored in KIRKBY (1984, 1985). In general it may be expressed in the form:

$$-\partial z_L/\partial t = L - S/h \qquad (10)$$

where

$-\partial z_L/\partial t$ = the rate of lowering by landslides,

L = the rate of potential lowering, unconstrained by deposition from above, and

h = the mean travel distance for landslide material.

In KIRKBY (1984), the process laws for slides were taken as:

$$L = \gamma g(g - g_o) \qquad (11)$$

$$h = h_o/(g_* - g) \qquad (12)$$

where

γ, h_o = rate constants,

g_o = the ultimate lower threshold for sliding and

g_* = the lowest gradient on which slide material will come to rest; i.e. the talus gradient.

The analysis presented by IIDA & OKUNISHI (1983), or by DIETRICH et al. (1986) shows that landsliding should have a distance dependence, and that this should probably influence the threshold gradient g_o, causing it to decrease downslope in response to wetter soils. Such a dependence has not been found to lead to hollow formation however, and equation (11) has here been replaced by a form with a power law increase with distance downslope:

$$L = \lambda g(g - g_o)x^\gamma \qquad (11a)$$

for an exponent γ greater than zero.

This process law for landslides is intended to represent long term slide rates and not rates of movement during a slide event. It is used here to forecast slope profiles in equilibrium with a constant rate T of downcutting, to obtain the region of convexity. As has been seen above, this coincides with the region of hollow stability, even when the assumption of constant downcutting is not met. Equations (8) to (11a) above have been applied to the component of slide lowering, by subtracting the creep/splash component. For constant downcutting:

$$\partial S_L/\partial x = -\partial z_L/\partial t = T - kdg/dx \quad (13)$$

where the suffix L refers to landsliding.

Integrating, under the assumption of constant downcutting:

$$S_L = Tx - kg \quad (14)$$

Substituting into equation (10), and inserting the process laws (11a) and (12):

$$-\partial z_L/\partial t =$$
$$T - kdg/dx = L - S/h$$
$$\lambda g(g - g_o)x^\gamma$$
$$-(Tx - kg)(g_* - g)/h_o \quad (15)$$

The landslide slopes illustrated below solve this equation for the profile in equilibrium with constant downcutting, using an explicit numerical method.

Solutions to equation (15) generally show longer convex sections as gradient declines in resp onse to reduced rates of lowering. Fig.7 illustrates the form of the profiles produced for $\gamma = 0.5$. It may be seen that all show a clear convexity and a gentle concavity. For any given value of γ, there is a well defined negative power law relationship between

critical slope length to support a hollow, and mean gradient from divide to stream head (i.e. to the point of inflexion for this constant downcutting profile). The exponent in this relationship falls as γ is increased, as is shown in fig.8. A close match to the empirical exponents (0.7) found by DIETRICH et al. (1986) is obtained for $\gamma = 0.5$. It should be noted that hollow shape is implicit in this formulation, and increasing degrees of flow convergence can only be represented by higher γ values.

5   DISCUSSION

The analysis of hollow formation by landsliding is thus able to give a better forecast of some observed rates of change of stream-head length or area with catchment gradient than the analysis of formation by wash processes. There are however two main difficulties with this interpretation of hollow formation. The more severe is that stream heads, although excavated in some cases by landslides, are nevertheless the sites of streams. In the analysis of hollow formation by slides, there is no requirement that stream processes will be powerful enough to remove the material initially excavated by a slide. In principle at least, hollows might be formed by slides and never occupied by a functioning stream channel, a possibility which seems to be at variance with observation. For all but the most arid sites, the relationships between critical length or unit area and hollow gradient are as shown schematically in fig.9, with a positive relationship for wash enlargement, and a negative relationship for slide enlargement. In the presence of both processes, hollows might be presumed to form in response to whichever process has the

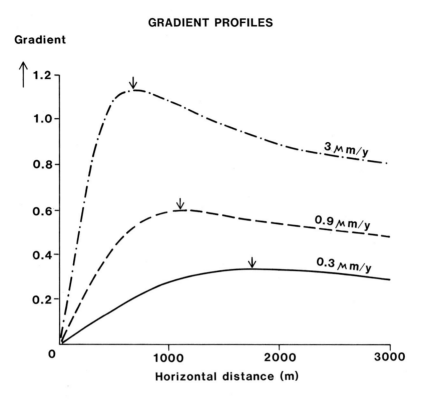

GRADIENT PROFILES

Fig. 7: *Example slope profiles in equilibrium with constant rates of downcutting, under erosion by landslides in combination with splash/creep.*

For this example $\gamma = 0.5$: Rates of lowering are shown on curves.

lower threshold, so that hollows would be wash controlled on low gradients and slide controlled on high gradients. This interpretation does not however avoid the original difficulty, in that wash hollows can exist without slides; whereas slide hollows do not appear to exist without streams. There is also the difficulty that the negative relationship for the Californian data extends down to slopes on $10°$ or less: that is well below geotechnically derived thresholds for slope stability.

The second difficulty is that observed hollows, in California at least (RENEAU et al. 1984), are occupied by a lens of colluvial fill which tends to taper out towards the stream head, forcing subsurface flow up towards the surface. A possible method for analysing this problem is by disaggregating the overland flows forecast by equation (3) in the wash case, to give sediment transport and hence rates of hollow enlargement or infilling on a storm by storm basis. A stochastic process is defined in this way, giving distributions of hollow depth and fill depth over time. A preliminary analysis based on equations (3) to (6), with a gradient exponent of $n = 1$ for wash, suggests that hollows begin to deepen appreciably for unit areas greater than

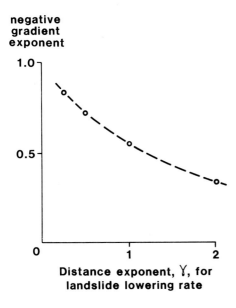

negative gradient exponent

Distance exponent, Y, for landslide lowering rate

Fig. 8: *Gradient exponent for critical slide unit length as a power of catchment gradient; expressed in terms of distance exponent γ in equation (11a).*

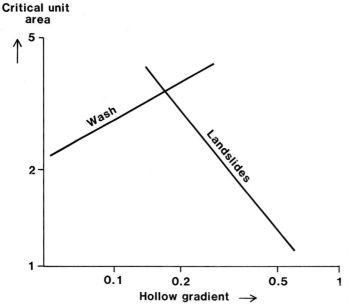

Critical unit area

Hollow gradient →

Fig. 9: *Hypothetical relationship between critical unit areas for wash and landslides, each in competition with splash/creep. At any gradient, the lower threshold should be the relevant one.*

about one tenth of the critical threshold value for hollow stability, but are typically full of colluvium until the unit area approaches the threshold. If subsurface flow is largely confined to this colluvial layer, over a relatively impermeable bedrock, then flow will be brought up to the surface at the base of the colluvial lens, as observed by DIETRICH et al. (1986). The siting of the functional stream head near the point of critical threshold area will be further reinforced by this mechanism.

This paper raises a number of questions about the position of stream and valley heads. Two processes have been discussed as possible candidates for valley enlargement. Wash is thought to be capable of eroding a valley provided that the critical tractive stress for soil aggregates is exceeded, and that storms are of long duration relative to the time of overland flow travel down hillsides (i.e. not in arid climates under HORTON overland flow). As the climate becomes more humid, and sub-surface flow more important, the area needed to support a stream head is forecast to increase as catchment gradients fall, suggesting an increase in drainage density as the landscape is lowered by erosion. Landslides have also been shown to be capable of producing valley heads, provided that long-term slide transport rates increase substantially with unit area or distance downslope, but it is not clear from the analysis that landslide hollows should necessarily contain a stream. For landslide hollows, drainage density should gradually decrease as gradients fall during catchment erosion, and hollows should be eliminated when gradients fall below an ulimate geotechnical threshold.

REFERENCES

BEVEN, K.J. & KIRKBY, M.J. (1979): A physically-based, variable contributing area model of basin hydrology. Hydrological Sciences Bulletin 24(1), 43–69.

CROZIER, M.J., EYLES, R.J., MARX, S.L., McCONCHIE, J.L. & OWEN, R.C. (1980): Distribution of landslips in the Wairarapa hill country. New Zealand Journal of Geology and Geophysics 23, 575–586.

DIETRICH, W.E. & DUNNE, T. (1978): Sediment budget for a small catchment in mountainous terrain. Zeitschrift für Geomorphologie, Supp.Bd. 29, 191–206.

DIETRICH, W.E., WILSON, C.J. & RENEAU, S.L. (1986): Hollows, colluvium and landslides in soil-mantled landscapes. In: Hillslope Processes (Ed. A.D. Abrahams), Allen and Unwin, 361–388.

IIDA, T. & OKUNISHI, K. (1983): Development of hillslopes due to landslides. Zeitschrift für Geomorphologie 46, 67–77.

KIRKBY, M.J. (1976): Implications for sediment transport. In: Hillslope hydrology. (Ed. M.J. Kirkby, John Wiley, 325–363.

KIRKBY, M.J. (1980): The stream head as a significant geomorphic threshold. In: Thresholds in geomorphology (Ed. D.R. Coates and J.D. Vitek), Allen and Unwin, 53–73.

KIRKBY, M.J. (1984): Modelling cliff development in South Wales: Savigear re-viewed. Zeitschrift für Geomorphologie 28(4), 405–426.

KIRKBY, M.J. (1985): A model for the evolution of regolith-mantled slopes. In: Models in Geomorphology (Ed. M.J. Woldenberg), Allen and Unwin, 213–237.

KIRKBY, M.J. (1986): A two-dimensional simulation model for slope and stream evolution. In: Hillslope Processes (Ed. A.D. Abrahams), Allen and Unwin, 203–222.

MUSGRAVE, G.W. (1947): Quantitative evaluation of factors in water erosion — a first approximation. Journal of Soil and Water Conservation 2, 133–138.

RENEAU, S.L., DIETRICH, W.E., WILSON, C.J. & ROGERS, J.D. (1984): Colluvial deposits and associated landslides in the Northern San Francisco Bay area, California, U.S.A. Proceedings of the 4th International Symposium on Landslides. International Society for Soil Mechanics and Foundation, Engineering, Toronto, Ontario, Canada, 425–430.

SIMONETT, D.S. (1967): Landslide distribution and earthquakes in the Dewani and Torricelli Mountains, New Guinea. In: Landform studies from Australia and New Guinea (Ed. J.N. Jennings and J.A. Mabbutt). Methuen, London.

SMITH, T.R. & BRETHERTON, F.P. (1972): Stability and the conservation of mass in drainage basin evolution. Water Resources Research **8(6)**, 1506–1529.

Address of author:
Mike Kirkby
School of Geography, Leeds University
Leeds, UK

A THEORETICAL STUDY
OF SOIL DETACHABILITY

D. **Torri**, Firenze

SUMMARY

The influence of soil characteristics on rainfed superficial soil erosion is usually not clearly defined. Some of the proposed definitions simply take into account the process of soil erosion globally. This fact can often give rise to misleading definitions, usually poorly physically based.

Here a general definition of one of the components of soil erodibility, namely soil detachability, is proposed. This definition is physically based and matches the findings of a number of experiments. Texture, aggregate stability and soil shear strength are the main soil characteristics that are relevant in defining soil detachability.

1 INTRODUCTION

Rainfed superficial erosion is greatly influenced by soil characteristics. They determine directly the resistance of soil particles and aggregates to detachment and transportation by overland flow and raindrop impact. Moreover, soil characteristics influence overland flow through infiltration rate, soil moisture and superficial conditions.

Soil characteristics are taken into account in different ways according to the type of modelling of soil erosion processes. Examples are the erodibility factor of the universal soil loss equation (WISCHMEIER & SMITH 1978) and the soil detachability and transportability of the splash model proposed by POESEN (1985).

Soil erodibility, as defined in the universal soil loss equation, would represent more or less all the ways in which soil characteristics are involved in soil erosion. Consequently this factor is far from being physically based (KIRKBY 1980) and all the limits inherent to a statistical parameter apply to it.

A serious step towards a more physically based soil erosion model is represented by POESEN's (1985) splash model. Within this single process, soil detachability and transportability are already recognized as distinct components of soil erodibility and treated separatedly. However, they are only sketchily defined. POESEN & SAVAT (1981) defined detachability as the amount of soil detached per unit of surface, per unit of rain kinetic energy. Unfortunately this definition is incomplete since the way in which the rain is applied can produce different amounts of detached soil. Even if the total kinetic energy is constant, slaking and interference between drop impact and depth

ISSN 0722-0723
ISBN 3-923381-10-7

of a water film, covering the soil surface (MUTCHLER & YOUNG 1975, TORRI & SFALANGA 1986), can cause the total detached amount to vary.

It follows that a more suitable definition of the soil characteristics influencing detachability and transportability is needed. This paper focuses on detachability. A general definition will be proposed, although complete parametrization has not yet been achieved.

2 DETACHMENT PROCESSES

Let us focus on the processes responsible for soil detachment. Raindrop impact, sheet flow and rill flow are the agents that provoke detachment. They obviously act by means of detaching forces against which the soil opposes resisting forces that keep soil particles and aggregates in place. In general terms, it is always possible to write an equation like the following one:

$$F_{TOT} = F(t) - R(t) \qquad (1)$$

where
F_{TOT} = resultant;
F = detaching force;
R = resistive force;
t = time.

It is well known that the detaching forces in rill and sheet flow are due to shear stress, Bernoulli lift and turbulence, as discussed in many textbooks (e.g., RAUDKIVI 1976, YALIN 1977, THORNES 1980). On the other hand, some confusion exists on the nature of the forces produced by an impining raindrop. Those forces are usually taken into account through kinetic energy or momentum. Those parameters, however, are only estimators of the real forces.

Going through the literature it is possible to characterize the nature of the real forces involved.

Following the findings of ENGEL (1955), HARLOW & SHANNON (1967), GHADIRI & PAYNE (1981), DE PLOEY & SAVAT (1968), HUANG et al. (1983) the general scheme of particle detachment can be summarized as follows:

1. when a drop hits a soil surface it initially resists change of shape. Then radial flow begins;

2. the radial flow is characterized by very high flow velocities (up to $10 \times$ the falling velocity of the drop). Some evidence exists that cavitation also occurs. High values of shear stress are produced at the solid-liquid interface, determining soil particle detachment.

One can conclude that the detaching forces are essentially similar, despite the name of the detaching agent (drop impact, sheet or rill flow) since they are always due to a fluid in motion. Hence a general mathematical structure can be proposed for all the detachment processes.

Returning to equ. (1) and taking into account the variation of the resistive force with time, the following considerations can be made. The resistive force can be set equal to a certain value Ro, as long as the soil particle is still. Once the particle starts gliding, rolling or jumping, equ. (1) describes transport rather than detachment. As proposed by FLAXMAN (1966) the usual case is:

$$Ro > R(t > 0) \qquad (2)$$

This means that once the particle is detached it can be washed away. Hence the conditions for detachment can be written as follows:

$$F(0) > Ro \qquad (3)$$

Let us suppose that the shear stress component of F is the dominant one. Hence equ. (3) can be written as:

$$\tau_t A_t > \tau_s A_s \qquad (4)$$

where
τ_t = shear stress exerted by the fluid;
A_t = particle surface over which τ_t acts;
τ_s = soil shear strength;
A_s = particle surface over which τ_s acts

A_s depends on the soil particle size and shape while A_t can also depend on the depth of the fluid provided that the particle is not completely immersed in the flow. Hence the ratio A_t/A_s can be written as follows:

$$\frac{A_t}{A_s} = \psi(h, \varphi, sh)\xrightarrow[h>\varphi]{} \psi'(\varphi, sh) \qquad (5)$$

where
ψ, ψ' = functions;
h = depth of the flow;
φ = particle size;
sh = particle shape factor.

Introducing (5) into (4) it follows:

$$\tau_t > \tau_s/\psi(h, \varphi, sh) \qquad (6)$$

or:

$$\tau_t \frac{\psi}{\tau_s} > 1 \qquad (7)$$

Hence soil detachability (D) can be defined as follows:

$$D = \frac{\psi(\overline{h}, \overline{\varphi}, \overline{sh})}{\tau_s} \qquad (8)$$

where
$\overline{h}, \overline{\varphi}, \overline{sh}$ = averages of the corresponding
                variables for a given condition.

3   SOIL SHEAR STRENGTH

Soil shear strength is due to a frictional term (due to pressure and particle packing) and a cohesive term (due to bonds among particles). On some soil the former is negligible with respect to the latter (e.g., on clay soils). For other soils the situation reverses (e.g., on loose coarse sand soils). In order to determine when the frictional term becomes negligible one can proceed as follows. Let us suppose cohesion is equal to k-times the frictional term. Then shear strength becomes:

$$\tau_s = (1 + k)P \tan\alpha \qquad (9)$$

where
P = pressure;
α = angle of internal friction.

Rearranging this equation it follows:

$$k = \frac{\tau_s}{p\tan(\alpha)} - 1 \qquad (10)$$

In order to solve equ. (10), data published by POESEN (1986) can be used. He measured a soil vane-shear strength of 0.2 kPa on the fine sand sediment (median diameter = 0.127 mm; % of sand = 89.3). The frictional term can be considered as due to a column of saturated sediment of 1 cm (average depth of the surface on which the shear is applied) while the internal friction angle can be set equal to 45° (which probably is an overestimation). Substituting these values in equ. (10) k equals 0.28. This means that cohesion is 0.044 kPa. This value must be compared with the frictional term acting on a particle partially exposed in the flow. Here pressure depends only on particle weight. Hence, considering a spherical quartz particle of 1 mm in size with a friction angle of 45°, the frictional term equals 0.011

kPa. This value is only 1/4 of cohesion indicating that this usually is the most important component of soil shear strength also on fine sand.

4   THE FUNCTION ψ

It has been said that ψ depends on the depth of the fluid and on the size and shape of the soil particle. The way in which ψ is influenced by the flow depth can be discussed for two cases:

(a) flow produced by lateral jets of an impinging rain drop;

(b) rill flow.

Case (a) is characterized by a very small value of h, hence ψ should depend on h.

Let us suppose that ψ can be expressed as the product of two functions:

$$\psi = t_1(h)t_2(\varphi, sh) \tag{11}$$

Equ. (7) can consequently be written as follows:

$$\tau_t t_1(h) > \frac{\tau_s}{t_2(\varphi, sh)} \tag{12}$$

The right side of inequality (12) depends mainly on soil characteristics while the left side depends mainly on raindrop characteristics. The literature (e.g. RIEZEBOS & EPEMA 1985) suggests that rainfall kinetic energy may be a good approximation of the left side of equ. (12).

At the opposite extreme of the range of h, when a rill flow is established, h is usually larger than φ and the soil particles are often completely immersed in the flow. Hence the function ψ becomes:

$$\psi = f(\psi, sh) \tag{13}$$

During sheet flow, intermediate situations can arise.

5   EXPERIMENTAL EVIDENCE OF THE ROLE PLAYED BY SOIL COHESION

AL DURRAH & BRADFORD (1982) pointed out that splash detachment is inversely proportional to soil shear strength. They proposed the following equation:

$$A = a\frac{kE}{\tau_s} + b \tag{14}$$

where
A = soil loss;
a, b = empirical constants;
kE = drop kinetic energy;
τ_s = soil shear strength measured with a Swedish falling cone penetrometer.

This means that soil detachability by splash (D_s) is:

$$D_s = \frac{a}{\tau_s} \tag{15}$$

TORRI et al. (1987a) found that:

$$D_s = \frac{t(\varphi)}{\tau_s} \tag{16}$$

where
f = function
φ = stable aggregate-particle size distribution;
φ_s = soil shear strength measured with a vane-test apparatus.

Those two last equations clearly resemble each other indicating the prominent role played by soil shear strength on splash detachment.

Some evidence exists that rill erosion also depends on soil shear strength. It can be partially found in the literature on flow in cohesive bed channels (FLAXMAN 1963, ABDEL-RAHMANN 1964). GOVERS (1985) and GOVERS & RAUWS (1986) pointed out that a threshold exists above which rills can be incised in loamy soils. Data collected by TORRI et al. (1987b) confirm the previous findings. Their data indicate a mean value of 10^{-4} for the ratio between the critical shear stress and soil shear strength when rills start eroding the soil. The low value of the ratio can be explained considering that the most weakly linked particles are the first to be entrained by the flow, while the shear stress is an underestimation of the total force exerted over the particle. This is still more convincing if we consider that the critical shear stress for particle entrainment decreases exponentially with increasing protrusion of the particle into the flow (FANTON & ABBOTT 1977).

6   CONCLUSIONS

The processes of detachment of soil particles and aggregates are due to similar forces, despite differences in the detaching agent, namely, drop impact, sheet flow, or rill flow. Actually the forces causing detachment are always those produced by a fluid in motion.

Soil detachability is different according to which of the three detaching agents is active. This depends on the effect produced by the depth of the flow. However, soil shear strength is always inversely proportional to soil detachment.

The definition of detachability, proposed in this paper, is supported by some experimental evidence. It can be used, once completely parametrized, for estimating soil detachability and, probably, soil detachment rate. Moreover, as it is more rigorous than previous definitions, it can both allow better understanding of the processes of soil erosion and provide a more reliable base for comparing data of different authors.

REFERENCES

ABDEL-RAHMANN, N.M. (1964): The effect of flowing water on cohesive beds. Contribution 56, Versuchsanstalt für Wasserbau und Erbau an der Eidgenössischen Technischen Hochschule, Zürich, Switzerland, 1–14.

AL DURRAH, M.M. & BRADFORD, J.M. (1982): Parameters for describing soil detachment due to single waterdrop impact. Soil Sci. Soc. Am. J. **46**, 836–840.

DE PLOEY, J. & SAVAT, J. (1968): Contribution à l'étude de l'érosion par le splash. Zeitschrift für Geomorphologie, **2**, 174–193.

ENGEL, O.G. (1955): Waterdrop collisions with solid surface. Journal of Research of the National Bureau of Standards, **54**, 5, 281–298, Research Paper 2591.

FANTON, J.D. & ABBOTT, J.E. (1977): Initial movement of grains on a stream bed: the effect of relative protrusion. Proc. R. Soc. Lond. A, **352**, 523–537.

FLAXMAN, E.M. (1963): Channel stability in undisturbed cohesive soils. Journal of Hydraulics Division, ASCE, **89**, HY2, Proc. Paper 3462, 87–96.

FLAXMAN, E.M. (1966): Discussion of 'Sediment transportation mechanics: initiation of motion'. Task Committee on preparation of Sedimentation Manual, Committee on Sedimentation of the Hydraulics Division, V.A. Vanoni, Chmn., Journal of the Hydraulics Division, ASCE, **92**, Proc.-Pap. 4959, 245–248.

GHADIRI, H. & PAYNE, D. (1981): Raindrop impact stress. J. of Soil Science, **32**, 41–49.

GOVERS, G. (1985): Selectivity and transport capacity of thin flow in relation to rill erosion. CATENA, **12**, 35–49.

GOVERS, G. & RAUWS, G. (1986): Transporting capacity of overland flow on plane and on irregular beds. Earth Surface Processes and Landforms, **11**, 505–524.

HARLOW, F.H. & SHANNON, J.P. (1967): The splash of a liquid drop. J. of Applied Physics, **38**, 10, 3855–3866.

HUANG, C., BRADFORD, J.M. & CUSHMAN, J.H. (1983): A numerical study of raindrop impact phenomena: the elastic deformation case. Soil Sci. Soc. Am. J., **47**, 855–861.

KIRKBY, M.J. (1980): The problem. In: Soil erosion. Kirkby, M.J. & Morgan, R.P.C. (eds.), J. Wiley, Chichester, 1–16.

MUTCHLER, C.K. & YOUNG, R.A. (1975): Soil detachment by raindrops. In: Present and prospective technology for predicting sediment yields and sources. Proceedings of the Sediment Yield Workshop, Oxford, Mississippi, USDA-ARS 40, 113–117.

POESEN, J. (1985): An improved splash transport model. Zeitschrift für Geomorphologie, **29**, 2, 193–211.

POESEN, J. (1986): Surface sealing as influenced by slope angle and position of simulated stones in the top layer of loose sediments. Earth Surface Processes and Landforms, **11**, 1–10.

POESEN, J. & SAVAT, J. (1981): Detachment and transportation of loose sediments by raindrop splash. Part II: detachability and transportability measurments. CATENA, **8**, 19–41.

RAUDKIVI, A.J. (1976): Loose boundary hydraulics. Pergamon Press, Oxford.

RIEZEBOS, H.T. & EPEMA, G.F. (1985): Drop shape and erosivity. Part II: Splash detachment, transport and erosivity indices. Earth Surface Processes and Landforms, **10**, 69–74.

THORNES, J.B. (1980): Erosional processes of running water and their spatial and temporal controls: a theoretical view point. In: Soil erosion. Kirkby, M.J. & Morgan, R.P.C. (eds.), J. Wiley, Chichester, 129–182.

TORRI, D. & SFALANGA, M. (1986): Some aspects of soil erosion modelling. In: Prediction of agricultural nonpoint source pollution: model selection and application. Elsevier Pu. Co., Amsterdam.

TORRI, D., SFALANGA, M. & DEL SETTE, M. (1987a): Splash detachment: runoff depth and soil cohesion. CATENA, **14**, 149–155.

TORRI, D., SFALANGA, M. & CHISCI (1987b): Threshold conditions for incipient rilling. CATENA Supplement **8**, 97–105.

WISCHMEIER, W.H. & SMITH, D.D. (1978): Predicting rainfall erosion losses. Agricultural Handbook 1537, U.S. Department of Agriculture, Washington, D.C.

YALIN, M.S. (1977): Mechanics of sediment transport. Pergamon Press, Oxford.

Address of Author:
Dino Torri
C.N.R. Centro di Studio per la Genesi, Classificazione e Cartografia del Suolo
P.le Cascine, 15
Firenze, Italy

CATENA SUPPLEMENT 10   p.21–29   Braunschweig 1987

A MODEL
OF PROGRESSIVE SLOPE FAILURE
UNDER THE EFFECT OF THE
NEOTECTONIC STRESS FIELD

N.S. **Ai** and T.D. **Miao**, Lanzhou

SUMMARY

The possible effects of the neotectonic stress field on the occurrence of landslides are reviewed. It is shown that the likelihood of slides depends on the orientation of the slope with regard to the principal stress directions and on the intensity of the general geomorphic activity in the area. The landslide genesis passes through three stages: buildup, development of progressive failure and actual "burst". Methods for the mathematical analysis of these stages are given. Finally, an example is presented from China in which it is shown that the mathematical analysis can be used for predicting the course of the events leading to a slide.

1 THE EFFECTS OF THE NEOTECTONIC STRESS FIELD ON LANDSLIDES

The stability of a slope is an important problem for geomorphologists, civil engineers and others who are concerned with the safety of structures and populations. This paper is a progress report on the state of the art in the study of the relationship between the neotectonic stress field and the stability of slopes.

Twenty years ago, RADBRUCH-HALL & VARNES (1967) indicated that a local neotectonic stress field certainly plays an important role in causing landslides, but not much was known about the manner in which this occurred. Subsequently, the section of geophysics of the Technical University of Vienna has been studying the problem of geodynamic control of slides. In a slide area of the Felber Valley (Salzburg Prov., Austria), the mountain-fracture "scars" along which slow mass movements occurred are roughly normal to the minimum compression direction (CARNIEL et al. 1975). For an unstable valley slope in the Lesach Valley (East Tyrol, Austria), the average displacement-direction corresponds closely to the maximum compression direction (HAUSWIRTH et al. 1979). The two cases reveal that the average direction of mass movement is parallel to the principal compression direction of the local neotectonic stress field in these cases. However, a statistical analysis of the distribution of the displacement vectors and the joint orientation in the Gastein Valley (Salzburg Prov., Austria) showed that the displace-

ISSN 0722-0723
ISBN 3-923381-10-7

F. AHNERT (EDITOR): GEOMORPHOLOGICAL MODELS — THEORETICAL AND EMPIRICAL ASPECTS

ment is parallel to one of the preferred joint orientations. From this it was inferred that geotectonic shearing motions could also give rise to the mass displacements (HAUSWIRTH & SCHEIDEGGER 1980).

The above investigations refer to slow landslides. For fast slides, a statistical analysis of groups has shown the existence of a relationship between the neotectonic stress field and the average displacement direction of the slide group. An analysis of 411 displacement directions of two great old shocks in Gansu Province, Chine (the Tianshui earthquake on July 21, 1654 [M = 8.0] and the Tongwei earthquake on June 19, 1718 [M = 7.5, or 8.0], showed that the average motion direction is parallel to the principal compression direction of the local neotectonic stress field (AI et al. 1984)). In Dongxiang country of Gansu Province, 189 displacement-directions of old and new landslides (most of them were fast slides) were statistically analysed and it was found that these directions were parallel to the two shear directions of the local neotectonic stress field (AI & ZUO 1985).

To sum up, the effect of the neotectonic stress field on landslides manifests itself in the three following aspects (AI & SCHEIDEGGER 1984):

1. there exist shearing surfaces in the neotectonic stress field which promote the formation and occurrence of landslides;

2. the orientation of the sliding directions in a group of landslides is related to the orientation of the local tectonic stress field;

3. there is commonly an increase in the frequency of landslides along the

direction perpendicular to the principal compression direction of the neotectonic stress field.

Therefore, if the principal orientations of the local neotectonic stress field have been calculated, the stability of slopes in an area may be estimated.

2   RESEARCH METHODS

The research results mentioned above were obtained on the basis of SCHEIDEGGER's principle of antagonism (SCHEIDEGGER 1979). According to this principle, valley trends, joint orientations, fault plane solutions of earthquakes, and some other geological or geophysical phenomena may be effects of endogenic forces arising from the neotectonic stress field. The features caused by the actions of endogenic and exogenic forces are statistically different: the former are systematic, whereas the latter are random (SCHEIDEGGER 1979).

The different expression of the two types of forces in the landscape can make a separation of endogenic from exogenic effects by mathematical methods possible. There are three methods for recognising a systematism of orientations. The first of these is the KOHLBECK-SCHEIDEGGER method (1977). The method is accurate, but the program is rather difficult for ordinary computers to manage. However, now two simpler substitute methods have been designed at Lanzhou University which can be run on microcomputers. One is the concentrated-degree-method (YU et al. 1985) and the other is the power-density-method (ZAO & AI 1985).

By using the methods mentioned above, the best "mean" directions can be chosen from many direction data. Then, the principal compression (or tension) direction of the tectonic stress field can be easily estimated if the principal directions are taken as the bisectrices of the shear fracture surfaces.

In addition to the principal directions, the intensity of a neotectonic stress field may be estimated by means of STRAHLER's curve (STRAHLER 1952). According to SCHEIDEGGER's principle of antagonism, the action of the endogenic and exogenic forces occurs simultaneously; one can estimate the intensity of the antagonistic action by means of an analysis of exogenic features since it is easier to measure exogenic effects than endogenic ones.

STRAHLER (1952) has suggested that the hypsometric curve of an area can be used to identify the landscape stages of DAVIS (1924) quantitatively. However, SCHEIDEGGER (1985) suggested that the stages are nothing but the expression of the antagonistic intensity. The terms "young", "mature" and "old" used by DAVIS do not refer to an evolutionary stage, but rather to the intensity of the antagonism which might be "high" (> 1 mm/year), "average" , or " low" ($<< 0.1$ mm/year) in the respective "stages". An analysis of the integral of STRAHLER's hypsometric curves for four drainage areas near Tianshui and Wudu (China) shows that the integral-value of the curve can be used as an indicator of the geodynamic intensity of the respective area (AI 1985). The larger the integral-value and the more convex the curve, the more intense is the antagonism (SCHEIDEGGER 1987) and therefore, the more serious is the landslide hazard.

GERBER & SCHEIDEGGER (1969) have discovered that the most important feature in a notch running across a maximum principal horizontal stress direction is the occurrence of a stress concentration at the bottom of the notch. A photoelastic simulation made by us (fig.1) and a numerical simulation using a computer program (fig.2) also verify this. Accordingly, a stress concentration is created at the bottom of s slope under the action of the principal compressional force of the neotectonic stress field. If the compressional force is strong enough, the bottom of the slope will fail first. The failure will gradually move from the bottom to the top of the slope, the lateral compressional force decreases continuously to zero, and then the tensional force increases continuously which leads to a crack somewhere on the top. With the development of fractures, a landslide will occur eventually. The rheological failure process of the slope with time described above is called "progressive failure".

The stage from the beginning of the failure at the bottom to the appearance of tensional fractures at the top is the first stage of landslide preparation called the "buildup stage".

3 THE BUILDING STAGE OF A LANDSLIDE

3.1 MECHANICAL ANALYSIS

The method of slices (TIMLAW & LUMB 1978) for the convential analysis of slope stability is used here to avoid a complex calculation using elasticity and plasticity theory.

We consider a simple homogeneous soil slope and assume the soil as an ideal rigid-plastic material and the slopes having a circular arcuate sliding surface when a landslide occurs (fig.3). The slices like that shown in fig.3a and fig.3b show

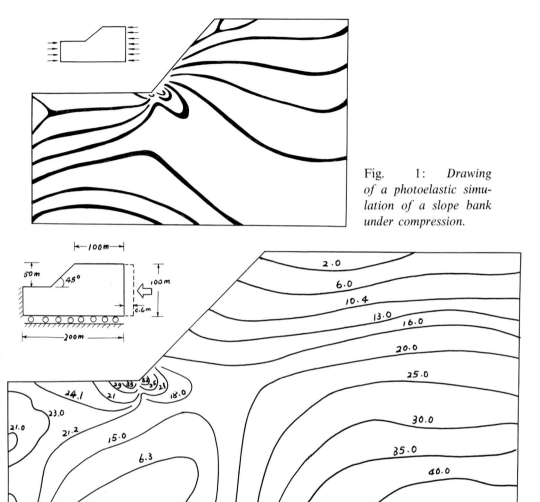

Fig. 1: *Drawing of a photoelastic simulation of a slope bank under compression.*

Fig. 2: *Drawing of a computer simulation of a slope bank under compression.*

the forces acting on each slice, for instance, on that numbered (i), where

1. W_i is the weight of the slice,

2. $P_i = N_i - ub_i sec\ \alpha_i$ (1)

   is the effective pressure on the slide bottom where u is the pore water pressure,

3. S_i is the shear force at the bottom,

4. E_i, E_{i+1} are the normal forces and X_i, X_{i+1} are the vertical shear forces between the slices.

   Next, we will discuss the basic equation. For each slice (i), as a body subject to a plane-force system, the following equilibrium equations hold:

$E_{i+1} = E_i + S_i cos\ \alpha_i - N_i sin\ \alpha_i$ (2)

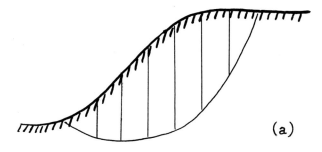

(a)

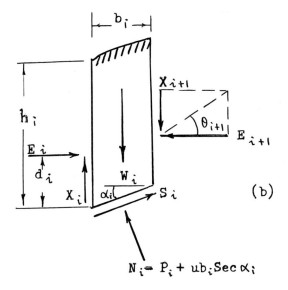

(b)

$$N_i = P_i + ub_i Sec \, \alpha_i$$

Fig. 3: *Slices in a landslide with an arcuate sliding surface.*

$$X_{i+1} = X_i + S_i sin \, \alpha_i - N_i cos \, \alpha_i - W_i \qquad (3)$$

$$N_i \frac{b_i}{2cos \, \alpha_i} =$$

$$W_i \frac{b_i}{2} + E_{i+1}d_{i+1} - E_i(d_i - b_i tan \, \alpha_i) \qquad (4)$$

where d_i, d_{i+1} indicate the load points of E_i and E_{i+1}, respectively.

Soil usually fails by shearing. By the well-known law of Coulomb's the maximally permitted shear force (shear strenght) is

$$S_{pi} = C_p b_i sec \, \alpha_i + (N_i - ub_i sec \, \alpha_i)tan \, \phi_p \qquad (5)$$

where C_p is the maximum value of the cohesion and ϕ_p is the friction angle of the soil. The failure condition of the slice (*i*) is

$$S_i = S_{pi} \qquad (6)$$

However, by considering of the soil strength-loss caused by the underground water, the stresses of the collapsed slice drop rapidly to a residual state when local failure takes place:

$$S_{ri} = C_r b_i sec \, \alpha_i + (N_i - ub_i sec \, \alpha_i)tan \, \phi_r \qquad (7)$$

where C_r is the residual cohesion and ϕ_r is the residual friction angle.

To complete the above basic equations, we have to make some assumptions:

for the plastic-collapse region

$$d_i = \frac{1}{3}h_i \qquad (8)$$

for the rigid region, in addition to (8),

$$\frac{X_i}{E_i} = tan\ \alpha_i \qquad (9)$$

3.2 THE ANALYSIS OF THE ABOVE

1. The radius and the position of the sliding surface (circular arc) should be determined first by the traditional method of stability analysis of a slope which can be found in many books on soil mechanics.

2. The sliding part of the slope has to be divided into a series of slices.

3. If the first slice at the bottom of the slope has collapsed under a stress concentration, then the lateral forces E_2, X_2 can be found from the equations (2)–(4), (7) and (8) with $E_1 = 0, X_1 = 0$ given by the boundary conditions. The stress in the slope body must redistribute itself after this local failure. When the shear force S_2 approaches S_{p2} (condition (6)), a failure of the second slice follows. Thus for the first slice, one can calculate E_3, X_3 by the same equations for $i = 2$ with E_2, X_2 known from the last step. This procedure is repeated until a slice is reached, e.g. the slice (k), where $E_{k+1} = 0$. Next to the slice (k), the normal forces E between the slices change to tension (E is a compression for the slices (1) to (k)). For the slices with numbers greater than (k), the soil has not collapsed yet (rigid region), thus the forces E_{k+1}, E_{k+2} etc. can be obtained by the equations (2)–(4), (8) and (9).

4. The place where the tension crack occurs has to be found by using the fracture condition, supposing that the crack will be at the slice (n),

$$E_n \geq [\sigma^+]h_n \qquad (10)$$

in which $[\sigma^+]$ is the tensional strength limit of the soil.

3.3 EXAMPLE

We assume that there is a simple soil slope with the inclination angle $\beta = 45°$, height $H = 25$ m (fig.4a), and $R = 1.8$ T/m³, $\phi_r = 19°$, $C_r = 0$, $u = 0.25r$, $[\sigma^+] = 350$ T/m².

Following the procedure given above, we find that for this slope the radius of the sliding arc is 30 m, with the center of the arc corresponding to $\beta_1 = 15°$. The variation of the lateral force E against $sin\ \alpha$ is plotted in fig.4b in accordance with the calculated results, by which it can be seen that from the slice (5) onward, the compressional force E decreases gradually to zero, then it changes to a tensional force and a fracture crack occurs near the slice (11) at the top of the slope. This example shows clearly the evolutionary process of the landslide buildup stage.

4 THREE STAGES OF LANDSLIDE EVOLUTION

According to our model of progressive failure, a landslide normally undergoes three stages in a certain order. Besides the buildup stage, the other two stages are the developing and bursting stages.

The developing stage of landslide evolution occurs between the time of the initial tensional fractures at the top of the

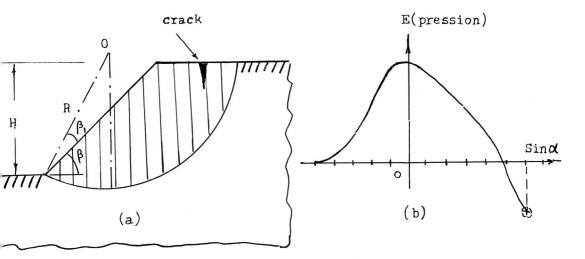

Fig. 4: *Method fo slices for a circular sliding surface and result for the example given.*

slope until the actual burst of the land-slide. This is the process of viscoplastic expansion of the fracture. Generally speaking, the evolutionary speed of this stage is faster than that of the first one. If the landslide evolution is in the second stage, prediction of the accident or burst time will be possible. A successful test has been made by SAITO (1965) who forecast the occurrence time of a landslide according to rheology theory, measuring the width-expansion of a surficial fracture.

The third stage is the bursting stage. If one considers only two factors, that is, the form factor T and the soil property factor G, the state of the landslide system can be determined by the following formula (MIAO & AI 1986):

$$4\eta^3 + 2u\eta + v = 0 \qquad (11)$$

This means that the system can pass into a cusp of catastrophe theory (fig.5). For this purpose, the following characteristic equation has been postulated:

$$1 + T^3 + (1 + T^2)\sqrt{1 + T^2} = 2G^3 \qquad (12)$$

Only when the control variables T and G satisfy the equation (12), (i.e. the landslide state is situated on the line OB), will the landslide burst suddenly. Thus a landslide burst can be divided into two types: on the line OB it may be a fast landslide, on the left of this line, the burst will be slow.

Because of internal or external changes due to environmental conditions, the evolutionary process of the three stages may be interrupted and then no landslide will occur. Thus, not all landslides in a buildup stage will evolve into a burst.

5 PRACTICAL APPLICATION OF PROGRESSIVE FAILURE FOR SLOPES UNDER STRESS

On 18th August, 1985 we took part in the investigation and discussion of measures to insure the stability of a slope on Shilaquan Mt. (AI & MIAO 1986). The slope of the mountain is quite sim-

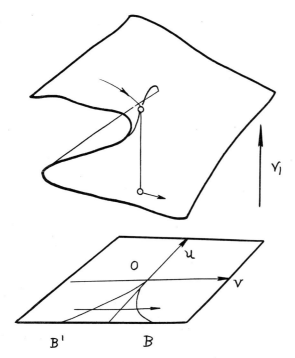

Fig. 5: *Catastrophe-theory model with a cusp.*

ilar to that of Sale Mt., where a catastrophic landslide occurred on March 7th, 1983. In the Sale Mt. landslide three villages were completely destroyed and 220 people were killed. At the top of the slope of Shilaquan Mt. a series of fractures have been appearing since 1983. In the last two years the fractures have further developed. Thus, there is a great concern for the safety of the village which is located at the foot of Shilaquan Mt., because of the possibility of another catastrophic landslide occurring similar to that of Sale Mt. in 1983.

On the top of Shilaquan Mt. we inspected the fractures which can be divided into two types. The first type of fractures found during 1985 are rather long, reaching 200 metres, but their width was not big, and in some places they were only faintly visible. The fractures have a NW-SE strike with some

sections having a strike of 310°. This 310° direction is just perpendicular to the principal compression direction of the local neotectonic stress field which has been calculated to be N38°E by AI & SCHEIDEGGER (1984).

The second type is represented by small arc-shaped fractures around the gully head. These fractures are developing rather rapidly, indicating that a small landslide is going to occur.

According to our model the appearance of fractures related to the local neotectonic stress field shows that the slope has failed and the landslide is building up. However, these fractures related to the stress field are not developing rapidly. The observation instruments put in the slope since the summer of 1985 have not shown yet any abnormal variation. The geostructure of Shilaquan Mt. is similar to that of Sale Mt., but the hydrogeological conditions of the former are better than those of the latter. Thus, we forecast that the developing stage of the Shilaquan landslide should be longer than that of the Sale landslide. However, the village on the foot of the slope has to be moved to another place in any case.

REFERENCES

AI NANSHAN (1985): Effects of a Neotectonic Stress Field on Landslides. Proc. 4th Intern. Conf. and Field Workshop on Landslides. Tokyo, 433–436.

AI NANSHAN, LIU BAICHI & ZHOU JUNXI (1984): New report on old Earthquake-Landslides. J. of Lanzhou University (Natural Sciences) 20(1), 174–178.

AI NANSHAN & MIAO TIANDE (1986): A new indicator of slope stability, an example of the Shilaquan Mountain. J. of Lanzhou University (Natural Sciences), 22(1), 129. (in Chinese)

AI NANSHAN & SCHEIDEGGER, A.E. (1984): On the connection between the neotectonic stress field and catastrophic landslides. 27th Inter. Geol. Congr. Reports VI, 180–188.

AI NANSHAN & ZUO FAYUAN (1985): A statistical analysis of moving direction data of landslides in Dongxiang region of Gansu Province. J. of Lanzhou University (Natural Sciences) 21(3), 133. (in Chinese)

CARNIEL, P., HAUSWIRTH, E.K., ROCH, K.H. & SCHEIDEGGER, A.E. (1975): Geomechanische Untersuchungen in einem Rutschungsgebiet im Felbertal in Österreich. Verh. Geol. B.-A., Wien, 4, 305–330.

DAVIS, W.M. (1924): Die erklärende Beschreibung der Landformen. Teubner, Leipzig.

GERBER, E. & SCHEIDEGGER, A.E. (1969): Stress-induced weathering of rock masses. Ecolog. Geol. Helv. 62, 405–415.

HAUSWIRTH, E.K., PIRKL, H., ROCH, K.-H. & SCHEIDEGGER, A.E. (1979): Untersuchungen eines Talzuschubes bei Lesach (Kals, Osttirol). Verh. Geol. B.-A. 2, 51–76.

HAUSWIRTH, E.K. & SCHEIDEGGER, A.E. (1980): Tektonische Vorzeichnung von Hangbewegungen im Raume von Bad Gastein. Interprävent 1980, Bd. 1, 159–178.

KOHLBECK, F. & SCHEIDEGGER, A.E. (1977): On the theory of the evaluation of joint orientation measurements. Rock Mech., 9, 9–25.

TIMLAW, K. & LUMB, P. (1978): A limit equilibrium analysis of progressive failure in the stability of the slopes. Canad. Geol. J. 15(1).

MIAO TIANDE & AI NANSHAN (1986): On catastrophe theory and landslides. Proc. III Nation. Sym. on Geotectonics & Geodynamics. Yichang (China). (in Chinese) (in press)

RADBRUCH-HALL, D.H. & VARNES, D.J. (1976): Bulletin of the Intern. Assoc. of Eng. Geol. No. 14, 205–216. (Title of paper not available)

SAITO, M. (1965): Forecasting the time of occurrence of a slope failure. Proc. 6th Int. Conf. Soil Mech. & Found. Eng., 2, 537–541.

SCHEIDEGGER, A.E. (1979): The principle of antagonism in the Earth's evolution. Tectonophys. 55, T7–T10.

SCHEIDEGGER, A.E. (1985): Principles of geodynamic studies. Exploration of Nature 4(2), 85–93. (in Chinese)

SCHEIDEGGER, A.E. (1987): The fundamental principles of landscape evolution. CATENA Suppl. 10, 199–210.

STRAHLER, A.N. (1952): Hypsometric (area-altitude) analysis of erosional topography. Bull. Geol. Soc. Am. 63, 1117–1142.

YU QINYU, JIANG ZHUZONG & AI NANSHAN (1985): A concentrated degree method for the calculation of valley trends. Scienta Geogr. Sinica 5, 1–9. (in Chinese)

ZHAO ZHEN & AI NANSHAN (1985): A computational method for the density diagram of boulder fabric. Acta Sedim. Sinica 3(1), 124–127. (in Chinese)

Addresses of authors:
N.S. Ai
Department of Geography, Lanzhou University
Lanzhou, China
T.D. Miao
Department of Mathematics and Mechanics, Lanzhou University
Lanzhou, China

PROCESS-RESPONSE MODELS OF DENUDATION AT DIFFERENT SPATIAL SCALES

F. **Ahnert**, Aachen

SUMMARY

The landform development model program SLOP3D, which is based on the mass balance concept, is used to investigate

1. the interaction between weathering and denudation at a point on a slope,

2. the dependence of slope form upon the prevalent denudation process,

3. the relationships between slope form, mean denudation rate and summit denudation rate and

4. the height limit of young mountain ranges as a function of their width.

The results show that it is possible to apply a single theoretical model program to geomorphological problems at greatly differing spatial and temporal scales.

1 INTRODUCTION

Since the work of GILBERT (1877), all models of denudation are directly or indirectly based on the denudational mass balance, which in its simplest form may be written

ISSN 0722-0723
ISBN 3-923381-10-7

$$C = C' + (W + A - R)\triangle t \qquad (1)$$

where
C = regolith thickness (dimension: L) at the end of a time span $\triangle t$

C' = regolith thickness (dimension: L) at the beginning of that time span

W = weathering rate, i.e. the thickness added per time unit (dimension: LT^{-1}) to the regolith thickness by weathering of the bedrock; expressed geomorphologically this is the rate of waste production by bedrock weathering

A = waste supply rate, i.e. the thickness added per time unit (dimension: LT^{-1}) to the regolith thickness by transport from upslope

R = waste removal rate, i.e. thickness removed per time unit (dimension: LT^{-1}) from the regolith thickness by transport in the downslope direction or by solutional transport towards the water table.

The local denudation rate d, i.e. the net exogenic change of the local elevation from h' to h per time unit, may accordingly be written as

$$d = \frac{h' - h}{\triangle t} = R - A \qquad (2)$$

The dimension of h and of h' is L, that of d is LT^{-1}. The denudation rate d has positive values if there is local downwearing and negative values if there is accumulation.

This Gilbertian mass balance should be applicable to landforms and geomorphological processes at any spatial or temporal scale, from the changes at a single point during a single rainfall event to the denudation of a large drainage basin over millions of years.

It is used as the basic design principle for the denudational model program SLOP3D from which a great variety of specific models may be generated. The qualitative and quantitative structure of this program has been developed and modified over the last three decades (cf. AHNERT 1954, 1964, 1976). In this paper, an attempt is made to use SLOP3D to answer geomorphological questions at different spatial scales, namely,

1. What are the geomorphological consequences of the interactions between weathering and denudation at a point of the land surface?

2. Are there process-specific slope forms?

3. What are the relationships between slope form, mean denudation rate and summit denudation rate?

4. Is it reasonable to assume that there is a limit to the possible height of mountain ranges which is, in effect, a function of their width?

The SLOP3D model examples used in this paper are identified by a code number (for example, 28028601) which is made up of the date (here, 28 Feb. 1986) and the particular SLOP3D computer run (here, no. 1) at that date.

2   INTERACTIONS AT A POINT OF THE LAND SURFACE

At any slope point, the components of the mass balance are functionally linked with one another and with the local slope angle, as shown in fig.1. The regolith thickness C is a positive function of W and of A but a negative function of R, as equation (1) shows. However, the rate of bedrock weathering W is in most instances a negative exponential function of C: the thicker the regolith, the more slowly weathers the bedrock underneath. This is the first of the several negative feedbacks in the system. If the rate of waste removal R and of waste supply A are both zero (which should occur on a horizontal surface), then the weathering process reduces its own rate W progressively towards zero as the regolith thickness C increases.

Fig.1 contains two other feedback loops. They link C with R and A, respectively, by way of the local downslope and upslope angles. A local increase of the waste removal rate R without an immediately accompanying increase of the supply rate A, for example, has the initial consequence of a decrease of the local regolith thickness C. To this change of C there are responses of both W and A which tend to counteract it. One response is an increase of the rate of bedrock weathering W; thus the initial decrease of regolith thickness due to waste removal is counteracted by a follow-up increase of the rate of regolith production due to bedrock weathering. Since the addition to the regolith thickness occurs from below, through conversion of bedrock to regolith, it has no influence upon the surface elevation at the slope point in question except perhaps for a possible effect of bulk density changes (disregarded here) that accompany the weathering.

The initial local decrease of C due to increased removal means also that the local elevation has been lowered relative to the elevation of points upslope, and therefore that the upslope angle has locally steepened. This, in turn, leads to an increase in the rate of waste supply A which then counteracts both the initial decrease of C and its accompanying relative local surface lowering. A will

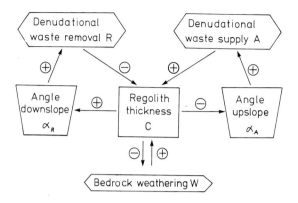

Fig. 1: *The functional structure of the local denudational mass balance system.*

tend to increase further as long as the local upslope angle continues to steepen, i.e. as long as $R > A$, until ultimately the supply rate A has caught up with the removal rate R. Conversely, a local decrease of R has the effect that both the local waste production by weathering and the local waste supply by denudational transport from upslope are initially greater that the removal. Accordingly, the regolith thickness increases both from weathering below and from net accumulation (i.e. a relative increase of the surface elevation) above. In response to these changes, however, the bedrock weathering rate W, the local upslope angle and the waste supply rate A tend to decrease until the sum $W + A$ equals the removal rate R, in which case C becomes constant.

From these interactions, which have been noted repeatedly by geomorphologists since the work of GILBERT (1877) and which are illustrated here in fig.1, it can be seen that any initial change of W, R or A triggers compensating changes in the other two processes so that the system tends towards the establishment of an equality, or "equilibrium", between $W + A$ and R. Because of the self-adjusting quality of the interaction be-

tween these processes, this equilibrium is correctly termed a dynamic equilibrium. It is characterised by the absence of local changes of the regolith thickness C, so that then in equation (1) $C = C'$, although all participating processes are active and the surface is being denudationally lowered. Not only the regolith thickness but also the local upslope and downslope angles — i.e. the local surface form — remain constant under these circumstances.

In order to avoid confusion, it is recommended to use the term "dynamic equilibrium" only when referring to the "equality of action", as GILBERT (1877) called it, between the rates of interacting processes or process groups such as $W + A$ and R; the term "steady state", by contrast, should be reserved to denote the accompanying constancy of the material and geometric system components — here, regolith thickness and local surface form — which are "static" in the sense of not containing the dimension of time. In short, dynamic equilibrium can only exist between the process components of a process-response system, as a self-regulating equality between input and output per time unit, while steady state is the visible material and/or geometric expression of that equality.

It is worth noting that in all process-response systems that contain more than two interacting process components, an externally induced change of one component may be compensated by any combination of responses of the other components. The magnitude of their combined response, of course, is governed by the magnitude of the initial change; however, the magnitudes of their individual responses are functions of their own interaction and depend furthermore upon the properties of the forms and materials that also are components of the system. In natural systems, these properties most often are insufficiently known, so that usually the individual responses of system components to an initial change cannot be predicted precisely. This indeterminacy is similar to that which exists for the relationships between width, depth and velocity in the continuity equation of hydraulic geometry (cf. LEOPOLD & MADDOCK 1953). One of the purposes of theoretical process-response models such as SLOP3D is to serve as a tool for theoretical experiments in which such complex responses (cf. SCHUMM 1973) may be simulated, and thus better understood, under a variety of controlled environmental, material and geometric conditions.

In SLOP3D the process rates of fig.1 are represented by equations. For example, the gross amount removed per time unit from a surface point by slow mass movement of the plastic flow type is

$$R_1 = k_1 \cdot (C \cdot sin\alpha - k_2) \tag{3}$$

and the amount removed by wash denudation is

$$R_2 = (k_3 + k_4 \cdot C) \cdot D^{k_5} \cdot sin^{k_6}\alpha \tag{4}$$

C is the local regolith thickness, D the effective local runoff depth, α the local slope angle and $k_i(i = 1, 2, 3, ...)$ in these and the following equations are constants (normally ≥ 0).

Purely mechanical weathering has the equation

$$W_M = W_o \cdot e^{-k_7 C} \tag{5}$$

where W_o is the weathering rate of bare bedrock. The rate of chemical weathering, however, can increase at first with increasing regolith thickness C according to

$$W_{Ch} = W_o \cdot (1.0 + k_8 \cdot \frac{C}{C_c} - \frac{C^2}{C_c^2}) \tag{6}$$

where C_c is a predetermined "critical thickness". W_{Ch} in equ. (6) reaches its maximum when

$$\frac{dW_{Ch}}{dC} = \frac{W_o}{C_c} \cdot (k_8 - \frac{2 \cdot C}{C_c}) = 0 \tag{7}$$

The regolith thickness C under which the highest rate of chemical bedrock weathering occurs is then the "optimal regolith thickness"

$$C_{opt} = \frac{k_8}{2} \cdot C_c \tag{8}$$

By substituting this expression for C in equ. (6) one obtains the maximum weathering rate as

$$W_{Ch(max)} = W_o \cdot (1.0 + \frac{1}{4} \cdot k_8^2) \tag{9}$$

In SLOP3D equ. (6) is used only for $C \leq C_c$. Whenever C exceeds the "critical thickness" C_c, chemical weathering continues according to

$$W_{Ch} = W_o \cdot k_9 \cdot e^{-k_{10} \cdot (C - C_c)} \tag{10}$$

i.e. in a way similar to that of equ. (5). Mechanical and chemical weathering may be combined in various proportions governed by a prescribed proportionality coefficient $0 \leq P \leq 1.0$:

$$W = P \cdot W_M + (1.0 - P) \cdot W_{Ch} \qquad (11)$$

By choosing particular combinations of values for $k_7, k_8, k_9, k_{10}, C_c$ and P, various environmental and lithologic conditions of weathering may be simulated.

Fig.2 illustrates the interaction of the mass balance components through time (fig.2). The initial profile is horizontal. The "motor" of the system is the local baselevel lowering (or stream incision) rate d_f at the slope foot. It produces a gradient and thus initiates the denudation processes. In fig.2 d_f has a prescribed constant gross value of 1 m per time unit: however, its net value decreases gradually to 0.222 per time unit (at about $T = 45$) because waste from the slope is brought to the slope foot at an increasing rate and needs to be removed there before further baselevel lowering can occur. The process of net downcutting is stopped arbitrarily by the program at $T = 61$. Weathering in this model is chemical. It starts according to equ. (6); however, very early the critical regolith thickness C_c (here 1 m) has been transgressed and further weathering goes on according to equ. (10).

From time $T = 0$ to time $T = 50$, the process rates d_f, W, R, A and the local denudation rate d gradually approach dynamic equilibrium: weathering W and denudation d become equal to the rate of baselevel lowering d_f and $W + A$ becomes equal to R so that the regolith thickness C becomes constant ($C = C'$, cf. equ. (1)). Gradually $d = d_f$ at all points of the slope, so that local relief becomes also constant. This is the state

of dynamic equilibrium in the sense of GILBERT (1877) and others (for example, JAHN (1954), AHNERT (1954) and HACK (1960)).

After the end of baselevel lowering at $T = 61$, all process rates decrease, but not equally. The slope summit continues to be worn down while the slope foot remains at the same elevation: the state of the model changes from the steady state of constant form and from the dynamic equilibrium of processes to the disequilibrium of relief decline. The sum $W + A$ becomes larger than R so that the regolith thickness C now increases; following the same tendency, the local denudation rate d becomes smaller than the weathering rate W. The interdependence of the processes remains intact, but with the "motor" d_f switched off, the system slowly runs down. This disequilibrium of relief decline corresponds to the "graded valley sides" (at fixed baselevel) of DAVIS (1909, 268); it is a "quasi-equilibrium" (cf. LEOPOLD et al. 1964, 267) in the sense that the processes continually adjust themselves to one another and thus maintain a tendency towards a state of equilibrium which, however, they cannot reach except at the trivial end when all process rates are zero.

In this seemingly simple scheme, a particular complication is brought in by the functional relationship between chemical weathering W_{Ch} and regolith thickness C (fig.3). Between the weathering rate W_o on bare bedrock ($C = 0.0$) and the maximum rate of weathering $W_{Ch(max)}$ which occurs when the regolith cover has reached its optimum thickness, the same weathering rate W ($W_o < W < W_{Ch(max)}$) may occur at two different waste thicknesses ($C_1 < C_{opt}$ and $C_2 > C_{opt}$, cf. fig.3); but these two possibilities have quite different ge-

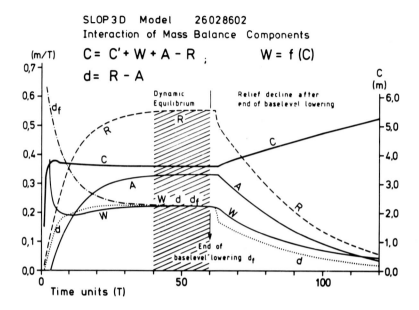

Fig. 2: *The interaction of the mass balance components through time (SLOP3D model no. 26028602).*

C: regolith thickness; C': previous regolith thickness; W: weathering rate; A: rate of waste arrival from upslope; R: rate of waste removal in the downslope direction; d: local denudation rate; d_f: lowering of the slope foot (local baselevel).

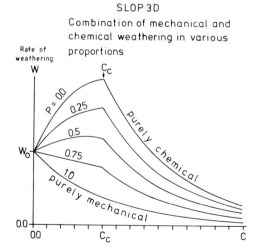

Fig. 3: *Weathering as a function of regolith thickness in the SLOP3D model program.*

P is the proportionality factor for the combination of mechanical and chemical weathering. In this diagram $k_8 = 2.0$, so that $C_{opt} = C_c$.

omorphological results. One case is shown in fig.2. Here very soon after the start of the development the regolith thickness becomes greater than C_{opt}; in this case, the negative feedback loop $W = f(C = f(W))$ shown in fig.1 and in equation (10) is at work: a decrease of C produces an increase of W and thereby increases regolith production that tends to offset the initial decrease of C. Consequently, C approaches and holds a constant value until the stream incision d_f at the slope foot changes or ceases.

However, if the rate of weathering W occurs under a regolith thickness $C < C_{opt}$, there are only positive feedbacks: a decrease of C due to increased denudation causes a decrease of W, so that even less regolith is produced and the regolith thins out even more until it has disappeared entirely and the slope surface consists of bare bedrock that weathers at the rate W_o. Potential denudation then is greater than actual denudation, and the latter is controlled by the rate W_o, at which parts of the bedrock are made mobile and thus become available for denudational removal. If on the other hand the regolith thickness C increases (still with $C < C_{opt}$), the rate of weathering W also increases until $C = C_{opt}$. In other words, the positive feedbacks that occur in this situation lead either to bare bedrock or to a production (and perhaps even transgression) of the optimum waste thickness. The geomorphological consequences of these two models of development are illustrated by Model Nr. 28028601 (fig.4): although the bedrock is homogeneous throughout, there is a surface differentiation between areas of bare bedrock where denudation is weathering-limited (on the divide because $A = 0$ and potentially $R > W$, on the valley shoul-

der because potentially $R > A + W$) and regolith-covered areas of gentler gradient where $C > C_{opt}$ and where denudation is transport-limited. Because the rate of chemical bedrock weathering is smaller on bare rock than under a regolith mantle of moderate thickness, the rocky divide is less rapidly worn down than the adjacent waste-covered lower slope; it thus gradually comes to stand with a steeper slope above its surroundings — an inselberg system on homogeneous rock, caused by the spatial differentiation of exogenic processes. This quantitative model corroborates the qualitative concept of "differentiated weathering" as described by BREMER (1973).

3 DENUDATIONAL PROCESS TYPE AND SLOPE FORM

The preceding example has already led away from the mass balance interactions at a single surface point to the relationships that exist among a series of surface points along a profile; it illustrates the fact that changes of landform shapes are brought about by the spatial differentiation of the local mass balances, i.e. when different surface points are degraded or aggraded by different amounts. The basic landform unit is the slope, that is, the segment of the land surface which is limited at its upper margin by a divide, i.e. a line from which process paths diverge, and at its lower margin by a thalweg, i.e. a line towards which process paths converge. The main reason why slopes (rather than, for example, drainage basins) are considered as basic surface units by most geomorphologists may be the fact that slopes are the largest easily delimited land surface

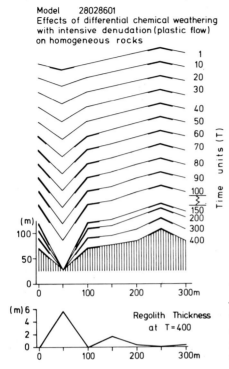

Model   28028601
Effects of differential chemical weathering
with intensive denudation (plastic flow)
on homogeneous rocks

Fig.   4: *The development of an inselberg
system on homogeneous rock by spatial differentiation of exogenic processes (SLOP3D
model no. 28028601).*

Thick profile line: bare bedrock surface and weathering-
limited denudation; thin profile line: regolith-covered surface
and transport-limited denudation.

units one can see completely from a single viewpoint on the ground.

Slopes represent the second spatial
scale at which SLOP3D is to be applied
here; it is the scale for which the model
program had been originally designed.
The questions to be investigated concern
the shape of process-specific slope profile forms and the spatial distribution of
denudation rates on these profiles — in
particular, the difference, if any, between
the mean denudation rate and the summit denudation rate.

3.1   SLOPES PRODUCED BY
SLOW MASS MOVEMENTS

In the first case (fig.5), slow mass movement such as creep or solifluction is the
only denudation process at work. Downcutting takes place with a constant gross

rate at the slope foot for the first 1200
time units; after that, the local baselevel
remains fixed.   After an initial phase
of profile differentiation, a steady-state
convex profile is being lowered parallel
to itself until the stream incision stops.
This indicates a dynamic equilibrium between the rate of uplift represented by
stream incision and the rate of denudation which in this phase is equal at all
slope points.   The convex shape is due
to the fact that the slow mass movement
(plastic flow) is a slope-dependent process; the model process is described by
equation (3), where k_1 is a mobility coefficient (representing, for example, frequency of freeze-thaw cycles and/or soil
moisture contents) and k_2 is a cohesion
term ($k_2 = 0$ in fig.5). Since the amount
of waste that has to be transported in-

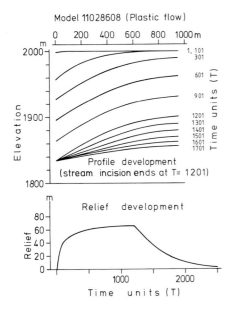

Fig. 5: *Characteristic slope profile development by slow mass movement (creep or solifluction).*

The numbers on the right side of the profile lines denote elapsed time units.

creases progressively from the top to the bottom of the slope, a dynamic equilibrium in which all slope points are being lowered at the same rate is accompanied in this case by a downslope increase of the slope angle; the characteristic slope form for slope-dependent slow denudation processes is therefore convex.

This convex shape remains the characteristic form also for the further slope development after the end of stream incision — a reminder that convex slopes can — and quite commonly do — occur no matter whether stream incision is present or not. W. PENCK's (1924) concepts of slope development are decidedly wrong in that respect. The relief development curve in fig.5 shows very well the three phases

1. initial profile differentiation,

2. dynamic equilibrium with constant relief (steady-state) and

3. relief decline.

In the last phase, the relief approaches zero asymptotically because the downwearing of the convex slope form diminishes the local slope angles and thus the rate of the slope-dependent denudation.

3.2 SLOPES PRODUCED BY SUSPENDED-LOAD WASH

Quite different is the regime of wash denudation. In the SLOP3D program, this process conforms to the empirical results of ZINGG (1940), namely, that the sediment yield from wash denudation is a power function of both the slope angle and the slope length; instead of slope length, however, SLOP3D uses the depth of local runoff as one of the independent variables because it relates more closely to the process than mere slope length (equ. (4)). This local runoff depth may or may not be proportional to the distance from the divide; it is generated by a simple subroutine of SLOP3D which has been explained in an earlier paper (AHNERT 1977). For the sake of simplicity, the coefficient k_4 of equ. (4) is set here at zero so that there is no influence of regolith thickness upon sediment mobility.

Suspended-load wash denudation means that the waste material removed from any slope point does not get redeposited anywhere on the slope but is transported away. Consequently, this type of denudation is described sufficiently if one calculates with equation (4) only the amount of autochthonous material that is removed from every slope point. The term A of the mass balance equation (1) remains zero because no redeposition occurs. ZINGG (1940) had found for the sediment removal from a finite length of a slope with the gradient S that the sediment loss was approximately proportional to $L^{1.5} \cdot S^{1.5}$; for a point rather than a length, it would then be approximately proportional to the first derivative of that term with respect to L, that is, to $L^{0.5} \cdot S^{1.5}$ or, written in the transformed way of SLOP3D, proportionately to $D^{0.5} sin^{1.5}\alpha$. Thus in equ. (4) k_5 and k_6 have been given the values 0.5 and 1.5, respectively, for suspended-load wash.

Fig.6 shows the characteristic profile development for this denudation process, with stream incision at a constant rate until $T = 601$. The slope is concave throughout, with and without stream incision. Between about $T = 300$ and $T = 601$ the relief is constant, indicating a dynamic equilibrium between uplift (= stream incision) and denudation, with the same denudation rate at all points. The local runoff depth D has been programmed in this case to increase linearly downslope. Obviously the constant denudation rate $d = R_2$ (cf. equ. (4)) at all slope points is then only possible if the downslope increase of D is compensated by a downslope decrease of sin

$\neq \alpha$, that is, if the equilibrium profile is concave. The point of the model is that this concave characteristic form establishes itself through the interaction of the processes involved (cf. fig.1).

After the end of stream incision, the slope form remains concave. Just as in the case of the mass movement slope (fig.5), the process-specific characteristic form establishes and maintains its qualitative properties with or without stream incision. In contrast to fig.5, however, the relief development diagram of fig.6 has a much more rapid relief decline after stream incision ends. This is so because throughout most of the relief decline the slope at the summit of the profile remains steep. The summit therefore continues to be worn down rapidly regardless of the overall relief.

3.3 SLOPE DEVELOPMENT WITH COMBINED MASS MOVEMENT AND SUSPENDED-LOAD WASH DENUDATION

In fig.7 the profile development proceeds with both mass movement according to equ. (3) and suspended-load wash according to equ. (4). During the initial phase of profile differentiation the slope is predominantly convex, but the equilibrium profile (represented by the profile at $T = 1001$) has a convex upper part and a mildly concave lower part. Here, too, the convexo-concave characteristic form is maintained during relief decline after the end of stream incision. The upper convexity indicates that slope-dependent mass movement dominates here because the runoff depth is still rather small; this part of the profile is also an unintentional but nevertheless valid corroboration of GILBERT's (1909) explanation

Model 27028701 (Suspended-load wash)

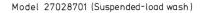

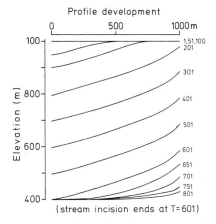

(stream incision ends at T=601)

Fig. 6: *Characteristic slope profile development by suspended-load wash denudation.*

Model 15028710
(Suspended-load wash and plastic flow)

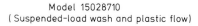

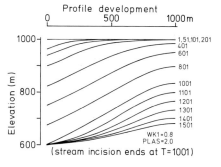

(stream incision ends at T=1001)

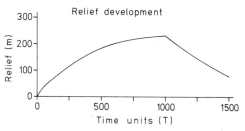

Fig. 7: *Slope profile development by the combination of slow mass movement and suspended-load wash denudation.*

k_1 (or PLAS) = 2.0, k_2 = 0.0, k_3 (or WK1) = 0.0; cf. equ. (3).

of the convexity of hilltops. On the lower slope the suspended-load wash denudation is effective enough to impose its shape characteristics upon the profile. The proportion between upper convexity and lower concavity depends upon the relative intensity of the two processes overall, which in SLOP3D is determined by the relative magnitude of the two coefficients k_1 (called PLAS in the FORTRAN notation) and k_3 (called WK1) in equations (3) and (4).

Fig.8 shows, for example, that the combination of k_1 (or PLAS) = 2.0 and k_3 (or WK1) = 0.4 produces a predominantly convex slope, while the combination of $k_1 = 2.0$ and $k_3 = 3.0$ leads to the development of a predominantly concave slope.

3.4 SLOPE DEVELOPMENT WITH BEDLOAD WASH DENUDATION UNDER DIFFERENT CONDITIONS OF PARTIAL AREAL CONTRIBUTION

"Bedload" wash denudation or "point-to-point" denudation refers to a slower overland flow transport system than that of suspended-load wash: instead of being transported clear out of the profile in one step, the sediment load moves downslope from one identified point of the profile to the next, and the mass balance equation (cf. equ. (1)) of that next point (and of all points below the slope crest) includes a term $A > 0.0$. The SLOP3D process equation is the same as that for suspended-load wash (equ. (4)) except that the two exponents k_5 and k_6 are both given the value 1.5.

Fig.9 shows four equilibrium profiles (with continuous constant-rate gross stream incision) after 2501 time units of development. The rate of gross stream incision, the equation for weathering and the equation for bedload wash denudation are identical in all four cases. The only difference lies in the duration of runoff-producing rainfall. Each of the slope profiles is identified in the model by the coordinates of 20 surface points. The constant IPAC = 20 in fig.9a (model No. 22028606) causes the runoff-producing precipitation to last until the rainwater that fell at the beginning of the rain at the crest of the slope has flowed all the way to the slope foot, across all 20 surface points of the slope. Because all points received rain during this time, the local runoff Q (and with it the runoff depth D) increased from the crest to the foot of the slope, and the entire slope length contributed water to the runoff depth at the slope foot. This is illustrated by the steady rise of the dashed curve "local Q" from right to left. The drawn-out line represents the slope profile; it is concave in the normal way one would expect for any slope shaped predominantly by wash denudation. On the second profile, fig.9b (model No. 22028605) with IPAC = 15, the rainfall lasts until the runoff from the crest of the slope has flowed across 15 of the 20 slope points, or over three-quarters of the length of the slope. As a result, the local runoff Q increases only on the upper three-quarters and remains constant on the lowest quarter of the slope length. Since the precipitation lasts for a shorter time than the time needed by the runoff to flow from crest to foot, the water that falls on the crest of the slope does not reach the foot of the slope (if one disregards possible afterflows); instead, only the lower three-quarters of the total profile length supply water to the slope foot and possibly to a stream that may be located

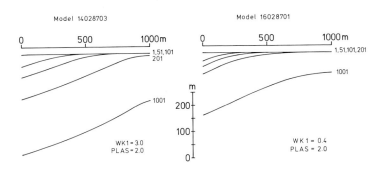

Fig. 8: *Characteristic profile shapes for slope development with differing relative intensities of suspended-load wash (WK1 or k_3) and slow mass movement (PLAS or k_1).*

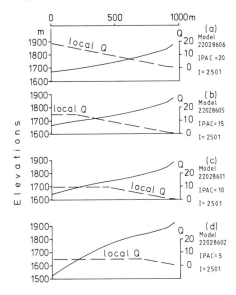

Fig. 9: *Four equilibrium profiles of slopes shaped by bedload wash denudation under differing conditions of partial area contribution of rainfall.*

IPAC = duration of effective rainfall events. I = elapsed time units of slope development; Q = local runoff height.

there; in other words, the actual hydrological drainage area of the slope foot is smaller than the topographical drainage area. This is the phenomenon that has been called partial area runoff contribution by YAIR et al. (1978) and partial area streamflow generation by others (cf. RICHARDS 1982, 39–41).

The slope profile in this case becomes concave only in the upper three quarters of its length, where the runoff discharge increases progressively; the low-ermost quarter with constant runoff has a slightly steeper gradient.

In fig.9c (model No. 22028601) with IPAC = 10, this tendency is more clearly visible; the lower half of the profile is noticeably convex. Fig.9d (model No. 22028602) with IPAC = 5 finally shows a concave wash profile only in the uppermost quarter of the profile and the lower three-quarters are convex.

Partial area runoff contribution is a common phenomenon in arid and semi-arid environments where rainfall events tend to have very short durations. Convexities of the lower profile segments as shown in fig.9 should be expected there; the shorter the "characteristic" duration of a rainfall event and the longer the slope along which the runoff flows, the more pronounced should be this "lower convexity". There is, however, at least one additional necessary condition: the particle size of the transported material must not become appreciably smaller from the crest to the foot of the profile; in the SLOP3D models of fig.9 the particle size has been assumed to be uniform.

Empirical evidence that profiles of this type exist for the reasons set forth here has been provided by SCHUMM (1961) who described profiles of semiarid ephemeral streams that are concave in their upper course and convex in their lower course. It should also be possible to find this profile type on pediments and alluvial fans in semiarid regions where there is little sorting or comminution of the transported material.

One particular aspect connected with the process-specific slope forms in fig.9 is the fact that, from the top profile with IPAC = 20 to the bottom profile with IPAC = 5, the elevation of the slope foot is progressively lower despite a gross rate of stream incision that is constant and equal in all four models. This difference is due to a difference in the net rate of stream incision during the phase of profile differentiation: the smaller IPAC, the smaller is the runoff depth and the sediment supply at the slope foot; the smaller also, accordingly, is the share of the gross stream incision rate that needs to be expended for sediment removal before net downcutting can take place, and the larger is the net incision rate.

4 SLOPE FORM AND DENUDATION RATES

Statements about denudation rates are usually made from measurements of the sediment load of rivers or from the amounts of sediment that have been accumulated in reservoirs (for example, by CORBEL 1959, SCHUMM 1963 and YOUNG 1969). Such data allow direct estimates of the mean denudation rate ($\bar{d}$) in the drainage basin that lies above the point of measurement. In large mid-latitude drainage basins, this rate is a linear function of the mean relief (AHNERT 1970). Attempts to estimate the rates of summit denudation (d_s) and thus of relief decline from these data have been made also but were based on hypothetical assumptions.

The model program SLOP3D offers the possibility to test the relationship between $\bar{d}, d_s$ and the relief directly for different process-specific profile forms. The test is carried out with the profile sequences of fig.5, 6 and 7.

The three different phases of profile development (cf. 3.1) contain different relstionships between local denudation values. The phase of profile differentiation in the early part of slope development is also a phase of relief increase: that is, the net stream incision rate (and the denudation rate at the slope foot) d_f is higher than the summit denudation rate d_s. The phase of dynamic equilibrium is marked by constant relief and by equality of local denudation rates all along the profile so that $d_f = \bar{d} = d_s$. This is an ideal state that can be approximated, in nature. Of particular interest, however, is the phase of relief decline after the end of stream incision, because it is also the phase of spatial differentiation of the denudation rate.

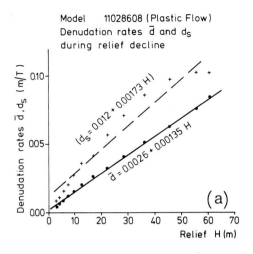

Model   11028608 (Plastic Flow)
Denudation rates $\bar{d}$ and d_s
during relief decline

$(d_s = 0.012 + 0.00173$ H$)$

$\bar{d} = 0.0026 + 0.00135$ H

(a)

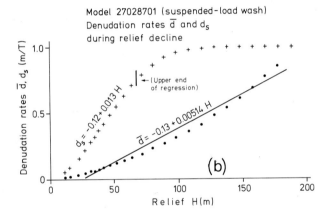

Model 27028701 (suspended-load wash)
Denudation rates $\bar{d}$ and d_s
during relief decline

(Upper end of regression)

$d_s = -0.12 + 0.013$ H

$\bar{d} = -0.13 + 0.00514$ H

(b)

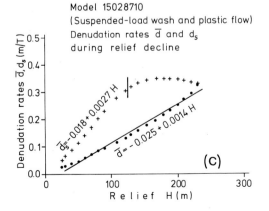

Model 15028710
(Suspended-load wash and plastic flow)
Denudation rates $\bar{d}$ and d_s
during relief decline

$d_s = 0.018 + 0.0027$ H

$\bar{d} = -0.025 + 0.0014$ H

(c)

Fig. 10: *Mean denudation rate $\bar{d}$ and summit denudation rate d_s as functions of available relief.*

a) For slow mass movement.

b) For suspended-load wash.

c) For a combination of slow mass movement and suspended-load wash.

Fig.10a shows the mean denudation rate $\bar{d}$ and the summit denudation rate d_s as functions of the available relief H in the model of slope development by slow mass movement (cf. fig.5). Not the absolute values but the relative changes of denudation with changing relief are of importance here. The function $\bar{d} = f(H)$ is very clearly linear and very similar to the function obtained from empirical data (cf. AHNERT 1970, 251). The summit denudation values d_s are also approximately proportional to the relief H, but in a non-linear manner; the linear regression line $d_s = f(H)$ in fig.10a is only a crude approximation of the actual distribution of the data points. The profile sequence after $T = 1201$ on fig.5 reveals the reason: during slope decline, the slope angle at the summit remains at first almost constant and later lessens only very gradually. Since the mass movement is a slope-dependent process (cf. equ. (3)), the angle of slope at the summit is the direct factor to influence d_s; relief is only an indirect factor to the extent in which the slope angle at the summit decreases as the relief becomes lower.

The dependence of the denudation rates upon relief is even smaller in the case of the suspended load wash denudation model (fig.10b and fig.6). The mean denudation rate d decreases rapidly with decreasing relief in the early phases of relief decline. This is due mainly to the rapid flattening of the lower part of the profile which afterwards cannot be worn down further by any significant amount. Mean denudation then becomes essentially the denudation on the upper part of the slope averaged out over the entire profile length. The summit denudation curve shows just the opposite trend: d_s remains approximately constant during the relief decline from $H = 188$ m to $H = 90$ m, because there is no great change in the magnitude of the denudation-determining factors (here, runoff height D and slope angle α) at the summit. Below $H = 90$ m, the slope at the summit decreases and with it d_s. This kind of relationship matches ver well the observations one can make in some badlands: sharp summits with steep slopes and intensive denudation, but small gradients and little net denudation on the lower profile.

The third example (fig.10c) shows the denudation during relief decline in the profile sequence of fig.7, with the combination of suspended-load wash and slow mass movement. Its mean denudation rate $\bar{d}$ is again nearly as linear a function of the relief as in fig.10a; the summit denudation rate d_s, however, varies in a manner similar to that in fig.10b.

If one compares these model results with the obviously linear relationship $\bar{d} = f(H)$ that was obtained from mid-latitude empirical data (AHNERT 1970), it seems that the relief development in mid-latitude regions is better matched by slope development models based either on slow mass movement (creep, solifluction) alone or on a combination of slow mass movement and wash denudation, rather than by models based on wash denudation alone. This corresponds well with existing knowledge of the denudation processes that have been active in these regions during the Quaternary.

A second conclusion concerns estimates of the summit denudation rate from mean denudation. They are easy in landform systems close to dynamic equilibrium because then the summit denudation rate is similar to the mean denudation rate. They become more difficult during relief decline. One may make a reasonable guess of d_s from known values of $\bar{d}$ if the dominant denudation process is creep or solifluction. Fig.10a indicates that d_s would be roughly 30% to 50% larger than $\bar{d}$. In regions with a dominant share of wash denudation, however, summit denudation is largely independent of relief or of mean denudation and therefore cannot be estimated in this manner. This means also, of course, that in such areas no estimate or projection of the rate of relief decline is possible from relief values or from mean denudation data.

5   THE HEIGHT LIMITS OF MOUNTAIN RANGES

Even at the macroscale of large drainage basins and mountain ranges SLOP3D can serve as a tool for the analysis of some aspects of relief development. In an earlier study it was found that in many young mountain systems of the world the ratio between the logarithm of the relative height ($logH$) of a major summit above the foreland and the logarithm of the distance from that summit to the foreland margin ($logL$) was nearly constant, with values between 0.772 and 0.823 (AHNERT 1984). The sample consisted of 21 mountain systems that were undergoing long-term uplift over the past several million years, from Cross Fell in the Pennines, Snowdon (Wales) and Feldberg (Black Forest) to Mt. Blanc, Aconcagua and Mt. Everest. Fig.11 shows the distribution of these data. The near-constancy of log H/log L means that the wider a young mountain range is, the higher are its main summits.

To explain this phenomenon, the following hypothesis was formulated:

1. The height of the main summits is a function of a) the long-term rate of

uplift and b) summit denudation.

2. There seems to be a geophysical limit to the maximum rate of long-term uplift; short-term movements such as glacio-isostatic uplift are not considered here, nor are height increases by compressional folding. This limit is set by the velocity of mantle currents in the asthenosphere that must flow into the uplift area in order to fill the space under the lithospheric mass being uplifted.

3. Erosion and denudation occur in response to the uplift, as relief is increased. If the long-term rate of uplift is approximately constant, the summit denudation rate will, after some lag time, catch up with the uplift rate. From that point onward the mountain system is approximately in dynamic equilibrium; although uplift continues there is no appreciable further relief increase.

4. If the mountain range is uplifted as a broad mass, the erosion and denudation response sets in at the margin of this mass and proceeds gradually towards the divides by headward erosion and slope denudation. Consequently, the wider the mountain range the more time will elapse before the headward progression of erosion and denudation reaches the main divide areas and catches up with the rate of uplift there.

5. It follows that in the divide region of a wide mountain range, the uplift rate tends to exceed the denudation rate for a longer time before equilibrium is reached than in the divide region of a narrow mountain range. Wide mountain ranges therefore can become higher than narrow ones.

6. Since the height of the main summits is so strongly a function of the vary-

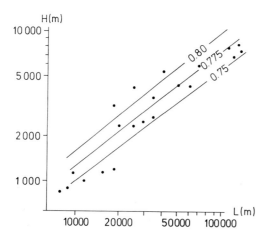

Fig. 11: *Relative height H as a function of the width L for various mountain ranges of the world.*

The straight lines indicate the ratios $log H/log L$ = 0.75, = 0.775 and = 0.8.

ing width of the mountain range (i.e. of the distance L to the margin), the long-term rate of uplift seems to be approximately identical in those different mountain ranges; of course this does not preclude considerable shorter-term fluctuations.

7. Implicitly, the hypothesis also suggests that the mountain ranges are approximately in a state of dynamic equilibrium.

An attempt was made to simulate this interaction with SLOP3D. Model profiles of different lengths L were subjected to the same rate of uplift (i.e. of gross stream incision) until equilibrium was reached, and the ratio $log H/log L$ of the equilibrium profile was determined. This was done for three different modes of denudation.

The results are shown in fig.12a. If denudation is by slow mass movement (plastic flow) only, the ratio $log H/log L$ (which is called "characteristic logarithmic slope") increases with increasing length L. Suspended-load wash denudation by itself has just the opposite effect: the greater the profile length, the smaller becomes the characteristic log-

arithmic slope. Because of the opposite character of these two trends, it was a natural conclusion to combine them. After several experiments with different combinations of the coefficients PLAS or k_1 (cf. equ. (3)) and WK1 or k_3 (cf. equ. (4)), the characteristic logarithmic slope was found to be nearly constant for different profile lengths if $k_s = 0.4$ and $k_3 = 4.0$. In this case the $log H/log L$ values varied between 0.7619 for $L = 500$ m and 0.7606 for $L = 1500$ m, that is, by only 0.0013 for a length ratio of 1:3. That is much less than the variation in the empirical data. The equilibrium profiles for this process combination are shown in fig.12b. Their overall shape is predominantly concave; the uppermost segment however is convex. The shape seems to represent the two exogenic process realms that together cause the denudation of mountain ranges: the concave (wash-dominated) part resembles the longitudinal profiles of the streams that have cut back into the mountain mass, the convex part near the summit is predominantly shaped by slow mass movements and resembles the valley side slopes in the interior of the mountain

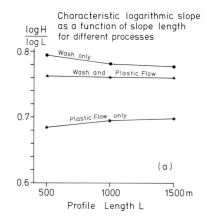

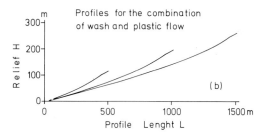

Fig.12a: *Characteristic logarithmic slope* $\log H/\log L$ *as a function of profile length for model slopes developed by differing denudation process systems.*

Fig. 12b: *Profiles of differing length, formed by wash and plastic flow, with constant* $\log H/\log L$.

area. The model experiment thus supports the hypothesis about the height limits of mountain ranges not only because of the nearly constant characteristic logarithmic slope but also because this constancy was obtained by a simulation with a geomorphologically plausible process combination.

6 CONCLUSIONS

In this paper, one theoretical model concept has been applied to geomorphological problems at very different spatial and temporal scales. The results show that it is possible to design models which remain valid regardless of scale and therefore are useful tools in the investigation of a great variety of geomorphological questions. Some results were produced directly by the model program without prior empirical information and may serve as starting points for empirical investigations; others corroborate existing empirical knowledge. In all cases, the advantage of linking empirical and theoretical work is obvious.

REFERENCES

AHNERT, F. (1954): Zur Frage der rückschreitenden Denudation und des dynamischen Gleichgewichts bei morphologischen Vorgängen. Erdkunde **8**, 61–64.

AHNERT, F. (1964): Quantitative models of slope development as a function of waste cover thickness. Abstracts of Papers, 20th Int. Geogr. Congr., London.

AHNERT, F. (1970): Functional relationships between denudation, relief and uplift in large mid-latitude drainage basins. Am. J. of Sci., **268**, 243–263.

AHNERT, F. (1976): Brief description of a comprehensive three-dimensional process-response model of landform development. Z. Geomorph. N.F. Suppl. **25**, 29–49.

AHNERT, F. (1977): Some comments on the quantitative formulation of geomorphological processes in a theoretical model. Earth Surface Processes **2**, 191–201.

AHNERT, F. (1984): Local relief and the height limits of mountain ranges. Am. J. of Sci. **284**, 1035–1055.

BREMER, H. (1973): Grundsatzfragen der tropischen Morphologie, insbesondere der Flächenbildung. Geog. Z., Beiheft "Geographie heute — Einheit und Vielfalt" (Plewe-Festschrift), 114–130.

CORBEL, J. (1959): Vitesse de l'érosion. Z. Geomorph. N.F. **3**, 1–28.

DAVIS, W.M. (1909): Geographical essays. Boston.

GILBERT, G.K. (1877): Report on the geology of the Henry Mountains. Washington. (2nd edition 1880).

GILBERT, G.K. (1909): The convexity of hilltops. J. Geol. **17**, 344–350.

HACK, J. (1960): Interpretation of erosional topography in humid temperate regions. Am. J. Sci. **258-A**, 80–97.

JAHN, A. (1954): Denudacyjni bilans stoku Csas. Gogr. **25**, 38–64. English version: Denudation balance of slopes. (1968) Geogr. Polonica **13**, 9–29.

LEOPOLD, L.B. & MADDOCK, Th. (1953): The hydraulic geometry of stream channels and some physiographic implications. U.S.G.S. Prof. Paper **252**.

LEOPOLD, L.B., WOLMAN, M.G. & MILLER, J.P. (1964): Fluvial Processes in Geomorphology. San Francisco and London.

PENCK, W. (1924): Die morphologische Analyse. Stuttgart.

RICHARDS, K. (1982): Rivers. London and New York.

SCHUMM, S.A. (1961): Effect of sediment characteristics on erosion and deposition in ephemeral stream channels. U.S.G.S. Prof. Paper **552 C**, 31–70.

SCHUMM, S.A. (1963): The disparity between present rates of denudation and orogeny. U.S.G.S. Prof. Paper **454H**.

SCHUMM, S.A. (1973): Geomorphic thresholds and complex response of drainage systems. Proc. 4th Annual Geomorphology ymposium, Binghamton, 75–85.

YAIR, A., SHARON, D. & LAVEE, H. (1978): An instrumented watershed for the study of partial area contribution of runoff in the arid zone. Z. Geomorph. N.F. Suppl. **29**, 71–82.

YOUNG, A. (1969): Present rate of land erosion. Nature **224**, 851–852.

ZINGG, A.W. (1940): Degree and length of land slope as it affects soil less in runoff. Agricultural Engineering (21) **40**, 59–64.

Address of author:
F. Ahnert
Geographisches Institut der RWTH
D-5100 Aachen
Federal Republic of Germany

CATENA SUPPLEMENT 10   p.51–66   Braunschweig 1987

FACTORS INFLUENCING STRUCTURAL LANDFORM DYNAMICS ON THE COLORADO PLATEAU ABOUT THE NECESSITY OF CALIBRATING THEORETICAL MODELS BY EMPIRICAL DATA

K.-H. **Schmidt**, Berlin

SUMMARY

On the global scale climate is one of the most important controlling factors of structural landforms. If, however, form and process are studied on a more regional scale, other controls gain significance. Structural landform dynamics were investigated in the central parts of the Colorado Plateau, a semiarid area of relatively uniform climatic conditions. The controlling factors, directly or indirectly, exert influence on the dependent system variables (tab.1).

Empirical data on the system variables were collected for more than one hundred structural landforms. The influence of the controlling factors was statistically analyzed, and the causal links between the system variables were inquired into. The influence of the controlling factors is demonstrated for the characteristics of the lower scarp slope. It is shown that some controlling factors, such as the lithology and structure of the rocks

ISSN 0722-0723
ISBN 3-923381-10-7
©1987 by CATENA VERLAG,
D–3302 Cremlingen-Destedt, W. Germany
3-923381-10-7/87/5011851/US$ 2.00 + 0.25

involved, the direction of the dip, or the mode of production and transport of debris, have been paid too little attention to in some theoretical models.

1 INTRODUCTION

The purpose of this paper is to show that a collection, examination and quantitative evaluation of empirical field data may yield useful, sometimes necessary information for the development and improvement of theoretical models. Structural landform dynamics will serve as an example.

In this paper cuestas, hogbacks and horizontal plateaus are referred to as structural landforms. They have in common that their development and their form components are primarily controlled by geologic structure and bedrock lithology. Their backslope is protected by a resistant caprock, which is underlain by softer rocks more susceptible to erosion. The scarps of these landforms are heterogeneous, generally consisting of an upper steep slope in the resistant layer, and a lower moderately inclined slope in the less resistant rocks. The break of slope

INDEPENDENT VARIABLES	
(1)	lithology and structure of caprock
(2)	lithology and structure of underlying soft rock
(3)	thickness of caprock
(4)	thickness of soft rock
(5)	thickness ratio
(6)	dip
(7)	direction of dip
(8)	position of drainage lines
(9)	distance to base level
DEPENDENT VARIABLES	
(1)	groundplan (embayment ratio)
(2)	inclination of upper scarp slope
(3)	length of upper scarp slope
(4)	inclination of lower scarp slope
(5)	length of lower scarp slope
(6)	inclination of backslope
(7)	length of backslope
(8)	dissection of upper scarp slope
(9)	dissection of lower scarp slope
(10)	debris cover on scarp slope
(11)	dissection of backslope

Tab. 1: *Independent and de-pendent variables in the system of structural landform dynam-ics.*

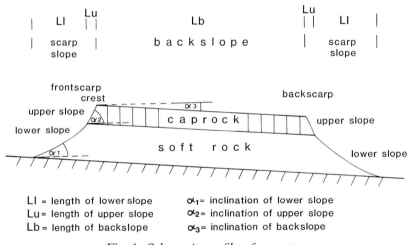

Fig. 1: *Schematic profile of a cuesta.*

is in most cases exactly at the geological contact (e.g. CARSON & KIRKBY 1972, 354). A distinction is made between frontscarps and backscarps. On a frontscarp the dip is into the scarp, whereas on a backscarp the dip is out of the scarp face. The backscarp corresponds to the "Achterstufe", a term in-troduced by MORTENSEN (1953). The relief elements of a cuesta are shown in a schematic profile (fig.1).

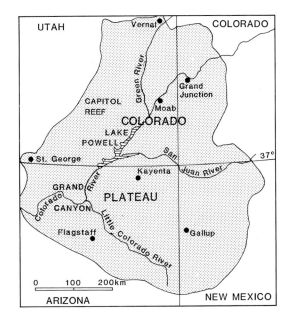

Fig. 2: *Location map.*

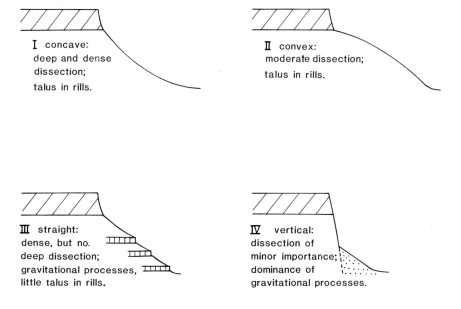

I concave:
deep and dense
dissection;
talus in rills.

II convex:
moderate dissection;
talus in rills.

III straight:
dense, but no.
deep dissection;
gravitational processes,
little talus in rills.

IV vertical:
dissection of
minor importance;
dominance of
gravitational processes.

Fig. 3: *Types of lower scarp slopes.*

2 SYSTEM VARIABLES IN STRUCTURAL LANDFORM DYNAMICS

There are a number of independent variables which affect the detailed pattern of form and process characteristics of structural landforms. On the global scale climte is, of course, one of the most important controlling factors (e.g. BLUME 1971). If form and process variations are studied on a more regional scale, other controls gain greater significance (tab.1). These factors, directly or indirectly, exert influence on the dependent system variables (tab.1).

Structural landforms were investigated in the central parts of the Colorado Plateau in the southwestern United States (fig.2), a semiarid area with relatively uniform climatic conditions. Here, as in an experimental setup, the independent variables show great differences in their specific attributes. Thus a great variation in the properties of the dependent variables is obtained. Empirical data on the system variables were collected for more than one hundred structural landforms. The influence of the controlling factors was statistically analyzed for the set of dependent form and process variables. The caussl links of the interrelations between independent and dependent system variables were also investigated.

3 THE CONTROL OF THE LOWER SCARP SLOPE CHARACTERISTICS

It is not the purpose of this article to go into the details of the influence of the controlling factors on each of the dependent variables and to present the operational procedure involved (see, for instance, SCHMIDT 1980). The paper concentrates on a small selection of results, namely on the control of the lower slope characteristics, which will demonstrate the multi-variate influence on cuesta scarp forms and processes. These variables will also be important in the discussion of the theoretical models which have been offered for structural landforms on the Colorado Plateau. The dependent form and process variables of the lower scarp slope discussed here are its inclination, dissection and its debris cover. These different attributes are closely linked in a systematic and effective self-regulating famework.

3.1 INFLUENCE OF THE PROPERTIES OF THE SOFT ROCK

The most important independent variables governing the processes and the resulting forms of the lower scarp slope are the lithology and structure of the slope forming soft rock ((2) in tab.1). According to the different rock types involved a classification into four slope categories is possible (fig.3).

The first type (I) is characterized by a concave slope, which generally turns into a pediment at the scarp foot. The average inclination of these slopes is about 35°. The slope is deeply dissected by a great number of rills, in which the debris of the caprock is concentrated (photo 1). Here, as in all other cases, large debris blocks can also be found at the scarp foot. This slope type is developed in highly impermeable and homogeneous shales like the Upper Cretaceous Mancos Shale.

The second slope type (II) has a convex profile with an average inclination of about 30°. It is less deeply dis-

Photo 1: *Slope type I; concave lower slope in the Upper Cretaceous Mancos Shale, deeply dissected, concentration of talus in rills. Caprock is the Point Lookout Sandstone.*

sected and the rill density is lower than in the first type (photo 2). The caprock debris is also concentrated in the rills, through which the debris is transported to the scarp foot. This slope type is found in bentonitic swelling clays, which contain large quantities of montmorillonite like those of the Petrified Forest Member of the Chinle Formation. When drying after precipitation events desiccation cracks develop, which reduce surface runoff and induce piping in a following event (photo 3). Microkarst features like sinkholes and 'karst-springs' at the scarp foot are typical for these slopes.

The third slope type (III) is composed of segments of different inclinations because of the interstratification of soft layers and thin more resistant beds, as for example in the Halgaito Tongue of the Cutler Formation. The resistant beds form secondary ledges on the slope. A line drawn from the upper end of the slope to the scarp foot runs straight with a short basal concavity. Due to the insertion of the more resistant beds the

Photo 2: *Slope type II; convex lower slope in the Brushy Basin Member of the Jurassic Morrison Formation, moderately dissected, talus in rills. Caprock is the Cretaceous Cedar Mountain Formation.*

average inclination of this lower slope type is about 40°. These beds also impede a deep dissection by the slope rills, the density of which, however, is great. The rills are not the major lines of transport of the caprock debris, they have the prime function of undermining the caprock and producing rockfalls and talus cones, which are also undermined by rills at their flanks, thus being separated from the scarp and forming talus flatirons (SCHIPULL 1980). By the production of talus cones the inclination becomes smaller, and the slope is locally stabilized (photo 4).

The fourth slope type (IV) has a vertical cliff in its upper part. At the base there is a talus cone with an inclina- tion approximately at the angle of repose consisting of caprock and soft rock material (photo 5). This complex lower slope is developed in evenly bedded series of fine sandstones, siltstones and shales with beds of gypsum like those of the Moenkopi Formation. Another important feature of these rock types are the vertical joints, along which rectangular blocks are formed that fall down to the base of the slope where they easily disintegrate. Extensive cliff failures may occur. Steep-sided gullies divide the vertical cliffs into individual column-like segments. These gullies are the prolongations of rills of the upper slope, and do not originate on the lower slope itself.

The subdivision into these four lower

Photo 3: *Desiccation cracks and microkarst features in the Petrified Forest Member of the Triassic Chinle Formation.*

slope categories is applicable throughout the study area. The average appearance of the slope types is modified by the influence of other controlling variables.

3.2 INFLUENCE OF THE OTHER CONTROLLING VARIABLES

The inclination of the lower slope is not influenced by lithology ((1) in tab.1) and thickness of the caprock (3): the slope types show the same character below different caprocks. The dissection, however, is indirectly influenced by the lithology and thickness of the caprock, because all drainage lines originating on the upper slope continue on the lower slope on their way to the scarp foreland.

To a large extent the debris cover of the lower slope is provided by the caprock material. The influence of caprock lithology and jointing on the size of talus is evident. Caprock thickness is important for the distribution, transport and the mode of destruction of talus material, because the thicker the caprock the higher is the potential energy of rock-

Photo 4: *Slope type III; straight lower slope in the Halgaito Tongue of the Permian Cutler Formation, ledges are formed by thin resistant beds, no deep dissection, undermining of caprock (Cedar Mesa Sandstone) leads to the production of rockfalls and talus cones.*

falls. Debris can be transported farther down the slope by gravity forces, and a high percentage of the rocks falling from the cliff disintegrates in transit or on impact (SCHUMM & CHORLEY 1966). It is also this group of thicker caprocks that provides the blocks found at the foot of the scarps. Only the upper portions of the lower slope are supplied with rockfall material, when the caprock is of only moderate thickness. The undermining process must be most intense in caprocks of very small thickness, because the weight of the rock alone does not cause rock failure. It is here that large overhangs in the upper slope may develop.

The thickness of the soft rock ((4) in tab.1) and the thickness ratio (5) have only a minor influence on lower slope inclinations. With increasing thickness the basal concavity in slope types I and III is more pronounced. Slope type IV is only vertically stable up to a threshold thickness of about 10 meters depending on the cementing material involved. If this threshold is passed, the basal debris cone develops. With increasing thickness of the soft rock the dissection of all slope types is intensified, because the drainage area of the rills gets larger. The tendency of channel convergence becomes stronger. A greater thickness of the soft rock and a greater thickness ratio facili-

Photo 5: *Slope type IV; vertical lower slope in the Triassic Moenkopi Formation with basal talus cone. Caprock is the Shinarump Conglomerate.*

tate the transport and destruction of the debris cover, which is thinner per unit area.

The dip of the strata ((6) in tab.1) has only a negligible influence on the lower slope characteristics. Much more important is the direction or the dip (7), a controlling factor to which too little attention has been paid in most models.

Slope inclination on backscarps is generally smaller than on frontscarps (fig.1). This can be best observed along canyons, which have been incised parallel to the strike of gently dipping strata. The differences between front- and backscarp inclinatins is always statistically highly significant.

As the drainage divide on a cuesta is generally situated close to the crest of the frontscarp, runoff in consequent valleys is directed towards the backscarp, which, therefore, is much more dissected than the corresponding frontscarp. This circumstance results in a much higher embayment of the backscarp (SCHMIDT 1980). Linear erosion in cuesta scarp

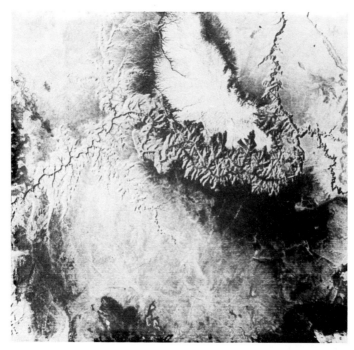

Photo 6: *Grand Canyon, the strata are dipping to the southwest, the South Rim (frontscarp) lies much closer to the Colorado River than the North Rim (backscarp), which is also much more embayed.*

development is of particular importance on the backscarps. The backwearing of backscarps, therefore, runs at a much faster pace. This fact has often been neglected, but can easily be deduced from the distance of back- and frontscarps from the drainage lines, by which they were initiated. The Colorao River in the Grand Canyon area is incised into strata which are gently dipping to the southwest. Thus the South Rim is a frontscarp, the North Rim a backscarp. The ratio of distances to the Colorado River is 1 to 3 (photo 6).

The average debris cover density and thickness are not greater on backscarps than on frontscarps, as might be expected, since the dip out of the scarp face should support the removal of the caprock by gravitational processes. If talus production exceeded talus destruction and transport to the foreland,

eventual longlasting talus accumulation would occur, and the equilibrium of talus input and output would be disturbed. To prevent this state of disequilibrium there is the internal self-regulating mechanism of gentler inclinations on backscarp slopes.

Lines of talus concentration, however, are found along the channels and canyons that reach down from the cuesta backslope through the embayments of the backscarp. Runoff concentration makes talus transport and removal very effective in the embayments. Moreover, the backscarps due to their higher embayment ratios are much longer than the corresponding frontscarps; so the sum of all talus production and removal processes along backscarps may be several times greater. This results in the aforementioned faster backwearing of backscarps.

The position of the drainage lines ((8) in tab.1) and the distance to the regional base level (9) also influence the form and process characteristics of the lower scarp slope. A subsequent valley at the scarp foot leads to greater steepness of the slope, and the basal concavity is shortened or not present at all; it may also be absent when there is a high vertical distance to base level. The relation between dissection of the slope and the position of drainage lines need not be discussed; high vertical distance to base level intensifies dissection, though short-lived changes of base level show no influence on slope dissection (VANDERPOOL 1982), only changes of long duration and greater magnitude due to the slopes' long relaxation times. A rising base level disturbs equilibrium of talus production and removal, with a debris surplus on the slope and a talus weathering ratio (SCHUMM & CHORLEY 1966) greater than one.

Inclination and dissection and the production, distribution, destruction and transport of talus material are in a delicate balance on the lower scarp slope as can be inferred from the preceding information. Where dissection is intense, slope inclination is moderate; where inclination is high, dissection plays only a minor role. Either dissection (type I) or steep inclination (type IV) or a combination of both (type III) are responsible for the destabilization of the caprock and the production of talus material (fig.3). Type II does not fit into this picture with its moderate inclination and dissection, but here landsliding processes in high intensity precipitation events are promoted by the lithological characteristics of the bentonitic material, which furnishes planes of slippage when saturated with water (STRAHLER 1940, MULLENS 1960).

When dissection is a major feature of the lower scarp slope, the rills facilitate the downslope transport of the talus material (type I, II); where dissection is less important, transport is accomplished mainly by gravitational processes (type IV), which may be supported by the undermining action of rills at the flanks of talus cones (type III).

On complex scarps, where different types of resistant and soft rock material are involved, the four slope types produce their specific attributes; their average appearance, especially as far as their inclination is concerned, remains the same beneath different types of caprock. On the complex scarp in the Capitol Reef area (location see fig.2), slope types II–IV can be observed in a single profile (photo 7).

The close spatial co-existence of concave, convex, straight and vertical slope types show that climatic interpretations of different slope profiles should be used with great caution, that the lithological properties of the rocks have to be considered carefully in model building and that the model assumption of a typical slope profile being most probable to develop in a specific region is far from real.

4 COMPARISON BETWEEN FIELD OBSERVATIONS AND MODEL SIMULATIONS

In the next step structural landform form and process characteristics as they are observed on the Colorado Plateau are compared with the results of model simulations with special emphasis on the lower slope attributes.

A limited number of models has been proposed for the Colorado Plateau, all

Photo 7: *Capitol Reef, complex scarp with three different lower slope types (II–IV) in a single profile (II in Church Rock Member, III in Petrified Forest Member of the Chinle Formation, IV in Moenkopi Formation).*

of them dealing with the Grand Canyon, a very special case, which, however, also reflects the essential mechanisms of structural landform dynamics in a sequence of different slopes in a complex scarp. Dissection and debris cover of the lower segments of the canyon walls are, of course, influenced by input processes from the upper segments. They receive more debris and are also more dissected than corresponding lower slope types on a simple caprock/soft rock cuesta scarp.

The models were described by POLLAK (1969), ARONSSON & LINDE (1982), and CUNNINGHAM & GRIBA (1973). Also a more general model by AHNERT (1976a, 1976b) will be discussed.

In POLLACK's model stream incision and lateral downslope transport in horizontal strata of different resistance and thickness are considered. It is stated that the expression of the strata is dependent on the state of development of the system (POLLACK 1969, 62). Comment: This is certainly true for soft rocks that have lost their protective caprock cover. This phenomenon has already been described by GILBERT (1877). But in heterogeneous scarps the rocks keep their intrinsic characteristics. The model needs a subparallel tributary canyon (fig.4a) to explain the asymmetrical development of the canyon, which, in reality, is caused by the direction of the dip (see photo 6).

In the model put forward by ARONSSON & LINDE (1982) the bedrock is also assumed to be horizontally stratified by layers of different competence. Intensity of vertical erosion for the individual layers is given by the notation ψ, intensity of weathering is given by the notation ϕ (fig.4b). Debris is quickly removed. The solution formula leads to big overhanging parts of the rock walls. Com-

ment: This is in disagreement with gravitational processes and crack formation induced by the undermining processes on the lower scarp slope. Overhangs are only produced below very thin caprocks. There are also other respects in which the model does not meet reality. The harder rocks produce the protruding benches, the steep slopes are formed in the softer rocks (fig.4b). But there is only a limited number of free face-makers in the soft rocks. Clearly, the importance of vertical erosion is exaggerated in comparison with the backwearing of slopes, caused by gravitational and aquatic processes. The authors contend that the canyon is symmetrical as in their model (ARONSSON & LINDE 1982, 596). The actual asymmetrical form is not accounted for.

In a model proposed by CUNNINGHAM & GRIBA (1973) the principal assumptions are

that the various rock formations are exactly horizontally disposed,

that linear stream action and mass wasting are the only destructive processes,

and that there is only backwearing of slopes, no downwearing of crests (CUNNINGHAM & GRIBA 1973, 46).

In the model free faces also originate in less resistant rocks, if they are controlled by vertical joints (fig.4c, layer D). Comment: This is in good agreement with the conditions in slope type IV. Vertical cliffs in soft rocks are found in parts of the Supai Group in the Grand Canyon, though slope types I and III dominate on the canyon walls.

In the model parallel retreat of slopes is only found in free face-makers. Otherwise the processes operating result in

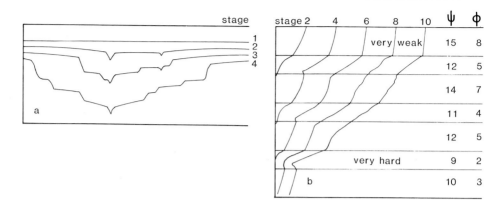

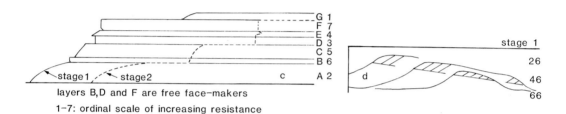

layers B,D and F are free face-makers

1–7: ordinal scale of increasing resistance

Fig. 4: *Model drawings after*

a) POLLACK (1969);
b) ARONSSON & LINDE (1982), ψ is the notation for the intensity of vertical erosion, ϕ for the intensity of weathering of the individual layers;
c) CUNNINGHAM & GRIBA (1973);
d) AHNERT (1976a, 1976b).

a reduction of slope angles (fig.4c, layer A). Comment: This statement contradicts field observations and the dynamics of structural landforms, for which parallel retreat of cuesta scarps is an essential mechanism. All over the Colorado Plateau identical rock types reveal identical slope types on heterogeneous cuesta scarps.

A major drawback of the model is that, with the exception of vertical cliffs in the free face-makers, it allows only convex slopes (fig.4c, layers A, C, E), whereas in the actual relief concave and straight slopes predominate. The error lies in the assumption of the model that linear stream action and mass wasting are the only processes operating; sheet and rill wash on the slopes are neglected. The only convex lower slopes on the Colorado Plateau are those in the bentonitic clays (fig.3), where sheet and rill wash are actually reduced due to underground drainage by piping. Clearly, aquatic slope processes have to be included in model simulations. The model, of course, cannot explain the asymmetrical profile of the canyon, because the strata are assumed to be horizontally disposed. The asymmetrical extent of backwearing is discussed and explained by greater recessional activity on the dip slope. The greater length of the northern tributaries and the greater dissection of the North

Rim are, however, not explained by the predisposition of backscarps for dissectional activity but by tectonic processes.

The last model to be commented on briefly is the one by AHNERT (1976a, 1976b), not specially designed for the Colorado Plateau, but for cuesta landscapes in general. Some of the limitations of the other models have been overcome here. The model includes sheet erosion as a denudational process, and the layers of diffrent resistance may have any dip. These additional model qualifications result in the development of concave slopes, the bench on the frontscarp is not sloping to the river, and the lower slopes on frontscarps are steeper than the corresponding backscarp slopes (fig.4d), a difference that is also observed in reality.

5 CONCLUSION

Theoretical models must be calibrated in comparison with the features of the natural system. The model's assumptions must be defined and the variables selected on the basis of empirical data evaluation. A constant rapport with empirical field observations is necessary. In the models concerning the development and dynamics of structural landforms some variables, like the specific lithological and structural characteristics of the rocks involved or the direction of the dip, and some system responses, like the presence or absence of sheet and rill wash or the mode of production and removal of debris have been frequently neglected. Negative feedback mechanisms in the internal self-regulating framework of the system variables also have to be taken into account, as the interaction of inclination, dissection and debris production and transport demonstrates.

REFERENCES

AHNERT, F. (1976a): Darstellung des Struktureinflusses auf die Oberflächenformen im theoretischen Modell. Z. Geomorph. N.F. Suppl.Bd. **24**, 11–22.

AHNERT, F. (1976b): Brief description of a comprehensive three-dimensional process-response model of landform development. Z. Geomorph. N.F. Suppl. Bd. **25**, 29–49.

ARONSSON, G. & LINDE. K. (1982): Grand Canyon — a quantitative approach to the erosion and weathering of a stratified bedrock. Earth Surface Processes, **7**, 589–599.

BLUME, H. (1971): Probleme der Schichtstufenlandschaft. Erträge der Forschung, Bd. **5**, 117 p., Darmstadt.

CARSON, M.A. & KIRKBY, M.J. (1972): Hillslope — Form and Process. 475 p., Cambridge.

CUNNINGHAM, F.F. & GRIBA, W. (1973): A model of slope development and its application to the Grand Canyon, Arizona, USA. Z. Geomorph. N.F. **17**, 43–77.

GILBERT, G.K. (1877): Report on the geology of the Henry Mountains. U.S. Geogr. and Geol. Survey, Rocky Mtn. Region, 160 p.

MORTENSEN, H. (1953): Neues zum Problem der Schichtstufenlandschaft. Einige Ergebnisse einer Reise durch den Südwesten der USA, Sommer und Herbst 1952. Nachr. Ak. d. Wiss. Göttingen, Nr. **2**.

MULLENS, T.E. (1960): Geology of the Clay Hills area, San Juan County, Utah. U.S. Geol. Surv. Bull. **1087** H, 259–336.

POLLACK, H.N. (1969): A numerical model of Grand Canyon. In: Four Comers Geological Society, Geology and Natural History of the Grand Canyon Region, 61–62.

SCHIPULL, K. (1980): Die Cedar Mesa-Schichtstufe auf dem Colorado Plateau — ein Beispiel für die Morphpdynamik arider Schichtstufen. Z. Geomorph. N.F. **24**, 318–331.

SCHMIDT, K.-H. (1980): Der Grundriß von Schichtstufen in Trockengebieten. Die Erde, **111**, 231–246.

SCHUMM, S.A. & CHORLEY, R.J. (1966) Talus weathering and scarp recession in the Colorado Plateau. Z. Geomorph. N.F. **10**, 11–36.

STRAHLER, A.N. (1940): Landslides of the Vermilion and Echo Cliffs, Northern Arizona. Jour. Geom. **3**, 285–301.

VANDERPOOL, N.L. (1982): ERODE — A computer model of drainage basin development under changing baselevel conditions. In: CRAIG, R.G. & CRAFT, J.L. (eds.): Applied Geomorphology, 214–223, London.

Address of author:
Karl-Heinz Schmidt
Institut für Physische Geographie
Geomorphlogisches Laboratorium
der FU Berlin
Altensteinstr. 19
D-1000 Berlin 33

CATENA SUPPLEMENT 10   p.67–72   Braunschweig 1987

SOME REFLECTIONS
ON MODELLING HILLSLOPE PROCESSES

J. **de Ploey** and J. **Poesen**, Leuven

SUMMARY

Recent hillslope process research has focussed on the basic understanding of the mechanical and physico-chemical interactions governing processes in order to predict the actual evolution of landforms. In the long run, this research will contribute to the explanation of landforms, provided that paleogeographic information on the sites under study is known explicitly and in detail.

In modelling these processes, a combination of both theoretical and experimental approaches is needed as illustrated by several examples from the Leuven laboratory. The main restrictions of hillslope process research are more and more caused by a lack of refined measuring techniques and by poorly developed theoretical models. In the near future, conceptual verbal approaches of complex geomorphological systems, supported by an integrated set of observations, measurements and mathematical models of elementary processes, will still remain dominant. It is hoped, however, that theoreticians will contribute to transform the proposed verbal models into mathematical expressions.

ISSN 0722-0723
ISBN 3-923381-10-7
©1987 by CATENA VERLAG,
D–3302 Cremlingen-Destedt, W. Germany
3-923381-10-7/87/5011851/US$ 2.00 + 0.25

1   INTRODUCTION

In geomorphological thinking, models have never been lacking. Moreover, geomorphology has experienced the disadvantageous influence of an excessively prolonged accentuation of pure theoretical, verbal models related to the socalled geomorphological cycle. The obsession to trace, on a pure morphographic and morphostratigraphic base, cyclic landform elements and to fit them in a global model of the geomorphological cycle, has ultimately retarded rather than activated the development of empirical process research. Through that, geomorphology has only recently become a natural science, relying on hypothesis, empirical testing and mathematical treatment of data. As HEMPEL (1970, 234) states "Any explanation of scientific character is amenable to objective checks; these include (a) an empirical test of the sentences which state the determining conditions (b) an empirical test of universal hypothesis on which the explanation rests ...". And further "The main function of general laws in the natural sciences is to connect events in patterns which are usually refered to as explanation and prediction". Modern process research tries to fulfill these conditions, mainly by introducing "empirical tests" which may lead to explanation and prediction. The ancient geomorphology of

W.M. DAVIS up to L. KING was not confronted with the ultimate "objective checks" since the main objective of these authors was to examen the extreme consequences of a set of concepts regarding the "cycle of development". In a certain way their deductive approach was outside of any experimental consideration. Experiments were mainly thought-experiments focused on the end-products of slope evolution rather than on the processes governing them. Of course, one may claim that geomorphology had to go through this phase before being able to develop the empirical approach. In fact, the bridge between physics and geography in physical geography is a rather recent phenomenon.

Recent process research has not only considered the direct volumetric-topographical effects of the main geomorphic agents. More and more investigations, convergently performed by geomorphologists and researchers in other disciplines, focus on the basic understanding of the mechanical and physico-chemical interactions which govern processes. This type of geomorphological study is not directly concerned with the explanation of landforms but indirectly, and in the long run, it will evidently contribute to this goal. However, a geomorphological interpretation of landforms not only assumes a very good knowledge of the processes and the working of process combinations but also the paleogeographic information on the sites under study needs to be known as explicitly and in detail. This, however, presupposes that Quaternary research is able to produce detailed chronostratigraphical and paleoenvironmental data sets. Many process geomorphologists doubt — in our opinion correctly — that this information will,ever be available in most areas.

If this is true, geomorphology should concentrate more on the prediction of the evolution of actual landforms. It means that we should test our models and concentrate our "objective checks" on selected morphographic units with a measureable seasonal or annual evolution.

2   THEORETICAL AND EMPIRICAL APPROACHES

In our opinion process research should be based on combined field and laboratory research. The priority of field work is evident since it determines the finality of all geomorphological study which for a large part is to elucidate the nature of process combinations, being active in given regional and complex ecosystems.

It becomes more and more questionable in how far slope hydrology, erosion and slope development, during semi-catastrophic events, are controlled by continuity equations. IMESON (personal communication) is of the opinion that site-specific conditions are often more important than general catenary conditions. This is certainly true in many cultivated areas as the Leuven laboratory experiences it in the Huldenberg test area, which belongs to the loess loamy belt. Therefore, it seems to us that, in most cases, field research should not be restricted to plots of limited size, but should concentrate more on complete toposequences. The Sde Boqer testsite, studied for years by YAIR and coworkers, has been one of the first validations of this principle.

Field studies are also needed to check models issued from laboratory research. The latter is essential since it allows one to test systematically the role played by certain factors, e.g. the impact of the important slope factor. Laboratory experiments at least promote the development of idealized models which form a base for further discussion of complex field situations.

Empirical research should not limit itself to the elaboration of mathematical expressions, resulting from curve fitting and current regression analysis. It is highly desirable that in the future, geomorphologists should pay more attention to physically-based theoretical considerations, expressed either verbally or mathematically. Such an approach is more in line with the work by AHNERT (1964, 1973) and KIRKBY (1980). It is important, if not necessary, to initiate and to pollinate empirical research by (simple) deterministic models.

An example is POESEN & SAVAT's (1981) splash transport model which starts from the simple, basic equation

$$q_s = VY - vy \qquad (1)$$

where

q_s = the net splash transport on a bare smooth interrill surface

V and v = the fractions of total volume of detached sediment splashed downslope and upslope respectively,

Y and y = the mean weighted projected splash distances in a downslope and upslope direction respectively.

Next, this basic equation was made explicit in terms of measurable quantities resulting in the final, more complex empirical equation (POESEN 1985):

$$q_s = f(KE, R, D_{50}, a, b) \qquad (2)$$

where

KE = the rainfall kinetic energy,

R = the resistance of the soil to detachment by raindrop impact,

D_{50} = the median grain size of the soil material,

a = the slope angle,

b = rainfall obliquity.

Meanwhile measurements at the Huldenberg test plot showed that upslope splash drift, resulting from strong cyclonic southwesterly winds, is often a reality (POESEN 1986). Hence, checking in the field, as a feedback operation, forces now to reconsider expression (2) and to replace factor b by a more complex expression, introducing slope orientation and mean velocity of the wind. This remodelling will require windtunnel tests with oblique rainfall simulation. Meanwhile, equation (2) is useful to calculate detachment rates on interrill surfaces under conditions of rainstorms without any important horizontal, wind-driven component.

Remodelling becomes a science of coefficients, trying to decipher the nature of "black-box coefficients" and to substitute more explicit mathematical functions for them. So stemflow modelling started with a theoretical expression (DE PLOEY 1982)

$$IC_r = f(I_r, t, S_b, \overline{L}, S_s, S_t, \overline{a}) \qquad (3)$$

where

IC_r is the total amount of rainwater collected at the base of the stem or sod;

I_r and t are respectively rainfall intensity and duration of rainfall;

S_b corresponds to the internodal, basal surface;

$\overline{L}$ is the mean length of stems or leaves;

S_s/S_t stands for the ground cover ratio;

$\overline{a}$ is the mean slope angle of stems or leaves.

The final stemflow model constructed after rainfall simluator experiments, introduced a black-box coefficient, a shape factor f_{sh}, which is now being analysed in more detail and needs specification for different types of vegetation.

In general, it can be stated that a process or subprocess P can be described by an equation of the general form

$$P = f(p_1, p_2, ..., p_i, c_b) \qquad (4)$$

where
$p_1...p_i$ are measurable parameters and
c_b is a black-box coefficient.

The extent to which the model becomes more explicit depends on two basic conditions:

a.   the discovery of new factors and parameters which play a role in P

b. the development of techniques which allow one to measure a larger number of significant parameters p_i.

It can already be seen that methodological restrictions and difficulties occur here:

a. It can be rather difficult to find a relatively simple mathematical expression for several components or factors. For example, in the case of the stemflow shape factor f_{sh} an adequate parametrisation of the complex geometry of leaves is experienced as problematic. The same is true for the dynamic characterisation of topsoil structures, an important factor in erodibility studies. In general difficulties are experienced in fitting structural-geometric properties into mathematical models.

b. There are also purely technological restrictions due to the lack of adequate measuring devices. Many examples may illustrate the situation. It is still impossible to allocate the kinetic energy of falling raindrops to various component processes such as the breaking of physical and chemical bonds between soil particles (= detachment), the deformation of the soil matrix and the ejection of detached particles. Adequate techniques

for measuring the degree of turbulence of sediment-laden thin water flows or air flows are completely lacking. Hydraulics and areodynamics still rest too heavily on the manipulation of a set of parameters, which have remained almost unchanged since the beginning of this century (total discharge, mean velocity, slope and hydraulic radius, viscosity). In the field of mass movements there is a more theoretical approach going on which supposes, at the experimental side, future progress of measurement techniques. An example is CULLING's (1983) rate process theory for geomorphic soil creep which demands new, sophisticated methods of data collection.

The Technical Bulletins of the BGRG offer interesting examples of how geomorphologists can contribute to the advancement of techniques. But probably more collaboration with engineers will be necessary in the future to promote this movement and to solve urgent problems.

Purely theoretical research becomes more important as an impetus for empirical investigations. At the same time one may call for theoretical models which introduce the maximum possible number of measurable parameters.

3   THE NEED FOR CONCEPTUAL—VERBAL APPROACHES

In a realistic view on the evolution of present-day geomorphology we cannot deny the basic impact of pure conceptual-verbal models, especially those encompassing complex, lumped models related to global geomorphological systems.

An example from our own recent experience may illustrate the situation. Recently a concept of "promoted erosion and controlled colluviation" was launched (DE PLOEY & YAIR 1985) which is only partially supported by one mathematical model, a colluviation model (DE PLOEY 1984) which states that

$$S_{cr} = A.c^{0.8}/q^{0.5} \qquad (5)$$

where
S_{cr} is the critical slope angle, in %, for starting colluviation;
c is the load concentration in g/l;
q corresponds to the unit discharge of the flow, in cm²/s;
A is a grain size factor depending upon the D_{50}-value.

Yet this model represents an important link in the total concept of controlled colluviation. But, still, it is true that the discussion of water and soil management on colluvial slope sections implies much more than the consideration of equation (5). An important question is to know if the concept is not in contradiction with verbally expressed but physically-based principles.

Whereas the development of empirical-mathematical models requires in some cases years of research, only the first qualitative insights related to complex process combinations and interactions have been acquired (e.g.: hillslope hydrology and the complex pattern of percolines and pipeflow; the poorly known interactions between vegetation and soil erosion ...). Hence, it seems logical and even inevitable that in the integrated discussion of processes and their morphogenetic effects conceptual-verbal models will remain dominant for a long period. One might expect that the most elementary subprocesses can be parametrically described more rapidly

than the integrated models, dealing with global erosion and sediment budgets in the framework of complex ecosystems. A recent report on slow, deep-seated mass movements and landslides in the Swiss Alps, mainly the results of investigations of a group of engineers of the Faculté Polytechnique de Lausanne, again illustrates this statement (BONNARD 1983, 1985). Formally and basically the rather voluminous report is a verbal construction, although partially supported by mathematical submodels. An evident reason for this is the final objective of the report; the establishment of landslide risk maps. These cannot be conceived by simple mathematical modelling of convergent but complex phenomena, belonging to the spheres of geology, geomorphology, climatology, historical and recent geodetic surveys, geotechnical analysis of materials and the study of past and present-day mass movements in the considered area.

4   CONCLUSION

Physically-based deterministic models (which can be tested, corrected and completed by experimental investigations), taken as a starting point, would greatly stimulate empirical research.

More and more progress in the empirical domain will depend upon the development of new measuring techniques which may require interdisciplinary research and, sometimes, expensive investments.

Finally we believe that, for a long time, complex geomorphic systems will still be described and explained in verbal terms, although supported by mathematical submodels. This is perfectly acceptable provided that terminology, definitions and reasoning are in good accordance with the state of knowledge in natural sciences.

REFERENCES

AHNERT, F. (1964): Quantitative models of slope development as a function of waste-cover thickness. Abstr. Papers 20th IGU Congress, London, p. 188.

AHNERT, F. (1973): A comprehensive model program for simulating slope profile development. Geocom Programs, **8**, 24 p.

BONNARD, C. (1983): Determination of slow landslide activity by multidisciplinary measurement techniques. International Symposium on Field Measurements in Geomechanics, Zürich, September 5–8, 619–639.

BONNARD, C. (1985): Détection et utilisation des terrains instables (DUTI),., Ecoly Polyt. Fed. Lausanne, 229 p.

CULLING, W.E. (1983): Rate process theory of geomorphic soil creep. CATENA Suppl. **4**, (Ed. j. DE PLOEY), 191–214.

DE PLOEY, J. (1982): A stemflow equation for grasses and similar vegetation. CATENA, **9**, 139–152.

DE PLOEY, J. (1984): Hydraulics of runoff and loess loam deposition. Earth Surface Processes and Landforms, **9**, 533–539.

DE PLOEY, J. & YAIR, A. (1985): Promoted erosion and controlled colluviation: A proposal concerning land management and landscape evolution. CATENA, **12**, 105–110.

HEMPEL, C.G. (1970): Aspects of scientific explanation. Collier-Macmillan ltd., London, 504 p.

KIRKBY, M.J. (1980): Modelling water erosion processes. In: KIRKBY, M.J. & MORGAN, R.P.C. (eds.): Soil erosion. John Wiley & Sons, Ltd., Chichester — New York — Brisbane — Toronto, 183–216.

POESEN, J. (1985): An improved splash transport model. Z. Geomorph. N.F., **29(2)**, 193–211.

POESEN, J. (1986): Field measurements of splash erosion to validate a splash transport model. Z. Geomorph. Suppl. Bd. **58**, 81–91.

POESEN, J. & SAVAT, J. (1981): Detachment and transportation of loose sediments by raindrop splash. Part II: Detachability and transportability measurements. CATENA, **8**, 19–41.

YAIR, A. (1977): Interdisciplinary research on runoff and erosion processes in an arid area, Sde Boqer experimental site, northern Negev, Israel. Proc. of the 5th Guelph Symposium on geomorphology, 109–131.

Addresses of authors:
J. de Ploey
Laboratory of Experimental Geomorphology, K.U. Leuven
Redingenstraat 16bis
B-3000 Leuven, Belgium
J. Poesen
Research Associate
National Fund of Scientific Research (Belgium)
Laboratory of Experimental Geomorphology
K.U. Leuven
Redingenstraat 16bis
B-3000 Leuven, Belgium

A VERTICAL EXCHANGE MODEL
FOR COARSE BEDLOAD MOVEMENT:
NUMERICAL CONSIDERATIONS

A.P. **Schick**, M.A. **Hassan** and J. **Lekach**, Jerusalem

SUMMARY

In a sand and gravel stream subjected to a uniform series of bed material transporting events, the number of surface particles which become buried within the scour layer during a given event is counterbalanced by a similar number exposed from previously buried locations. This principle of equilibrium vertical exchange exists for all paired combinating of particle burial rates and exposure rates. Starting with a tracer population which is entirely surficial, the number of particles on the surface and in the subsurface becomes quasi-constant at a level determinable from the burial and exposure rates, which, in turn, also control the number of events needed to achieve equilibrium exchange.

The system described is dependent on the relative concentration of the coarse tracer particles in the surface and subsurface layers of the channel bed, the depth of scour, and the rates of exposure and burial. The concepts involved agree well with the hitherto available limited experimental data from ephemeral streams in Israel and with measurements of scour as expressed in the Frijoles

ISSN 0722-0723
ISBN 3-923381-10-7
©1987 by CATENA VERLAG,
D–3302 Cremlingen-Destedt, W. Germany
3-923381-10-7/87/5011851/US$ 2.00 + 0.25

function (LEOPOLD et al. 1966). The equilibrium vertical exchange model has the potential of applicability to problems of fluvial armour development, to reconstructions of hydrometric history of ungauged streams, and in the environmental evaluation of ancient clastic sediments.

1   INTRODUCTION

In alluvial streams, coarse particles which are moved during transporting events also change their vertical position with respect to the channel bed. In tracing experiments (HASSAN et al. 1984), it is common for labelled pebbles to disappear through alluvial burial after a given event, only to be reexposed by a subsequent one. While the longitudinal transport of coarse particles is largely independent of size and highly skewed in relation to distance, the vertical movement is one of bidirectional exchange, in which particles buried during a given event are, in a statistical sense, 'replaced' by other particles exposed from inside the scour layer by the same event (SCHICK et al. 1987b).

Bedload tracing experiments (e.g. KONDOLF & MATTHEWS 1986, many others) invariably start with a surface population, which is being mixed — gradually over several events —

throughout the depth of the scour layer (SCHICK et al. 1987a). Under these initial conditions, the number of surface particles which become buried during a given event usually exceeds the number of labelled sub-surface particles which the same event exposes. In the long run, however, these two values must become similar, if the stream is to maintain geomorphic equilibrium. In such an equilibrium, the assemblage of forms which comprise the channel bed is in a steady state over time, though not necessarily stable in space. The building blocks of these forms, including specifically the coarse particles, should also be in a steady state over time. This means that the total number of coarse particles located on the surface should be constant over time, and the same is true of the number of the buried particles, as well as of the total number of the coarse particles within and on top of the alluvial body.

The concept of equilibrium vertical exchange enables a new insight into the problem of channel armour (ANDREWS & PARKER 1987). Well-armoured reaches, such as occur downstream of dams (WILLIAMS & WOLMAN 1984), can be related to the inhibition of peak discharges which had been, prior to the river closure, powerful enough to effectively mix the scour layer and thus disrupt the development of an armour. The new regime, after the dam closure, became one of regulated moderate and low-flow discharges which promote winnowing and favour the exposure of previously buried coarse particles at a considerably higher efficiency than the burial process, for which the required stream power is no longer available.

Because of the preponderance of a flashy flow regime in many arid areas,

desert streams are mostly characterized by a weak armour development; hence the concentration of the coarse particle fraction on the surface and within the scour layer is similar. Many perennial streams, on the other hand, exhibit a difference of several phi units in their median or D_{84} values between their surface and subsurface particle size distributions.

LEOPOLD et al. (1966) have defined an experimental relation between a discharge characteristic (discharge per unit width) and the depth of scour as determined from chain data. This relation, which became known as the Frijoles function, has been found to predict correctly the depth of scour as indicated by experiments with three-dimensionally tracable particles (SCHICK et al. 1987b). Independently of the above, the depth of scour can also be evaluated from considerations of vertical exchange of coarse particles within the scour layer. For a geomorphically 'dominant' event — i.e., one that, if repeated indefinitely, would keep the channel form assemblage in its present state — the number of coarse particles buried by the event must be offset by an identical number of similar-sized particle exposed. The depth down to which the active scour layer must reach in order to provide for these particles in terms of availability is a function of the density of the coarse particles within the scour layer; low-density alluvium requires, for the same number of pebbles to be exposed, deeper scour than high density alluvium. The as yet limited experimental data, obtained mostly from Nahal Hebron, Israel, indicate that, for several events ranging in frequency from about one to five years, the proportion of surface particles buried by each event, together with surface and subsurface particle size data, can be used to correctly predict depths of scour.

The experimental work on several aspects of the longitudinal transport and vertical exchange of coarse bedload is still under way and will continue for several years. However, it seems useful already now to formulate in a more rigorous way the variables and relations involved. It is hoped that such a formulation will aid in the development of a model which will explain fluvial coarse bedload transport in geomorphic and sedimentologic terms. Though not relying directly on hydraulic principles — a near impossibility because of the large number of variables and the complexity of the processes — it is based on their static and dynamic geomorphic statistical integrators. If successful, such a model would be important theoretically, and, moreover, it has the potential of applicability to practical problems such as the hydrometry of ungauged streams and the environmental evaluation of ancient clastic sediments.

The characteristics of the armour and sub-armour, in terms of coarse particle concentration and depth of scour, are clearly dependent on event size (SCHICK et al. 1987b, figs. 6 & 7), especially of the immediately preceding event. In this initial attempt of analysis, emphasis will be placed on the numerical development of the equilibrium vertical exchange model for coarse bedload movement resulting from a uniform event series. The refinement of using varying size events will be attempted at a later stage, as more and better experimental data become available.

2 DEFINITIONS AND EXAMPLES

Assume a simple experiment of tracing pebbles placed on the channel bed of a sand and gravel stream. The first flow event following emplacement, if powerful enough, moves some of the labelled pebbles, while scouring the bed at various places to various depths. In this paper we are not concerned with either the longitudinal displacement of the pebbles nor with the connection which exists between scour and transport, though both aspects will be alluded to in the summary. The focus here will be on the simple relation between pebble movement and location on or beneath the bed surface.

Obviously some of the pebbles initially placed on the bed are moved a given distance each by the flow and are subsequently, probably during the waning phases of the flow, deposited on the beds as it is at that moment. In some cases, the mobilized scour layer material will continue to deposit itself after the final settling of the pebble, which will thereafter become buried by a layer of alluvium. In other cases such a deposition will not take place, and the deposited pebble will remain on the surface, uncovered by any further deposition.

For a uniform series of discrete, equal-size flow events, the proportion of pebbles buried by an event in relation to the total number of surficial pebbles can be assumed to be constant from event to event. This rate variable, termed the rate of burial, b_r, is 50% in the example portrayed in fig.1. The first event after the initial emplacement of 1000 pebbles causes 50% of the surface population, i.e. 500 pebbles, to be buried as a result of the flood-generated mixing process. The other 500 are found after the event to

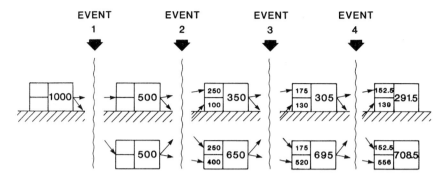

Fig. 1: *Hypothetical vertical distribution of bed material particles in an alluvial channel, caused by a series of equal-size discrete events.*

Initial tracer population: 1000 particles, surface placement. Burial rate: 50% per event; exposure rate: 20% per event. Further explanation in text.

have remained on the surface.

Due to similar considerations, and for an identical series of discrete, uniform events, also the proportion of pebbles of a given size class exposed by the flow, in relation to the number of subsurface pebbles prior to the event, can likewise be assumed to be constant from event to event. This second rate variable, termed the rate of exposure, e_r, is 20% in the example of fig.1. Out of the 500 tracer pebbles buried by event 1, 20% — or 100 particles — are reexposed by event 2. These 100 resurfaced particles are joined by 250 others which had remained on the channel bed out of the 500 which were on the surface prior to event 2. The other 250 have been buried by event 2, and have joined there the 400 particles which remained embedded within the scour layer out of the 500 which were there prior to event 2. The aggregate count after event 2 is, therefore: surface pebbles: 350; buried pebbles: 650.

Subsequent events continue to bring about a decrease in the surface population S, with a concomitant increase in the buried population B. After event 3,

the number of surface pebbles, S_3, becomes 305, and the number of buried pebbles, B_3, becomes 695. Intuition and fig.2 suggest that S and B tend to a limiting value, which is determined solely by the rates of exposure and of burial. Such a limit will be achieved when, as a result of a given event n, the number of subsurface pebbles exposed is exactly counterbalanced by the number of surface pebbles buried. Assume that, in such a state of equilibrium vertical exchange,

S_o = total tracer population, all surface, at begin of experiment;

kS_o = surface population at equilibrium ($o < k < 1$);

and hence,

$(1 - k)S_o$ = buried population at equilibrium.

Then, for the above example (figs.1 & 2a),

$$0.5kS_o = 0.2(1 - k)S_o \qquad (1)$$

yielding

$$k = 2/7(\text{ or } 286 \text{ out of } 1000) \qquad (2)$$

and

$$(1 - k) = 5/7(\text{ or } 714 \text{ out of } 1000). \qquad (3)$$

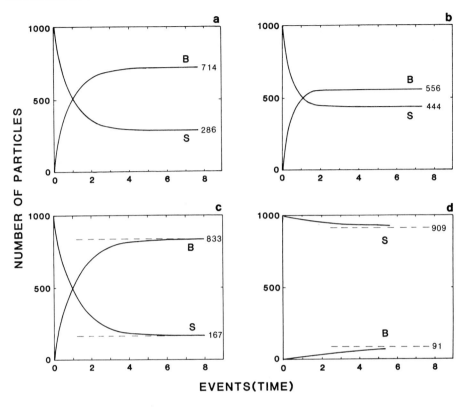

Fig. 2: *Temporal development of the number of surface (S) and subsurface (B) bed material particles.*

2a — burial rate 50%; exposure rate 20%; conditions as in fig.1; 2b — burial rate 50%; exposure rate 40%; 2c — burial rate 50%; exposure rate 10%; 2d — burial rate 2%; exposure rate 20%; simulating armour development.

And, in general terms,

$$S_\infty = [e_r/(b_r + e_r)]S_o \qquad (4)$$

and

$$B_\infty = [b_r/(b_r + e_r)]S_o \qquad (5)$$

The theoretical burial and exposure rates used in the above example (figs.1 & 2a) are actually fairly typical of some experimental data obtained in pebble tracing studies in the Negev Desert, Israel. Values such as indicated by this theoretical example, i.e. roughly 70% of the coarse population buried and 30% exposed, seem to be characteristic of stream channels with a good mechanism of vertical exchange, powerful enough to continually inhibit the systematic development of fluvial armour.

Of course, in a realistic field situation both temporal and spatial variations from a dominant mode value are likely. A series of moderate, low-flow events would tend to temporarily increase S and decrease B, while a single high-magnitude low-frequency event would do the opposite. Likewise, some gravel bars along a study reach might exhibit considerably more armour than the indicated mean, while nearby inner

channel bed material might be nearly de-
void of the coarse tracer sizes. The model
however, reflects the dominant situation
which obtains more or less closely over
most of the current geomorphic time
(subject to constancy of environmental
conditions) as well as over most of the
channel area and subsurface alluvial volume. Such a 'dominant' situation, though
produced in reality by a stochastic series
of randomly occurring small, medium,
and exceptional events, can probably be
simulated by a uniform event seris of a
'dominant' frequency on the order of 1–
2 years (WOLMAN & MILLER 1960,
WOLMAN & GERSON 1978).

Examples 2b and 2c (fig.2) illustrate
the effect of changing e_r while leaving b_r
unchanged at 50%. When e_r is doubled
to 40%, terminal S becomes 444. Under
these conditions, the channel bed will already appear at least partly armoured,
especially if the complementary 556 sub-
surface particles are well distributed over
a scour layer depth range which substantially exceeds the particle size of the
tracer.

Example 2c results from halving e_r (in
relation to the first example) to 10%,
with b_r still unchanged at 50%. Under
these conditions, only one in six pebbles
(167 out of 1000) will be on the surface,
a proportion indicating a very efficient
level of vertical exchange. If, in this
case, the 'dominant' depth of the scour
layer is six times the c-axis of the tracer
pebbles (assuming most pebbles are deposited with their a-b plane parallel to
the channel bed), the volumetric pebble
concentration in the surface layer and
in the subsurface become identical. For
one five year event monitored in Nahal
Hebron, the depth of the scour layer indeed approximated 5–6 times the c-axis
of the tracer pebbles. This correspon-

dence may be regarded as an indication
that events of such magnitude are effective in dismantling any armour-type surficial pebble concentration which might
have formed previously on the channel
bed.

Conditions promoting the development of armour are illustrated by example 2d (fig.2), which results from combining a very low burial rate of 2% with
an exposure rate of 20%. These conditions reflect the principle of hydraulic
winnowing and recall work done on
snowmelt and other non-flashy streams
both in the field (e.g. ANDREWS &
PARKER 1987) and in the laboratory
(e.g. PARKER et al. 1982). The terminal number of surficial tracer particles
is ten times higher than that of its sub-
surface counterpart — a ratio identical
to the ratio between the exposure rate
and the burial rate (an identity correct
also for all other examples). Evidently
a surficial pebble, embedded as it must
be in a structurally strong, perhaps even
somewhat indurated matrix of its neigh-
bours, has only a small probability (here,
2 in 909) of being dislodged, moved and
buried by a given event.

3   THE VERTICAL
   EXCHANGE MODEL:
   THE GENERAL CASE

Let us now explore the general case for a
uniform event series with varying burial
and exposure rates. Using the notation
as above,

$$S_1 = (1 - b_r)S_o + e_r B_o, \qquad\qquad (6)$$

$$S_2 = (1 - b_r)S_1 + e_r B_1, \qquad\qquad (7)$$

   and,

$$S_{(n+1)} = (1 - b_r)S_n + e_r B_n. \qquad\qquad (8)$$

Likewise,

$$B_1 = b_r S_o + (1 - e_r)B_o,$$ (9)

$$B_2 = b_r S_1 + (1 - e_r)B_1,$$ (10)

and

$$B_{(n+1)} = b_r S_n + (1 - e_r)B_n.$$ (11)

$$
\begin{aligned}
S_n + B_n &= const \\
&= S_o
\end{aligned}
$$ (12)

then

$$S_{(n+1)} = (1 - b_r)Sn + e_r(S_o - S_n).$$ (13)

Substituting

$$x_1 = (1 - b_r - e_r)$$ (14)

and

$$x_2 = e_r S_o$$ (15)

we obtain

$$
\begin{aligned}
S_{(n+1)} &= x_1 S_n + x_2 \\
&= x_1^n S_1 + x_2 + x_1 x_2 + x_1^2 x_2 \\
&\quad + x_1^3 x_2 + ... + x_1^{n-1} x_2 \\
&= x_1^n S_1 + x_2(1 + x_1 + x_1^2 + x_1^3 \\
&\quad + ... + x_1^{n-1}) \\
&= x_1^n S_1 + x_2[(1 - x_1^n)(1 - x_1)].
\end{aligned}
$$ (16) (17)

Also, for every $n \geq 1$,

$$
\begin{aligned}
S_n &= x_1^{n-1} S_1 \\
&\quad + (x_2 - x_2 x_1^{n-1})/(1 - x_1) \\
&= x_1^{n-1} S_1 + x_2/(1 - x_1) \\
&\quad - x_2 x_1^{n-1}/(1 - x_1)
\end{aligned}
$$ (18)

and, because the first and third terms approach zero due to $|x_1| < 1$,

$$
\begin{aligned}
\lim_{n \to \infty} S_n &= x_2/(1 - x_1) \\
&= e_r S_o/(e_r + b_r),
\end{aligned}
$$ (19)

a result already obtained above by a more direct way.

Likewise,

$$\lim_{n \to \infty} B_n = b_r S_o/(e_r + b_r).$$ (20)

A special case is

$$x_1 = 1$$ (21)

and therefore

$$b_r = e_r = 0$$ (22)

indicating complete inactivity of bed material, e.g. a fossil stream.

The above reasoning enables the computation of the terminal number of the surface particles S_n — as well as its complementary B_n — for all permissible combinations of burial and exposure rates. The results of this computation are shown in graphical form in fig.3. The theoretical examples a, b, c, and d (fig.2) are marked on the graph. Example b is close to the diagonal median of $S_n = 500$ and, by definition, also of $B_n = 500$, meaning that $e_r = b_r$, a relation also self-evident from the last two equations above. Small changes in e_r and b_r are not going to affect S_n substantially in this zone. The opposite is true for the conditions represented on the graph margins, as illustrated by examples c and d, with their very high or very low S_n values.

The three experimental sets of data available up to now – two from Nahal Hebron and one from Nahal Yael – all fall within a relatively small zone on the graph (fig.3), with their S_n being in the range of 300 ± 50. This is somewhat surprising, bacause only one of these three events can be regarded as being close in magnitude and frequency to the 'dominant' geomorphic event. Another one is a five year event, while for the third one not enough frequency information is available. Experimental data of exposure and burial require a fairly long period of three-dimensional monitoring of tracer

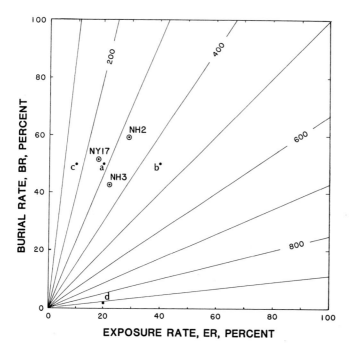

Fig. 3: *Theoretical ratio of surficial to total number of particles (S_n), in parts per thousand, as a function of burial and exposure rates, under conditions of vertical exchange equilibrium. NH2, NH3 and NY17 denote experimental data for Nahal Hebron and Nahal Yael, Israel.*

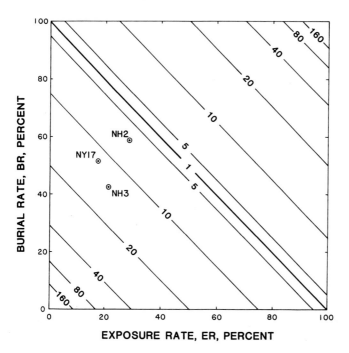

Fig. 4: *Theoretical number of events required for the ratio of surficial to total particles (S_n) to arrive within 0.001 of the terminal equilibrium ratio.*
NH2, NH3, and NY17 denote experimental data as in fig.3.

particles over a series of events. Since efficient methods to accomplish this are relatively new (HASSAN et al. 1984), not many sets of data are available. Dependable exposure values, in particular, can be obtained only after several events, because initial emplacement is on the surface, and enough time is needed for the tracers to be adequately admixed into the entire depth of the scour layer.

An intersting theoretical aspect of the vertical exchange model is the evaluation of the number of events necessary to achieve equilibrium exchange. Clearly, complete equality is not achievable, excepting the special case defined below, but recurring the dominant event many times over can get us as close as we wish. It can be shown that n, the number of events needed for S to approach S_∞ to within a predetermined ε, is approximated by

$$n = Round[(Ln\varepsilon/Lnx_1) + 0.5] \qquad (23)$$

On the basis of this equation, the number of events necessary to approach within $\varepsilon = 0.001$ of the limiting S_n, as a function of any combination of b_r and e_r, has been computed (fig.4). The resulting graph field is diagonally bisected by a singularity line of value $n = 1$ defined by

$$b_r + e_r = 1.0, \qquad (24)$$

this being the only condition which forces on the system the exact terminal S_n by the very first event; from then onwards it just perpetuates itself.

For all other cases, excepting those very close to the diagonal, more than five events are necessary for the system to approach S_n. Our three experimental cases indicate that the number of events needed is within the range $n = 10 \pm 4$.

For many arid and semiarid streams, this is equivalent to a period of 2–10 years, indicating, perhaps, that the vertical exchange process generates a relatively fast and sensitive geomorphic response to environmental conditions which reflect characteristics of flood flashiness and low flow characteristics.

Very high as well as very low paired values of e_r and b_r require an inordinately large number of iterations for S_n to approach a stable value. In extreme cases, represented by the upper right and lower left corners of the graph (fig.4), n may exceed 100. The low values seem to be associated with conditions of river armouring, slow to develop but relatively very stable. The very high values may indicate avalanche-like or debris flow type processes and their deposits.

4 CONCLUSION

The vertical exchange of coarse particles has not been hitherto recognized as an important factor in bedload transport and associated geomorphic dynamics. Tracer studies have clearly shown the interdependence between the alluvial burial of pebbles and their longitudinal transport; pebbles which have an inter-event buried phase in their history move significantly farther in their subsequent move than those who do not (SCHICK et al. 1987a, 1987b).

The discovery of this phenomenon, as yet not fully explained, has prompted us to investigate the process of pebble burial and its complementary process of pebble exposure in more detail. It soon became clear that a process of vertical exchange does indeed exist and can be proved statistically. Further, it was found that this process is affected in a regular, predictable way by measurable parameters such as event magnitude and frequency, depth of scour, and the concentration of coarse particles in the surface (armour) and subsurface layers. It also became possible to predict the depth of scour on the basis of the equilibrium assumption stating that the stream scours down to such a depth as determined by the availability of exactly the number of subsurface pebbles needed for resurfacing in order to counterbalance those surface pebbles buried by the same event. The depth thus predicted was found to compare well with the depth of scour as empirically predicted from unit discharge characteristics by the Frijoles function (LEOPOLD et al. 1966).

Thus the equilibrium vertical exchange concept, though initially developed mainly on theoretical grounds, has practical field implications in the fluvial dynamics of gravel bed streams. In this paper we concentrated on an analysis of the theoretical and numerical structure of the system as defined by the concept. We limited ourselves to a uniform event series, assuming that a 1–2 year event, if recurring many times, plays the role of a geomorphologically 'dominant' event, in the sense that it produces the same assemblage of process and form as the more realistic spectrum varying magnitude-frequency events (WOLMAN & MILLER 1960). If, however, the model is expanded in future to include a stochastically variable spectrum of events, various depths of scour will have to be taken into account as well as varying starting conditions — in particular burial and exposure rates — for each event as inherited from the previous one.

Further development and validation of the vertical exchange model, the evaluation of its more general significance, and in particular its connection with the longitudinal translation of the coarse particles will have to wait until more experimental data become availabe. Studies currently underway will hopefully supply these data in the not too distant future. Parallel future tasks are the improvement of the model so that it incorporates a stochastically varying magnitude-frequency event series, and correlative studies of scour, tracing, and armour in stream channels of varying environmental characteristics. The potential applicability of the vertical exchange model in evaluating ancient clastic sediments and in reconstructing recent flow spectra of ungauged alluvial streams from simple pebble tracing programs make such an effort worthwhile.

ACKNOWLEDGEMENT

This paper is based in part on the ongoing Ph.D. programs of Marwan A. Hassan and Judith Lekach. The Nahal Hebron and Nahal Yael research projects wer funded in recent years by grants from the Hebrew University Authority for Research and Development, the Israel Academy of Sciences and Humanities, and the Israel Water Commission's Division of Soil Conservation and Drainage. We would also like to thank Prof. Dr. F. Ahnert for inviting Asher P. Schick to attend the IGU/COMTAG International Workshop on Theoretical Geomorphological Models, Aachen, April 1986, which served as a spur for the preparation of this paper; Mr. Diab Abu-Aiadh for his help in overcoming mathematical and computer problems; and Mrs. Michal Kidron for drawing the figures.

REFERENCES

ANDREWS, E.D. & PARKER, G. (1987): The coarse surface layer as a response to gravel mobility. In: Sediment Transport in Gravel-bed Rivers. (C. THORNE, J. BATHURST & R. HEY, eds.), Wiley, Chichester, 269–325.

HASSAN, M.A., SCHICK, A.P. & LARONNE, J.B. (1984): The recovery of flood-dispersed coarse sediment particles — a three-dimensional magnetic tracing method. In: Channel Processes — Water, Sediment, Catchment Controls (A.P. SCHICK, ed.), CATENA Suppl. **5**, Braunschweig, 153–162.

KONDOLF, G.M. & MATTHEWS, W.V.G. (1986): Transport of tracer gravels on a coastal California river. Journal of Hydrology **85**, 265–280.

LEOPOLD, L.B., EMMETT, W.W. & MYRICK, R.M. (1966): Channel and hillslope processes in a semiarid area, New Mexico. U.S. Geological Survey Professional Paper **352-G**, U.S. Government Printing Office, Washington, D.C.

PARKER, G., DHAMOTHARAN, S. & STEFAN, H. (1982): Model experiments on mobile paved gravel bed streams. Water Resources Research **18**, 1395–1408.

SCHICK, A.P., LEKACH, J. & HASSAN, M.A. (1987a): Bedload transport in desert floods — observations in the Negev. In: Sediment Transport in Gravel-bed Rivers (C. THORNE, J. BATHURST & R. HEY, eds.), Wiley, Chichester, 617–642.

SCHICK, A.P., LEKACH, J. & HASSAN, M.A. (1987b): Vertical exchange of coarse bedload in desert streams. In: Desert Sediments — Ancient and Modern. Special Publication, Geological Society of London (L.E. FROSTICK & I. REID, eds.), 7–16.

WILLIAMS, G.P. & WOLMAN, M.G. (1984): Downstream effect of dams on alluvial rivers. U.S. Geological Survey Professional Paper **1286**, Government Pringing Office, Washington, D.C.

WOLMAN, M.G. & GERSON, R. (1978): Relative scales of time and effectiveness of climate in watershed geomorphology. Earth Surface Processes **8**, 189–209.

WOLMAN, M.G. & MILLER, J.P. (1960): Magnitude ad frequency of forces in geomorphic processes. Journal of Geology **68**, 54–74.

Address of authors:
A.P. Schick, M.A. Hassan and J. Lekach
Department of Physical Geography
Institute of Earth Sciences
Hebrew University
91904 Jerusalem, Israel

CHAOS AND ORDER
THE CHANNEL GEOMETRY OF
GRAVEL BED BRAIDED RIVERS

P. **Ergenzinger**, Berlin

SUMMARY

Hydraulic geometry and energy expenditure were studied in braided channels of a *torrente* in Calabria, Italy. There is a very effective regulation of channel geometry at a site with exponents close to 0.4 for both of the power functions relating discharge to width and depth.

The specific energy at the site, calculated for rectangularly shaped braids, results in a very close coincidence between mean depth and critical depth. The discharge in the braids is adjusted to achieve critical runoff (Froude number = 1). The braids in coarse erodible material act as threshold channels.

1   INTRODUCTION

In Calabria, the geometry of braided channels in gravel bed rivers is characterized by extreme bed mobility and a "chaotic" capacity for self-regulation. In the German language these braided systems are called "verwildert", which means that the behaviour of the river can be compared to wild, unruly children. It took only 150 years of water engineering

for there to be nearly no braided rivers left "uncultivated" in Germany. But was it wise to replace these untamed rivers by channelled rivers?

Italy is a country with *torrente* rivers, classical braided river systems. We started our investigations in Calabria in 1971. During our studies we became convinced that the braided rivers are not at all chaotic, but are extremely well-regulated fluvial systems with an optimum efficiency in carrying both water and bed load. By means of the Butramo data set from February 1975 we intend to prove this statement.

2   GEOGRAPHICAL SETTING OF THE BUTRAMO BASIN

The Butramo basin has an area of close to 40 km^2 and drains parts of the southwestern Aspromonte Mountains in Calabria. The long, narrow valley is 15 km long. The highest points of the basin are close to 1700 m; at the inflow into the Buonamico the height is about 100 metres above the Ionian Sea. The geology of the basin is simple: more than 40% is underlain by gneiss, the rest is covered by Miocene conglomerates and sandstones. Locally there are clays and red loams at the base of the conglomer-

ISSN 0722-0723
ISBN 3-923381-10-7
©1987 by CATENA VERLAG,
D–3302 Cremlingen-Destedt, W. Germany
3-923381-10-7/87/5011851/US$ 2.00 + 0.25

BUTRAMO FEBRUARY 1975: DISCHARGE / HYDRAULIC RADIUS / WIDTH

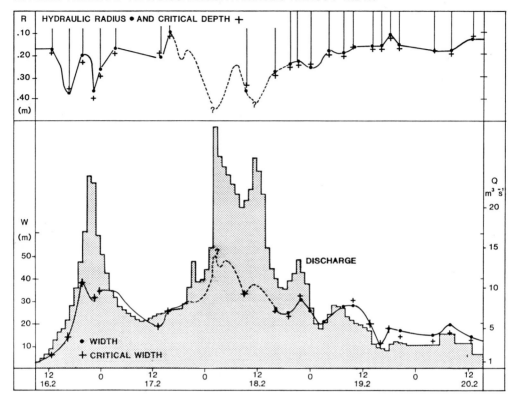

Fig. 1: *Discharge/hydraulic radius/width.*

ates. These areas are particularly prone to landslides. Generally the steep slopes are forested. Grazing by goats and sheep accelerates erosion. Many areas, especially the gentle slopes, are covered with degraded forests and macchia. Triggered by extreme precipitation, in springtime especially by rain on snow, there are corresponding floods and slope failures.

In February 1975 attempted to measure bedload transport. We failed to determine the bedload since the MÜHLHOFER basket sampler was unsuitable for the flow conditions of Butramo. MÜHLHOFER (1933) designed his sampler for the River Inn. At the

Butramo there is a high rate of bedload, but the water depht normally does not exceed half a meter. Under these conditions the wing of the sampler was never totally flooded and so the basket sampler was not forced to stay at a specific spot in good contact with the channel bottom.

The measuring site at Butramo is situated only 100 m above the upper end of the Butramo fan. The valley bottom is 50 m wide and an aqueduct crosses the river without piers. At both sides of the valley the slopes are very steep. In February 1975 the Butramo never covered the whole bottom width, the braids developed within the bottom in the coarse-

BUTRAMO FEBRUARY 1975: SUSPENDED LOAD, TEMPERATURE AND WEIGHT DENSITY

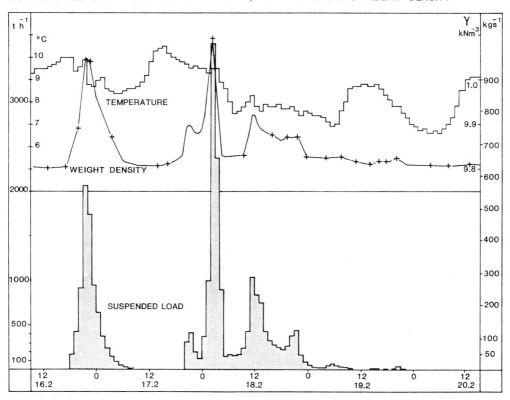

Fig. 2: *Suspended load.*

grained gravels. The fluvial sediments are dominated by gravels and pebbels. The average grain size of samples from bar and braid was always close to 40 mm, the 84% coarse grains are about 50 mm and the 16% fines are about 12 mm. There is some scattering of the results of grain size analysis by different portions of sand. In the area of the aqueduct the coarsest blocks are about 400 mm in size.

The inclination of the braids and of bar surfaces was as high as 0.034. During the floodwaves the slopes of the braids changed rapidly and often. Locally the inclination altered between 0.040 and 0.020. Since the angles were not mea-

sured every time in all braids, in the following calculations we always use the average inclination of 0.034.

The velocity of water was measured with an Ott meter. During the times with bedload transport only the velocity just below the water surface was measured. The average velocity was determined by multiplying these numbers by 0.8.

The geometry of the wetted perimeter was levelled with a tube-bar from the aqueduct. The measurements were made at 1 metre intervals and the accuracy in depth was estimated to be about 2 cm. During peak flow the irregularities in the braids became even bigger owing to the

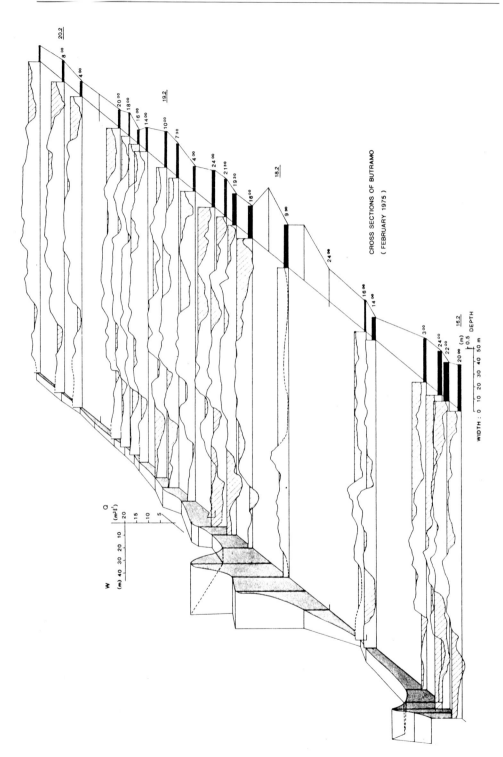

Fig. 3: *The changing geometry of the Butramo river bed in February 1975.*

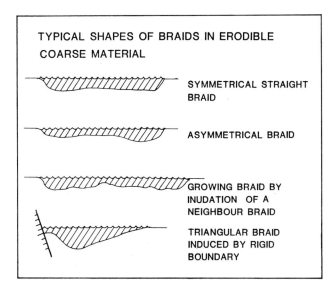

Fig. 4: *Typical shapes of braids in erodible coarse material.*

influence of waves and the unstable bottom layer. The tube also enabled us to hear the impact of the travelling stones and to determine the width of bedload transport.

Redistributed onto the 40 km^2 of the basin, this results in an average erosion of more than 2 mm. The relationship between discharge (Q) and suspended load (Q$_s$) can be described by the power function $Q_s = 0.04 \; Q^3$.

3 BUTRAMO DISCHARGE IN FEBRUARY 1975

The Butramo peaked several times between February 16 and 19, 1975. Over this period there was a precipitation of about 52 mm. Discharge for these days was $3.2 \; 10^6 \; m^3/88h$ or close to $10 m^3/s$ (fig.1). The discharge per km^2 was on average 250 l/skm^2. Because of intensive snowmelt there was more runoff than precipitation. There was also a high rate of suspended transport connected with the two flood waves (cf. fig.2). During the first flood wave the transport of suspended load was about 224 500 t/88h or an average of 710 kg/s. The maximum yield per unit area was 23 kg/s·km^2. Assuming a density of 2.5 t/m^3 the suspended volume was close to 90 000 m^3.

4 SHAPES OF BRAIDS

Along with the high rate of suspended load there was also a remarkable bedload transport. Several times even blocks with a b-axis of more than 400 mm rolled down the braids. The formation of the braids was always associated with much scour and fill. This is shown by the different shapes of the cross-sections (fig.3). The braid was never a stable gravel channel with maximum depth in the middle and a certain inclination from the banks to the centre-line (= threshold channel derived by LANE 1937). At Butramo the following basic types of braids were common (fig.4). The banks of the braids are steep (angles about 28°) and short. The cross-sections of the braids

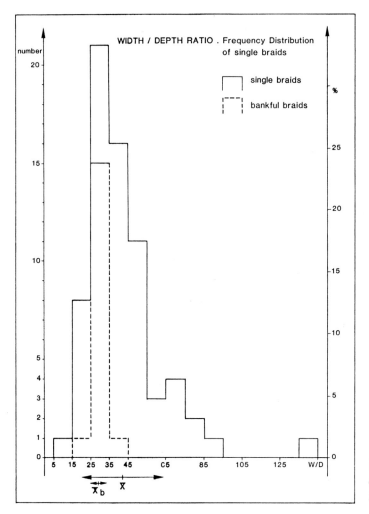

Fig. 5: *Frequency of width/depth ratios.*

are generally wide and shallow and can be assumed to be rectangular. Even the so-called triangular ones are wide and flat. The collected cross-section geometries have a very distinctive distribution of the width-depth ratios. As fig.5 shows, the maxima of the ratios are between 25 and 35. The longer tailing towards the higher ratios results from runoff situations during recession, when after flood crest the runoff is still using oversized old braids. If we take into account only the bankful braids, all width/depth ratios are between 15 and 45. The averages of the two samples are 42 ± 21 and 29 ± 3. These numbers show a great stability of braid form during different discharges. If the total discharge of Butramo is added into one hypothetical "superbraid" the width/depth ratio is between 30 (for a single braid runoff) and 240 (during recession). There is no simple relationship between width/depth ratios and the number of braids. Above 60 there is

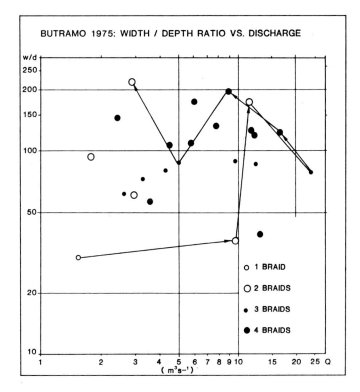

Fig. 6: *Width/depth ratio versus discharge.*

a tendency towards 3 braids, above 100 towards 4 braids (fig.6). But for every width/depth ratio there is also always the possibility of a two-braid system. This is especially common during the first half of the flood wave.

The comparable analyses of the relationships between discharge versus shear stress (τ) (fig.10) and discharge versus Manning friction (k_M) (fig.10) are

$$\tau = 22 Q^{0.38}$$

and

$$k_M = 25 Q^{-0.05}$$

for the bankful braids.

With both exponents the data for the braids can be described on logarithmic paper by a linear regression. The difference between the minimum variance (LANGBEIN 1964, 1965) theory and measurements is slightly higher for the friction function. After the calculation the exponent should be for τ 0.35 and for k_M -0.02. There is a weak tendency to diminish the friction of the total braids with increasing discharge, whereas the shear stress grows with approximately the same exponent as depth and width.

The result of the LEOPOLD analysis of the braided Butramo system is that seen from afar there may be the impression of a "chaotic" geometry, but in reality there is a high degree of self-regulation of the braids by erosion, transportation and accumulation of the non-cohesive material. The adjustment of the channels are even possible during flood waves; there is a strong tendency to create situations with bankful braid dis-

date	hour	LEFT BRAID area m^2	width m	depth m	veloc. m_s^{-1}	dis-charge $m^3 s^{-1}$	Froude no.	LEFT MIDDLE BRAID area m^2	width m	depth m	veloc. m_s^{-1}	dis-charge $m^3 s^{-1}$	Froude no.
16.2.	1400	1.18	5.8	0.20	1.45	1.7	1.02						
16.2.	2000	4.40	14.0	0.31	1.75	7.7	1.00						
16.2.	2230	8.05	18.8	0.43	2.00	16.0	0.97						
16.2.	0000	0.45	4.6	0.10	1.10	0.5	1.12	0.45	4.6	0.10	1.10	0.5	1.12
17.2.	0330	0.21	4.4	0.05	0.50	0.1	0.68	0.65	4.8	0.14	1.20	0.8	1.04
17.2.	1400	3.22	9.2	0.35	1.80	5.8	0.97	0.27	3.2	0.08	0.75	0.2	0.83
17.2.	1600	0.83	6.6	0.13	1.20	1.0	1.07						
18.2.	0930	0.58	3.6	0.16	1.20	0.7	0.96						
18.2.	1545	0.85	3.6	0.24	1.30	1.1	0.84	0.80	6.0	0.13	1.10	0.9	0.99
18.2.	1930	4.30	13.8	0.31	1.70	7.3	0.97						
18.2.	2130	4.50	12.8	0.35	1.80	8.2	0.98	0.80	3.8	0.21	1.40	1.1	0.96
18.2.	0000	0.48	4.0	0.12	1.05	0.5	0.96	0.25	3.2	0.08	0.80	0.2	0.90
19.2.	0400	0.06	1.5	0.04	-	-	-	0.16	2.9	0.06	-	-	-
19.2.	0730	2.35	11.4	0.21	1.35	3.2	0.94	0.44	2.9	0.15	1.20	0.5	0.98
19.2.	0945	2.55	11.3	0.23	1.45	3.7	0.96	0.17	3.0	0.06	-	-	-
19.2.	1400	0.55	3.6	0.15	1.15	0.6	0.94	0.25	4.1	0.06	0.45	0.1	0.58
19.2.	1600	0.60	3.5	0.17	1.20	0.7	0.90						
19.2.	1800	0.53	5.8	0.09	0.75	0.4	0.80	0.22	4.1	0.05	0.40	0.1	0.57
19.2.	2000	0.16	1.9	0.08	0.60	0.1	0.68						
20.2.	0400	0.38	4.1	0.09	0.90	0.2	0.96						
20.2.	0800	0.70	4.3	0.16	1.15	0.8	0.91						
20.2.	1300	0.23	3.1	0.07	0.45	0.1	0.54						

date	hour	RIGHT MIDDLE BRAID area m^2	width m	depth m	veloc. m_s^{-1}	dis-charge $m^3 s^{-1}$	Froude no.	RIGHT BRAID area m^2	width m	depth m	veloc. m_s^{-1}	dis-charge $m^3 s^{-1}$	Froude no.
16.2.	1400												
16.2.	2000	1.30	8.0	0.16	0.90	1.2	0.92	2.90	15.0	0.19	1.50	4.3	1.08
16.2.	2230	0.04	0.8	0.05	-	-	-	4.35	11.8	0.37	1.85	8.0	0.96
16.2.	0000	0.22	2.5	0.09	0.90	0.2	0.91	7.28	22.8	0.32	1.85	13.5	1.05
17.2.	0330	0.10	1.8	0.06	-	-	-	7.30	23.0	0.32	1.85	13.5	1.04
17.2.	1400	1.10	6.2	0.18	1.35	1.5	1.02						
17.2.	1600	1.80	10.7	0.17	1.30	2.3	1.01	0.93	11.5	0.08	0.85	0.8	0.97
18.2.	0930							11.95	29.0	0.41	1.90	22.3	0.93
18.2.	1545							6.10	16.8	0.36	1.80	11.0	0.95
18.2.	1930	0.55	4.6	0.12	1.10	0.6	1.01	1.15	6.9	0.17	1.30	1.5	1.00
18.2.	2130	1.60	6.7	0.24	1.45	2.3	0.94	1.55	7.5	0.21	1.30	2.0	0.90
18.2.	0000	2.20	9.8	0.22	1.50	3.3	1.02	3.35	10.0	0.33	1.80	6.0	1.00
19.2.	0400	2.27	8.3	0.27	1.65	3.7	1.01	1.85	8.5	0.22	1.35	2.5	0.91
19.2.	0730	2.00	8.0	0.25	1.45	2.9	0.92	0.82	5.1	0.16	1.20	1.0	0.95
19.2.	0945	1.25	9.0	0.14	1.20	1.5	1.02	0.86	5.9	0.15	1.15	1.0	0.95
19.2.	1400	1.15	5.6	0.21	1.30	1.5	0.91	1.68	6.9	0.24	1.40	2.3	0.91
19.2.	1600	0.06	1.5	0.06	-	-	-	1.85	7.1	0.25	1.45	2.7	0.93
19.2.	1800	0.24	2.7	0.09	0.75	0.2	0.80	1.30	6.2	0.21	1.30	1.7	0.91
19.2.	2000	0.17	3.8	0.04	-	-	-	2.55	9.0	0.28	1.60	4.1	0.96
20.2.	0400	0.07	1.4	0.05	-	-	-	2.05	7.3	0.28	1.40	2.9	0.90
20.2.	0800	0.65	4.8	0.14	1.10	0.7	0.92	2.30	7.8	0.29	1.65	3.8	0.98
20.2.	1300							1.68	9.7	0.17	1.15	1.9	0.87

Tab. 1: *Butramo 1975: The geometric properties of the braids.*

charge. During the two floodwaves there were 22 crossprofile measurements from 85 single braids. In 17 cases the braids were exactly bankful. If we take into account that all braids with width/depth rations between 15 and 45 (compare fig.6) are bankful or close to bankful, only 23 cases remain. The higher width/depth ratios are typical for braids which are underfitted during the floodwave recession.

5 HYDRAULIC GEOMETRY OF THE BRAIDS

Since the famous publication by LEOPOLD & MADDOCK (1953) on hydraulic geometry many publications have appeared on this subject (compare RICHARDS 1982, KNIGHTON 1984). It is astonishing that there are so few data on braided rivers compared to meandering rivers of all sorts (CHURCH & ROOD 1983). The most important pub-

date	hour	dis-charge	area cross	width	mean depth	wet: peri.	hydr. rad.	mean veloc.	Froude	crit. depth	crit. veloc.
		m^3s^{-1}	m^2	m	m	m	m	ms^{-1}		m	ms^{-1}
16.2.	1400	1.7	1.18	5.8	0.20	6.5	0.18	1.45	1.03	0.21	1.43
16.2.	1700	10.8	6.15	15.0	0.41	16.5	0.37	1.75	0.87	0.38	1.93
16.2.	2000	13.2	8.60	37.0	0.23	38.8	0.22	1.55	1.03	0.23	1.50
16.2.	2230	24.0	12.45	31.4	0.40	33.6	0.37	1.95	0.98	0.39	1.95
16.2.	0000	14.7	8.40	34.5	0.24	36.9	0.22	1.75	1.14	0.26	1.60
17.2.	0330	14.4	8.25	34.0	0.24	36.4	0.22	1.75	1.14	0.26	1.60
17.2.	1400	7.5	4.60	18.6	0.25	21.8	0.21	1.65	1.05	0.25	1.57
17.2.	1600	4.1	3.55	28.8	0.12	30.4	0.12	1.15	1.06	0.13	1.13
18.2.	0930	23.0	12.55	32.6	0.38	34.9	0.36	1.85	0.96	0.37	1.91
18.2.	1600	13.0	7.75	26.4	0.29	28.0	0.28	1.70	1.01	0.29	1.69
18.2.	1930	9.4	6.00	25.3	0.24	27.5	0.22	1.55	1.01	0.24	1.53
18.2.	2130	13.6	8.50	30.8	0.28	34.9	0.24	1.60	0.96	0.27	1.63
18.2.	0000	10.0	6.30	27.0	0.23	29.8	0.21	1.60	1.06	0.24	1.53
19.2.	0400	6.2	4.35	21.2	0.20	24.0	0.18	1.40	1.00	0.21	1.43
19.2.	0730	7.6	5.60	27.4	0.20	30.5	0.18	1.35	0.96	0.19	1.36
19.2.	0945	6.2	4.80	29.2	0.16	31.9	0.15	1.30	1.04	0.17	1.29
19.2.	1400	4.8	3.65	20.2	0.18	22.7	0.16	1.30	0.97	0.18	1.33
19.2.	1600	3.4	2.50	12.1	0.21	14.0	0.18	1.35	0.94	0.20	1.40
19.2.	1800	2.4	2.10	18.8	0.11	20.5	0.10	1.15	1.11	0.12	1.08
19.2.	2000	4.2	2.90	14.7	0.20	16.1	0.18	1.45	1.03	0.20	1.40
20.2.	0400	3.1	2.50	12.8	0.20	14.3	0.17	1.25	0.89	0.18	1.33
20.2.	0800	5.3	3.65	16.9	0.21	19.3	0.19	1.45	1.01	0.22	1.47
20.2.	1300	2.0	1.90	12.8	0.15	13.7	0.14	1.05	0.86	0.14	1.17

Tab. 2: *Butramo 1975: The geometric and hydraulic properties of the combined braids.*

	single braids	bankful braids	combined braid
Width W =	$5.79 \, Q_s^{0.38}$	$4.73 \, Q_b^{0.43}$	$8.43 \, Q_c^{0.48}$
Depth D =	$0.16 \, Q_s^{0.37}$	$0.17 \, Q_b^{0.37}$	$0.11 \, Q_c^{0.34}$
Velocity V =	$1.12 \, Q_s^{0.25}$	$1.22 \, Q_b^{0.20}$	$1.03 \, Q_c^{0.19}$

Tab. 3: *Butramo 1975: Hydraulic geometry of the braids.*

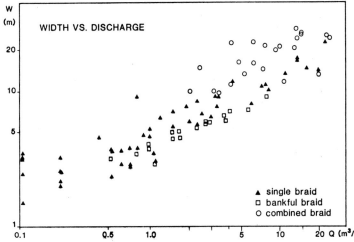

Fig. 7: *Width versus discharge.*

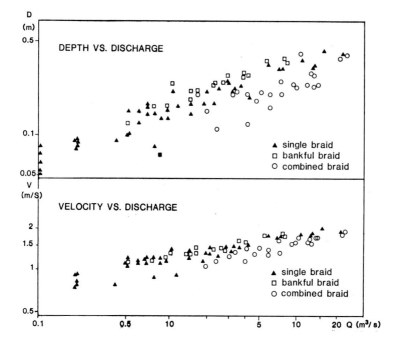

Fig. 8: *Depth versus discharge.*

Fig. 9: *Velocity versus discharge.*

lication on braided rivers (LEOPOLD & WOLMAN 1957) deals with sandy braided rivers in th southwest of the United States. The analysis of Butramo data was done in two steps. First, the hydraulic geometry of the single braids (with the bankful braids as a special group) and, second, the summed hypothetical "superbraid", the total of all braids during one short episode, will be studied. The numerical results are included in tab.1, the related figures are 7, 8, 9.

The resulting exponents of the power functions are typical for non-cohesive banks. They are comparable to the theoretically derived exponents of WILLIAMS (1978). The exponents for the width/discharge and depth/discharge are close to 0.4 and so the exponent for velocity discharge is close to 0.2. This is especially true for the case of the bankful braids.

The statement of minimization of the variance of important variables at a station means a minimum production of entropy. The high rate of width enlargement (exponent between 0.38 and 0.48) is also responsible for the high reduction of stream power ($\Omega = \gamma QS$) if this power is redistributed on the unit bed width ($\omega = \Omega/w$). According to measurements at Butramo the variability for Ω is 20-fold between low and high flow, for ω only 8-fold (cf. CHANG 1980, 1445). CHANG's proposition is that on the average stream power is at a minimum for the given discharge of water and solid material, and this means there must be a minimum channel slope. This result is confirmed by long-term developments. For a short-term analysis of different peaks of runoff the oscillation close to equilibrium is better reflected by minimum stream power per unit bed width (ω). Whenever there is a high exponent

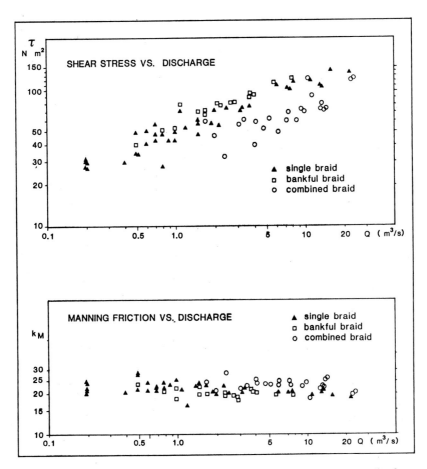

Fig. 10: *Shear stress versus discharge and Manning friction versus discharge.*

for the width/discharge power function at a station there is also a high tendency to minimize stream power per unit bed width. At Butramo station the exponent for the power function width of bedload transport vs. discharge is for example close to b = 0.67. The minimum of the relationship would be at b = 1 if there were no change in depth or velocity during a flood wave. This argument deals only with water discharge. For sediment discharge there must be another relationship with opposing tendencies.

6   SPECIFIC ENERGY

The SPECIFIC ENERGY for a given discharge is a measure of its mechanical energy determined with respect to the channel bottom. The specific had at any point of a rectangular cross section is (compare PRESS & SCHRÖDER 1966, 317–318)

$$H_s = D\cos\alpha + 1/2(V^2 g^{-1})$$

with

$$Q = WDV$$

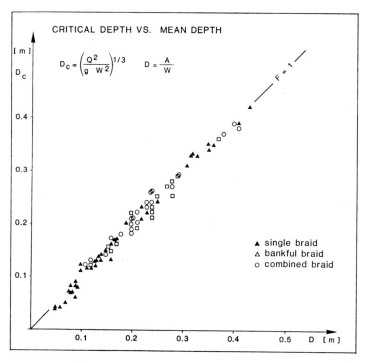

Fig. 11: *Critical depth versus mean depth.*

$$H_s = D\cos\alpha + 1/2(Q^2 g^{-1} W^{-2} D^{-2})$$

Since there is D and D^2 in the equation there are two different values of D and there is a minimum value for H_S.

Assuming $\cos\alpha = 1$ the minimum for H_s is

$$dH_s dD^{-1} = 0 = 1 - g^{-1} Q^2 W^{-2} D_c^{-3}$$

and
$$D_c = (g^{-1} Q^2 W^{-2})^{1/3}$$
$$D_c = g^{-1} V^2$$

(D_c = critical depth)

At critical depths the specific head is at its minimum value. By definition the Froude number is

$$F = g^{-0.5} D^{-0.5} V$$

For critical depth the Froude number is 1.

Whenever there is a Froude number close to 1 the related depth in rectangular cross sections should be critical, and every runoff close to 1 is a runoff with high efficiency.

In fig.11 the data for critical depth (D_c) and mean depth (D, D_b and D_t) are combined. The data match almost perfectly the midline between the two axes. Only the points for depth below 0.10 m are always below this line. It is easy to understand that for these situations on the coarse braid bottom there is nearly always subcritical runoff. Between the mean depth of 0.10 m and 0.32 m there is supercritical flow with $F < 1$.

In contrast to meandering systems the braided system with erodible banks

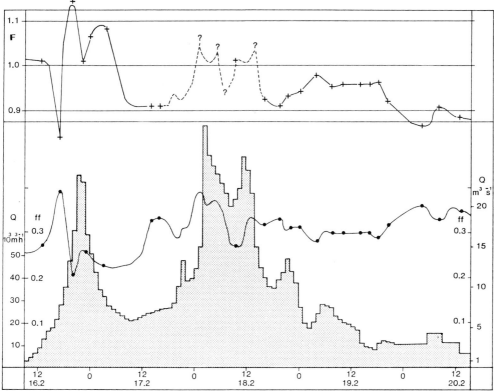

Fig. 12: *Discharge, friction and Froude number.*

shows a well-adjusted reaction even during times of great variation of discharge. The braids are adjusted to allow the water to discharge as efficiently as possible. Sediment transport, friction of grain and channel are regulated in such a way as to bring the flow close to critical depth and velocity (cf. fig.12). But this minimum rate of energy dissipation is, unlike the situation discussed by YANG et al. (1981), not attained in rectangular channels with width equal to twice the depth.

At least for the short time spans investigated at Butramo the channel is adjusted primarily to water discharge and

not "to carry sediment load ... as efficiently as possible" (KIRKBY 1977). But this is not necessarily a contradiction. Whenever there is supercritical shooting runoff, a hydraulic jump will occur. These jumps will stay at one spot or travel. In curved channel reaches there will be diagonal wave fronts creating even wavier conditions down to the bottom layer. The shallow runoff with critical depth, width and velocity is not only optimal for discharge but also creates optimal wide braids and even optimal erosion and transport conditions.

The channel geometry of braided sys-

tems with moveable coarse beds is very
closely related to very specific hydraulic
conditions.

ACKNOWLEDGEMENT

The investigations were funded by the
Deutsche Forschungsgemeinschaft. I am
indebted to H.-J. Lüder and K. Sijmons
for their assistance in the field.

The following symbols are used in the
paper:

A = cross-section area
C = concentration of suspended load
D = mean depth (A/W)
D_c = critical depth
D_b = bankful depth
D_t = depth of the combined braids
d = day
F = Froude number
ff = Darcy-Weißbach friction
g = gravitational acceleration
h = hour
k_M = Manning friction coefficient
P = wetted perimeter
Q = discharge
Q_s = discharge of suspended load
R = hydraulic radius (A/P)
S = slope
T = temperature
V = mean velocity
V_c = critical velocity
V_b = bankful velocity
V_t = velocity of the combined braids
W = width
W_b = bankful width
W_t = width of the combined braids
α = slope of the channel bottom
γ = specific weight of water
τ = shear stress
ω = stream power per unit width
Ω = stream power

REFERENCES

CHANG, H.H. (1980): Geometry of ravel-
streams. Journal of the Hydraulics Division.
Am. Society of Civil Engineers 106, HY9: 1443–
1456.

CHURCH, M. & ROOD, K. (1983): Catalogue
of Alluvial River Channel Regime Data. University of British Columbia, Dept. of Geography, Vancouver.

KIRKBY, M.J. (1977): Maximum sediment efficiency as a criterion for alluvial channels. In:
Gregory, K.J.: River Channel Changes, 429–
442. J. Wiley, London.

KNIGHTON, D. (1984): Fluvial forms and processes. Arnold, London.

LANE, E.W. (1937): Stable channels in erodible
materials. Transactions of the American Society
of Civil Engineers 102, 123–194.

LANGBEIN, W.B. (1965): Geometry of river
channels: Closure of discussion. Journal of the
Hydraulics Division, Am. Society of CivilEngi-
neers 91, HY3: 297–313.

LEOPOLD, L.B. & MADDOCK, T.J. (1953):
The hydraulic geometry of stream channels and
some physiographic implications. Prof. Paper.
U.S. Geological Survey 252, 1–57.

MÜHLHOFER, L. (1933): Schwebstoff- und
Geschiebemessungen am Inn bei Kirchbichl
(Tirol). Wasserkraft und Wasserwirtschaft 28.
Jg., 4. H., 37–41.

PRESS, H. & SCHRÖDER, R. (1966): Hy-
dromechanik im Wasserbau. W. Ernst, Berlin.

RICHARDS, K. (1982): Rivers, Form and Process in Alluvial Channels. Methuen, London,
New York.

WILLIAMS, G.P. (1978): Hydraulic geometry
of river cross-sections — theory of minimum
variance. Prof. paper, U.S. Geological Survey
1029, 1–47.

YANG, C.T., SONG, C.C.S. & WOLDEN-
BERG, M.J. (1981): Hydraulic Geometry and
Minimum Rate of Energy Dissipation. Water
Resources 17, 1014–1018.

Address of author:
Peter Ergenzinger
Institut für Physische Geographie
Freie Universität Berlin
Grunewaldstr. 35
D-1000 Berlin 41

CATENA SUPPLEMENT 10   p.99–110   Braunschweig 1987

LATERAL MIGRATION
OF STREAM CHANNELS

L.E. **Band**, New York

SUMMARY

A framework for the simulation of lateral stream and divide migration of non-alluvial valleys is presented. Stream channels and hillslopes are modelled as mutual boundary conditions, with the horizontal channel shifting determined by the asymmetry of sediment delivery from opposite valley walls, and the ability of the stream to rapidly remove that debris. The lateral stability of divides and drainage is sensitive to the specific form of sediment transport along the hillslopes and the stream incision rate. Conditions for the growth or decay of existing small tributaries are investigated along with implications for the development of stream junction angles in channel networks.

1   INTRODUCTION

The evolution of an integrated drainage network begins with the accelerated erosional lowering of small topographic hollows, characterized by convergence of surface or subsurface flow (DUNNE 1980). Once formed, the drainage lines serve as boundary conditions for the adjacent hillslopes, which in turn provide the lateral input of sediment and water to each segment of channel. This interaction forms a strong coupling between the dynamic evolution of the stream network and the interfluvial topography.

One aspect of this interaction that has received little attention is the lateral migration of stream channels. In virtually every attempt to model a stream-slope system, the drainage lines have been considered fixed in horizontal position or are given a lateral displacement that is set independent of the simulated processes. By virtue of the physical impossibility of the lower portion of a hillslope incising below the channel that serves as its local base level, a stream segment cannot shift laterally by the differential erosional lowering of the landscape. The process must occur as the result of motion directed orthogonally to the channel incision, by the progressive erosion of one of the banks. This can be modelled by treating hillslopes and drainage channels as mutual boundary conditions, with an explicit theory of lateral stream migration induced by interaction with the adjacent hillslopes. Note that the action of stream piracy does not shift a channel, it beheads and abandons streams such that the drainage, but not the actual channel, is moved.

Despite the obvious significance of the lateral stream migration problem, very little is known about the causative fac-

ISSN 0722-0723
ISBN 3-923381-10-7
©1987 by CATENA VERLAG,
D–3302 Cremlingen-Destedt, W. Germany
3-923381-10-7/87/5011851/US$ 2.00 + 0.25

tors in the absence of structural control. In this paper, the framework for the simulation of this stream-slope interaction is constructed. We restrict our attention to actively incising, non-alluvial channels, addressing the model to the active headwater region of the drainage basin. Stream activity as part of floodplain development is not considered. Following the suggestion of MELTON (1960), SMITH & BRETHERTON (1972) and my own and other's observations in rapidly incising channel networks, lateral shifting is modelled as a function of the differential rates of sediment delivery from opposing valley sides, and the ability of the stream to rapidly remove that debris. Physically, this assumes that a greater sediment flux from one canyon wall promotes the preferential erosion of the opposite slope toe, unless the channel is able to rapidly remove the debris. In general, it seems unlikely that the process is so localized that it depends only on the hillslope sediment delivered at a point (or small unit channel length), but rather is an integrated affect over a larger length of stream. This could include the contribution of a number of rills, debris chutes, or even small tributaries.

At present, the model is one-dimensional; we consider a profile taken through a tributary stream and model its potential to laterally migrate towards the mainstream. This may be taken as a mechanistic approach to the study of non-alluvial stream junction angles. The present study uses simulation in an exploratory manner. Several assumptions regarding the form and process of the model landscape are made, some of which are more speculative than others. The results of the simulation should therefore be viewed as tentative. However, the model may serve as the theo-

retical basis for empirical field or laboratory work, seeking to support or refute its assumptions and/or its results. Such empirical work may in turn improve the simulation model by providing modifications, or total replacement of various facets of the model.

2   IMPLICATIONS OF PREVIOUS WORK

Little work has actually been done on lateral stream migration. GILBERT (1877, 125) recognized the significance of the problem but suggested that once formed, drainage lines and divides may be horizontally stable in the absence of structural control. SCHUMM (1956), however, observed that tributaries in the Perth Amboy badlands shifted systematically relative to the mainstream. Comparative mapping of these streams revealed a tendency of their junctions to move upstream along the main channel with a commensurate lateral readjustment of the tributaries. PARKER (1977) reported similar behavior in a set of experimental badlands produced in the Colorado State University Rainfall Erosion Facility. In an analysis of valley asymmetry, MELTON (1960) suggested that a systematically unequal delivery of sediment from opposite valley slopes would tend to steepen the slope shedding less debris owing to the consistent shifting of the stream towards its bank, while promoting slope decline on the opposite bank. While this was empirically supported in a sample of hillslopes in Wyoming, canyons in the Verdugo Hills, California (STRAHLER 1950) did not show asymmetry. MELTON (1960) reasoned that the greater ability of the drainage lines to remove debris, suggested by the high channel gradients and active incision, prevented the development of the asymmetry. My own observations in the Verdugo Hills and similar nearby terrain suggest that preferential erosion of one bank does tend to occur in high-gradient tributaries. This may promote lateral migration while maintaining symmetric valley form as the canyon walls are kept at the angle of repose.

Perhaps the most compelling evidence for this activity may be found in empirical work on stream junction angles. Models have recently been developed for analysis and prediction of systematic trends of these angles with position in the drainage basin (ABRAHAMS 1980, PIERI 1980). These models are based on static geometric description of the junction region first proposed by HORTON (1945):

$$cos\theta = \frac{S_m}{S_t}$$

where θ is the junction angle, S_m is the mainstream declivity, and S_t is the tributary declivity. This model was subsequently modified by HOWARD (1971) to include junctions of more nearly equal size tributaries.:

$$\theta = \theta_1 - \theta_2, \; cos\theta_1 = \frac{S_3}{S_1}, \; cos\theta_2 = \frac{S_3}{S_2}$$

where θ_1 and θ_2 are the planimetric angles formed by the tributaries and the continuation of the trend of the confluent stream above the junction, and S_3, S_2, and S_1 are the declivities of the mainstream and two tributaries, respectively.

This model is strictly true only for the situation of an unincised stream (or rill) entering the mainstream, as a unique solution may only be found if the stream is constrained to exist in the valley-side plane as a line of steepest descent. As the minor tributary becomes more incised or the two tributaries become more nearly equal in size, this basic model, and consequently any model incorporating these predictions, beomes a poorer description of the local topographic geometry.

Despite this observation, junction angles seem to roughly follow the predicted trends, with systematic deviations occurring only in specific details of the system. In natural drainage networks, tributaries enter a mainstream at a more acute angle as their declivities decrease. Although the basic assumptions of the trigonometric model are not realistic, this observation indicates that some process or set of processes exist that dynamically adjust the angular geometry of the junction as the relative slopes of the tributaries and mainstream change, and in such a manner as to produce similar trends in the junction geometry to those predicted by the HORTON and HOWARD models.

For this to occur, streams that are initiated as rills on a hillslope must migrate towards the mainstream as they incise and lower their slope. This involves the preferential erosion of the interior bank of the tributary over long periods of time, and the complementary migration of at least part of the drainage divide as the tributary grows.

Lateral migration of stream channel and drainage divides as the result of observable erosion processes must therefore serve as the dynamic base necessary to formulate a model of the development and adjustment of the stream junction. There is clearly no discernible contribution to this question that may be offered by a purely geometric approach.

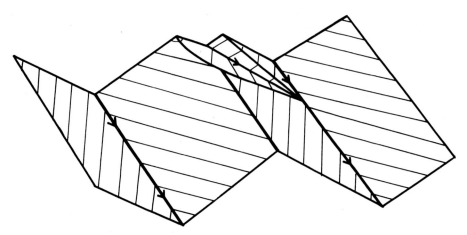

Fig. 1: *Idealized, small tributary entering a mainstream.*

3 MODEL CONSTRUCTION

The processes controlling the stream-slope interaction are numerically modelled by arranging two hillslope systems on opposing sides of a common drainage line. Each system consists of two slopes with a common divide, bounded by a fixed basal stream and the common drainage line. In its current implementation, this represents a small tributary to a mainstream (fig.1), although the boundary conditions can easily be altered to model a variety of situations. Each hillslope system is modelled independently, their only interaction being the shared boundary condition.

The effect of the drainage line on the hillslope may be directly modelled and has been approached by a number of studies (CULLING 1960, 1963, KIRKBY 1971, HIRANO 1975, BAND 1984, and others). Without directly modelling the fluid and sediment transport within the stream channel, we must formulate a strategy for the influence of the side slopes on the lateral displacement of the stream. The approach taken

here, regarding the influence of asymmetric sediment delivery and the vertical stream incision rate is expressed:

$$\frac{dx}{dt} = \lambda \frac{q_{sr} - q_{sl}}{\frac{-dz}{dt}} \qquad (1)$$

where x and z are the coordinates of the drainage line, q_{sr} and q_{sl} are the sediment flux from the left and right banks, respectively, expressed as a (substrate) volumetric rate per unit length of stream channel ($L^2 T^{-1}$) and λ is a proportionality constant with dimensions T^{-1}. Note that, at present, this approach is pure hypothesis. Although the qualitative effect of asymmetric sediment delivery and stream transport capacity may appear reasonable on the basis of the observations cited above, the quantitative form and significance of these factors have not been tested in the field or laboratory. The results that follow from this analysis, therefore, are also considered hypotheses, which should be subject to empirical testing.

The hillslope simulation model, applied to each side of the tributary valley, is described in detail elsewhere (BAND

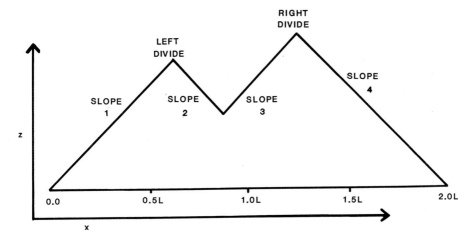

Fig. 2: *Cross section taken from the mainstream in fig.1, through the tributary basin, and down to the adjacent mainstream. L is a length scale equal to one half the horizontal distance along the cross section between the two mainstreams. View of the cross section is looking upstream.*

1983, 1985a). The model is constructed by first writing a statement of mass continuity for a profile:

$$\frac{\partial z}{\partial t} = -\frac{\partial q_s}{\partial x} \qquad (2)$$

and substituting a transport law combining hydraulic transport and the diffusion term representing soil creep and rainsplash

$$q_s = K_h q_w^m (-\frac{\partial z}{\partial x})^n + K_c(-\frac{\partial z}{\partial x}) \qquad (3)$$

where z is the height above a base level, q_s is the sediment transport, x is the horizontal coordinate and K_h, m, n and K_c are empirically determined parameter constants. Parameterization and testing of the model was done on a set of hillslopes developing in an abandoned hydraulic gold mine in northern California (BAND 1985a, 1985b). On these hillslopes, $q_w = rx$, where r is a runoff rate. The parameter set determined for

these slopes is employed here, although the magnitude of the diffusive processes of soil creep and rainsplash, and the tributary channel incision rates are varied to investigate the sensitivity of the response.

Before proceeding, dimensionless variables are introduced to generalize the solution:

$$\zeta = \frac{x}{L}, \qquad \eta = \frac{z}{L}, \qquad \tau = \frac{t}{t_c}$$

where L is a length scale, taken here as half the horizontal distance between the two fixed boundaries of the hillslope system, and t_c is a time scale, defined below. Substituting these variables into eq. (2) and (3) and rearranging gives:

$$\frac{\partial \eta}{\partial \tau} = -\frac{\partial}{\partial \zeta}(\zeta^m(-\frac{\partial \eta}{\partial \zeta})^n - \beta(\frac{\partial \eta}{\partial \zeta})) \qquad (4)$$

where $\beta = \frac{K_c}{K_h r^m L^m}$, and $t_c = \frac{L}{K_h r^m L^m}$. The incision rate of the tributary stream is $\frac{\partial \eta}{\partial \tau}$, such that $\frac{\partial \eta}{\partial \tau} = -1.0$ corresponds to a vertical incision of L in

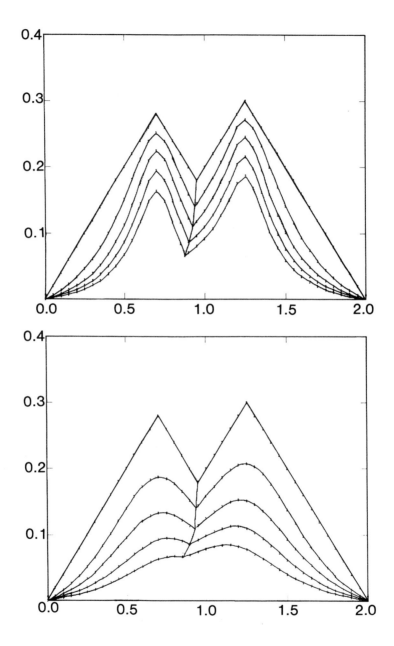

Fig. 3: *a & b: Simulated cross sectional profiles taken at* τ = 0.0 *(initial conditions),
and* τ = 0.25, 0.50, 0.75 *and* 1.0. *Horizontal and vertical axes are dimensionless distance* (ζ) *from and dimensionless height* (η) *above the first mainstream, respectively.
Tributary stream incision is at an exponentially decreasing rate, and* β = 0.01 *(3a)
and* β = 0.10 *(3b)*.

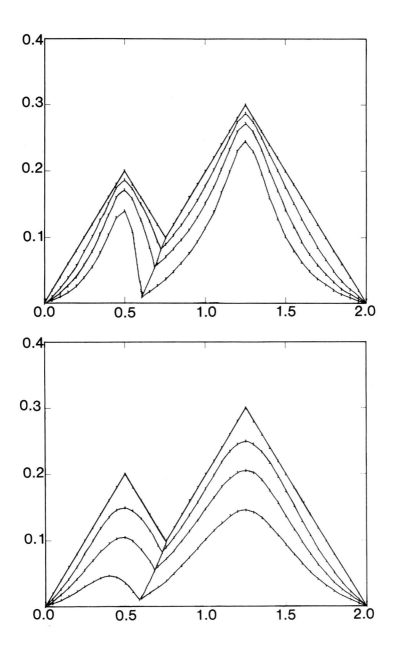

Fig. 4: *a & b: Simulated cross sectional profiles taken at* $\tau = 0.0, 0.1, 0.25$ *and* 0.5. *Horizontal and vertical axs are as in fig.3. Incision rates of the tributary channel are set as* $\frac{\partial \eta}{\partial \tau} = -1.0$ *and* $\beta = 0.01$ *(4a) and* 0.10 *(4b).*

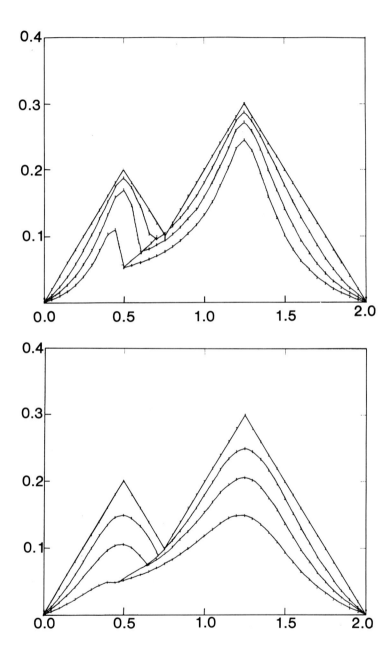

Fig. 5: *a & b: Simulated cross sectional profiles taken at* $\tau = 0.0, 0.1, 0.25,$ *and* 0.5*. Horizontal and vertical axes are as in fig.3. Incision rates of the tributary channel are set as* $\frac{\partial \eta}{\partial \tau} = -0.6$ *and* $\beta = 0.01$ *(5a) and* 0.10 *(5b).*

t_c. Eq. (3) is solved by use of a CRANK-NICOLSON discretization and a NEWTON-RAPHSON iteration.

4 SIMULATION

The model was run for $\beta = 0.01$ and 0.1, representing a variation in the magnitude of the diffusive processes. Note that the variation in β can be caused by any of the terms in the denominator, but this indicates a concomitant change in the time scale and incision rate. Initial conditions were taken as a set of rectilinear slopes at the same declivity, arranged with varying degrees of asymmetry of slope length about the tributary channel (fig.2).

The first simulation set (ζ_d, η_d), the initial position of the drainage line, as (0.95,0.18), with an exponentially decreasing incision rate, $\frac{\partial \eta}{\partial \tau} = -\eta$. β is first set to 0.01, and then 0.1, interpreted here as an order of magnitude increase of K_c, the diffusivity constant. With $\beta = 0.01$, the hillslopes are largely concave, with a small convexity at the divide and a low rate of crest lowering (fig.3a). The lateral stream migration is low, reflecting the near symmetry of opposing slope lengths, but increases with time as the vertical incision slows. With $\beta = 0.1$, the greater magnitude of diffusive processes accelerates the lowering of the slope crests, such that at $\tau = 1.0$, the tributary stream is barely lower than the left divide (fig.3b). This divide also shows a significant migration toward the tributary stream in response to the developing asymmetry of slope declivity across the crest, which accelerates the shortening of slope 2. This, in turn, causes a small increase in the acceleration of the lateral stream migration as the vertical incision rate decreases.

The imminent loss of the tributary stream in the latter case may be in-dicative of the mechanisms by which tributary-source links are abstracted from drainage basins following the reduction of relief, recognized by ABRAHAMS (1977). After the period of maximum channel network extension, the decreasing incision rates of the tributaries do not keep pace with the rates of divide lowering, given sufficient soil creep and rainsplash. Additionally, the acceleration of the lateral stream migration that accompanies the decreasing incision rates and growing slope length asymmetry would eventually lead to the loss of the left divide as the tributary approaches the mainstream. In either case, the tributary appears to be an unstable feature which will disappear on a time scale commensurate with the local scale and process rates outlined above, unless there are some other stabilizing processes that would offset this behaviour.

In order to separate the effects of decreasing incision rates and growing valley asymmetry on lateral stream movement, the simulations are repeated with two steady incision rates; setting $\frac{\partial \eta}{\partial \tau} = -1.0$ and -0.6 (figs. 4a, b and 5a, b, respectively). Initial conditions are more asymmetric, with (ζ_d, η_d) set at (0.8,0.1). With the higher, steady incision rates and higher β (fig.4b), both of the drainage divides are displaced away from the downcutting channel, expanding the tributary drainage area. When the incision rate is lowered (fig.5b), the higher β leads to a greater migration rate that results in the abstraction of the drainage line by $\tau = 0.5$. The high migration rate steepens slope 2 and forces the left divide toward the mainstream. This is better illustrated by the simulation with β set to 0.01, in which the divide shows a significant lateral shift towards the mainstream despite the lower magnitude of the diffusive process. This migration is not noticable with the lower value of β and high incision and shows that the types and rates of horizontal drainage divide migration are sensitive to the magnitude of the diffusive processes and the tributary activity.

5 DISCUSSION

More simulations need to be performed with a variety of initial and boundary conditions and transport law parameters, in order to generalize interpretations of system behaviour. However, at this point there are some basic patterns that can be drawn from these experiments. For the case of a small tributary developing on the side of a mainstream, there are interesting implications for the link's stability.

As the tributary link develops, it must incise rapidly relative to the magnitude of diffusive transport processes which determine both the rates of crest lowering and lateral displacement. A high relative incision rate results in a displacement of both divides away from the tributary, expanding its drainage area. It also maintains a low, lateral stream migration rate, depending on the initial asymmetry. This promotes the stability and growth of the link drainage area over time. If the incision rate then decreases, or the diffusive processes increase (perhaps due to a climatic change), the tributary may begin to be abstracted. Accelerated lateral migration of the channel forces the tributary toward the mainstream. The left divide may then be eradicated at a rate proportional (in part) to the magnitude of the diffusive transport processes.

If this occurs preferentially in the region near the confluence with the mainstream, the junction migrates up-valley, as observed by SCHUMM (1956) and

PARKER (1977). If it occurs away from the confluence, a similar but more pronounced junction realignment will occur by capture as the divide is breached. During this process, the tributary junction angle and the orientation and planimetric shape of the link are changing. The nature of this change is dependent on the differential response of the link that occurs as one moves towards or away from the junction.

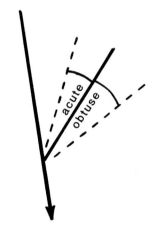

Fig. 6: *Tributary entering a mainstream. The angle between the divides (dashed) separating the tributary from the mainstream is partitioned into the acute and obtuse semi-divide angles, after ABRAHAMS (1980).*

ABRAHAMS (1980) has observed that the acute semi-divide angle of a channel junction is generally less than the obtuse angle (fig.6). While this tributary valley asymmetry may be partially explained by the processes described here, it in turn leads to the asymmetric sediment delivery required to force the lateral channel migration. This pattern suggests that link migration will generally be toward the mainstream, away from the longer hillslope. If the ratio of left to right slope lengths is approximately constant along the link, the ratio of left to right sediment delivery at various distances from the junction is a function of the dependency of the hydraulic transport on the contributing slope area. The more nonlinear this becomes (m increasing in eq. (3)), the greater is the sediment delivery asymmetry as one moves along the link, away from the junction. However, this is accompanied by an increased incision rate, if local downcutting is proportional to height above the local base level, which would counteract the effect of unequal sediment delivery, and tend to stabilize the link. Therefore, a greater nonlinearity in eq. (3) would promote an increasing rate of migration as one moves away from the junction. A less well expressed nonlinearity would promote a more uniform, or even a decreasing rate. This relative motion would be sensitive to the pattern of link incision and the dominant hillslope transport processes and may lead to a distinct, characteristic tributary geometry between different environments or micro-environments.

A simple hypothesis that can be drawn from these arguments, is that link junction angles tend to be less, and link shape more concave to the mainstream, in regions dominated by transport processes with a strong, nonlinear increase with slope length. Further, in such regions, the tributary links may be much more transitory as they rapidly migrate laterally to the mainstream, unless prevented by some other process. One possibility is that the channel curvature may induce a stabilizing influence as the centrifugal displacement of the flow along the outside bank may offset the asymmetry of sediment delivery.

There are a number of other empirically observed regularities in stream network structure that may be approached with the methodology discussed here. These include the initiation of meanders in non-alluvial valleys and their relation to tributary link spacing (ABRAHAMS 1982), the preferential occurrence of low magnitude tributaries on the outside valley wall of larger streams near a junction (FLINT 1980), and the cis-trans link problem (JAMES & KRUMBEIN 1969). However, before further speculations are made, the basic assumptions outlined here should be subject to empirical verification. This could be approached either by direct testing of model or actual landscapes (which is generally extremely difficult), or by indirect testing of the expected results in terms of stream network geometry.

REFERENCES

ABRAHAMS, A.D. (1977): The factor of relief in the evolution of channel networks in mature drainage basins. American Journal of Science, **277**, 626–645.

ABRAHAMS, A.D. (1980): Divide angles and their relation to interior link lengths in natural channel networks. Geographical Analysis, **12**, 157–171.

ABRAHAMS, A.D. (1982): The relation of chain length to chain curvature in natural channel networks. Earth Surface Processes and Landforms, **7**, 469–473.

BAND, L.E. (1983): Measurement and simulation of hillslope development. Unpublished Phd. dissertation, University of California, Los Angeles.

BAND, L.E. (1984): On the development of characteristic slope profiles. Modeling and Simulation, **15**, 13–18. Proceedings of the Pittsburgh Conference.

BAND, L.E. (1985a): Simulation fo slope development and the magnitude and frequency of overland flow erosion in an abandoned hydraulic gold mine. In: Woldenberg, M.J. (ed.), Models in Geomorphology, 191–212. Allen & Unwin.

BAND, L.E. (1985b): Field parameterization of an empirical sheetwash equation. CATENA, 12, 281–290.

CULLING, W.E.H. (1960): Analytical theory of erosion. Journal of Geology, 68, 336–344.

CULLING, W.E.H. (1963): Soil creep and the development of hillside slopes. 71, 127–161.

DUNNE, T. (1980): Formation and controls on channel networks. Progress in Physical Geography, 4, 211–239.

FLINT, J.J. (1980): Tributary arrangements in fluvial systems. American Journal of Scienc, 280, 26–45.

GILBERT, G.K. (1877): Report on the geology of the Henry Mountains. United States Geological and Geographical Survey, Washington, D.C.

HIRANO, M. (1975): Simulation of developmental process of interfluvial slopes with reference to graded form. Journal of Geology, 83, 113–123.

HORTON, R.E. (1945): Erosional development of streams and their drainage basins: hydrophysical approach to quantitative morphology. Geological Society of America Bulletin, 56, 275–370.

HOWARD, A.D. (1971): Optimal angles of stream junctions: geometric stability to capture, and minimum power criteria. Water Resources Research, 7, 863–873.

JAMES, W.R. & KRUMBEIN, W.C. (1969): Frequency distribution of stream link lengths. Journal of Geology, 77, 544–565.

KIRKBY, M.J. (1971): Hillslope process-response models based on the continuity equation. Institute of British Geographers Special Publication, no. 3, 15–30.

MELTON, M.A. (1960): Intravalley variation in slope angles related to microclimate and erosional environment. Geological Society of America Bulletin, 71, 133–144.

PARKER, R.S. (1977): Experimental study of drainage basin evolution and its hydrologic implications. Hydrology Paper, no. 90, Colorado State University, Fort Collins.

PIERI, D.C. (1980): Martian valleys: morphology, distribution, age and origin. Science, 210, 895–897.

SCHUMM, S.A. (1956): Evolution of drainage systems and slopes in badlands at Perth Amboy, N.J. Geological Society of America Bulletin, 67, 597–646.

SMITH, T.R. & BRETHERTON, F.P. (1972): Stability and conservation of mass in drainage basin evolution. Water Resources Research, 8, 1506–1529.

STRAHLER, A.N. (1950): Equilibrium theory of erosional slopes approached by frequency distribution analysis. American Journal of Science, 248, 673–696 and 800–814.

Address of author:
Lawrence E. Band
Department of Geology and Geography
Hunter Colloge — City University of New York
New York, New York 10021, USA
Current address:
Dept. of Geography
University of Toronto
Toronto, Canada MSS 1A1

CATENA SUPPLEMENT 10   p.111–119   Braunschweig 1987

A MATHEMATICAL MODEL
FOR THE GEOMETRY
OF MEANDER BENDS

U. **Wieczorek**, Augsburg

SUMMARY

Taking up previous investigations by the author, the attempt is made to deduce a general function for the approximation of the geometry of meander bends in the plane of the valley floor, in which no restriction for the geometry is made. Two cases must be distinguished:

1. the amount of the migration of the meander bend downvalley is the same at each point of the bend,

2. the amount of that migration is not the same at each point of the bend.

For case 1 it is possible to deduce a certain type of an approximation function. That is not possible for case 2 in general, because there the migration of each meander bend can be quite individual. For a specially simulated migration, which can be described by a function, a relation f_1^* is computed. By connecting that relation with certain functions, which will be deduced in this presentation, an approximation curve for the meander bend can be found. That approximation curve is charactized by the simulated migration.

ISSN 0722-0723
ISBN 3-923381-10-7
©1987 by CATENA VERLAG,
D–3302 Cremlingen-Destedt, W. Germany
3-923381-10-7/87/5011851/US$ 2.00 + 0.25

Approximation curves with a central angle $\geq 180°$ can result only in case 2.

1 INTRODUCTION

Meanders of rivers and creeks are one of the rhythmic phenomena we can observe on the earth surface. Size and geometry of meander bends depend on hydrological, geological and topographic parameters. Investigations of those dependencies have been performed e.g. by HJULSTRÖM (1957), LEOPOLD & WOLMAN (1960), LANGBEIN & LEOPOLD (1963), ZELLER (1967), DURY (1971, 1981) and FERGUSON (1977). The geometry of meander bends in the plane of the valley floor is the result of a random process which controls the movement of the water particles. Assuming such a random process SCHELLING (1951) deduced that the angle φ between the momentary direction of a particle being moved in a plane and that direction which is resulting from adding all the momentary directions can be approximated by a sine-function of the dimension "lenght of the path along which the particle is moved" (L). The term of that function is defined by

$$\varphi(x) = c \cdot sin(d \cdot L) \qquad (1)$$

in which c and d are the constants.

The problem is to find a function that will approximate meander bends in Euclidean x, y-coordinates as well as possible. Such a function has been derived for meander bends with a central angle of less than 180° (WIECZOREK 1985). An essential condition in this case was to assume the same amount of downvalley migration of the meander bend at each point, so that the entire meander bend shifted parallel to itself. In the present paper, this condition shall not be presupposed. To compare the two cases — same amount of migration in each point of the bend or not — it is necessary to show briefly how the approximation function for meander bends with a central angle of less than 180° is derived.

The parameters of this function do not directly depend on hydrological, geological and topographic parameters; rather, they depend primarily on the geometry of the meander bend. However, the geometry in turn depends on hydrological, geological and topographic parameters so that these parameters have an indirect influence also on the function parameters.

2 DEDUCTION OF AN APPROXIMATION FUNCTION FOR MEANDER BENDS IN EUCLIDEAN x, y-COORDINATES

For obtaining the approximation function it is necessary to connect three functions:

$$f_1 : x \mapsto L, \quad g_2 : L \mapsto \Phi, \quad g_3 : \Phi \mapsto y$$

in which x and y are Euclidean coordinates and L is the length of the meander bend beginning at a turning point, which is the starting point of the bend. The final point of the bend should be the next turning point downward. In the function of SCHELLING (equation (1)), L is the length of the meander bend beginning at the summit of a bend. So g_2 must be properly a cosinefunction. But if we consider that the integral function of a cosine function and if we replace the angle φ by a variable Φ, we can define g_2 as a sine function with

$$g_2(L) = c \cdot \sin(r \cdot L)$$

c defines the amplitude of the curve given by g_2. The function g_3 will be defined as a correction function for the amplitude c in such a way that the value of the first derivative of g_2 at the starting point and at the end point will not be changed. The amplitude of the curve which is defined by $y = g_3(g_2(L))$ is determined by the amplitude of the meander bend. The function g_3 is defined by the following term:

$$g_3(u) = \frac{u}{c^{-1} \cdot u \cdot (\frac{c}{A} - 1) + 1}$$

in which u has to be replaced by $g_2(L)$.

For deriving the function f_1, we have to regard the impulse $m \cdot \Delta \dot{x}$ which is transmitted from a water-particle to the channel bank in the x-direction and in which the water particle decelerates by $\Delta \dot{x}$.

After Newton's second law we have

$$m \cdot \ddot{x} = m \cdot \frac{\Delta \dot{x}}{\Delta t} \cdot \Delta t$$

Applying the mean theorem of the differential calculus, replacing $\frac{\Delta \dot{x}}{\Delta t}$ by $\alpha \cdot \ddot{x}$ and multiplying the equation with $\frac{\Delta x}{\Delta t}$ we obtain

$$m \cdot \Delta \dot{x} \cdot \frac{\Delta x}{\Delta t} = \alpha \cdot m \cdot \ddot{x} \cdot \Delta x \qquad (2)$$

Because only the impulse is considered which is transmitted from the water particle to the channel bank, the right side of the equation shows the energy which the water particle has lost to the channel bank. Only a part of this energy causes bank erosion. If this part of the energy is $\beta \cdot \alpha \cdot m \cdot \ddot{x} \cdot \Delta x$, β must be less than 1. New we multiply equation (2) with β and assume $\beta \cdot \Delta \dot{x}$ as that fraction $\gamma \cdot \dot{x}$ of the velocity of the water particle which is lost by eroding the channel bank. γ is a constant which depends on properties of the flowing water and on properties of the bank material. If we replace $\frac{\Delta x}{\Delta t}$ by $\vartheta \dot{x}$ and take into consideration that the energy on the right side of equation (2) is lost by the water particle, then the right side is taken as negative and we obtain

$$\gamma \cdot \vartheta \cdot \dot{x}^2 = -\alpha \cdot \ddot{x} \cdot \Delta x. \qquad (3)$$

For this equation two cases must be investigated:

Case 1: Δx is constant, i.e. the migration of the meander bend in the x-direction is the same at each point of the bend.

Case 2: Δx is not constant, i.e. the migration of the meander bend in the x-direction is not identical at each point.

Now the deduction of the term of function f_1 will be continued and the results will be discussed for the two cases.

Case 1:

We can change the preceding equation into the equation

$$c_o \cdot \dot{x}^2 = -\ddot{x}$$

If we integrate this equation twice we obtain

$$x = c_o^{-1} \cdot \ln(t + c_1) \qquad (4)$$

and therefore

$$t = e^{c_o x} - c_1,$$

in which t has the dimension "time".

If we multiply equation (4) with the flow velocity u which is assumed as being constant, we obtain ($c_1 = 1$, because $x = 0$, if $t = 0$)

$$L = u \cdot e^{c_o x} - u.$$

Multiplying this equation with the constant factor d from equation (1) and replacing $d \cdot u$ by a and c_o by b we obtain

$$g_2(f_1(x)) = c \cdot sin(a \cdot e^{bx} - a)$$

The constants a, b, c are computed from the conditions ($\alpha_1, \alpha_2, \lambda$ as in fig.2):

(I) $g_2(f_1 x) = 0,$

if $x = 0$ or $x = \lambda$

(II) $\dfrac{d}{dx} g_2(f_1(x)) = tan(\alpha_1),$

if $x = 0$

(III) $\dfrac{d}{dx} g_2(f_1(x)) = tan(\alpha_2),$

if $x = \lambda$

We obtain for the constants a, b, c from these conditions:

$$a = \frac{tan(\alpha_1) \cdot \pi}{tan(\alpha_2) - tan(\alpha_1)}$$

$$b = \frac{1}{\lambda} \cdot \ln(\frac{tan(\alpha_2)}{tan(\alpha_1)})$$

$$c = \frac{tan(\alpha_1)}{a \cdot b}$$

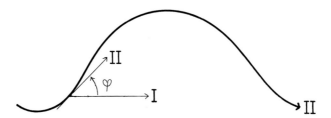

Fig. 1: *Definition of the angle* φ *between the current direction of a water particle in the channel and the fall direction of the valley floor.*

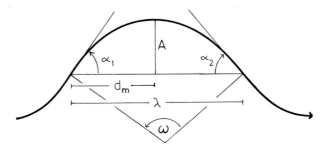

Fig. 2: *Shape parameters of a meander bend.*

For $\alpha_1 < 90°$ and $\alpha_2 < 90°$ and $\alpha_1 \neq \alpha_2$ the approximation function is defined by

$$y = g_3(g_2(f_1(x)))$$

If $\alpha_1 = \alpha_2$, we have to compute the limit of $g_3(g_2(f_1(x)))$ for $\alpha_1 \to \alpha_2$. Using the series for the sine function and the e-function we obtain as limit the term

$$y = \frac{tan(\alpha_2) \cdot \lambda}{\pi} \cdot sin(\frac{\pi}{\lambda} \cdot x)$$

It has been shown already (WIEC-ZOREK 1985) that natural meander bends are stable if there is a good approximation by the derived approximation function. Furthermore, natural meander bends are stable if the pair of quotients $(\frac{c}{A}; \frac{d_m}{d})$ has a position near the point (1;1) in an Euclidean coordinate system. d_m is the x-coordinate of the

summit of the natural meander bend, d is the x-coordinate of the summit of the approximation curve. For deriving the approximation function d_m has not been taken into consideration so that the comparison of d_m and d may serve as an indicator of the quality of the approximation. For all parameters of the approximation function we can find a random distribution if we compute those parameters for a number of bends. This may be an indicator for the random generation of meander bends. However, the approximation function shows a law for the geometry of meander bends which is only modified by random processes.

Case 2:

Δx in equation (3) is not assumed as constant. We can define Δx by the term $f(t)$ of a function f and we obtain from equation (3)

$$c_o \cdot \dot{x}^2 = -\ddot{x} \cdot f(t) \tag{5}$$

If we change this equation into

$$\frac{c_o}{f(t)} = \frac{-\ddot{x}}{\dot{x}^2}$$

and integrate this equation twice, we obtain

$$x = \int \frac{dt}{c_o \int \frac{dt}{f(t)}} \tag{6}$$

The term $f(t)$ must be determined for each natural meander bend by measurements which have to be repeated after certain time intervals. The length of the intervals depends on the velocity of the migration of the meander bend. Surely it will be reasonable in most cases to compute the mean of the different measurements at each point of the bend for determining an approximation for $f(t)$.

If we replace c_o by b and assume $\frac{1}{b} \cdot F(t)$ as a solution of the integral at the right side of equation (6) we obtain

$$b \cdot x = F(t)$$

If we assume F^{-1} as the reverse relation of F, we can write this equation

$$F^{-1}(bx) = t$$

Multiplying this equation with $\delta \cdot u$, in which u is the constant flow-velocity, we obtain

$$\delta \cdot u \cdot F^{-1}(bx) = L$$

or, replacing F^{-1} by f_1^* and $\delta \cdot u$ by a, we get

$$a \cdot f_1^*(bx) = L$$

and so we have

$$f_1(x) = a \cdot f_1^*(bx)$$

and

$$g_2(f_1(x)) = c \cdot sin(a \cdot f_1^*(bx))$$

If in equation (2) Δx is constant, then $f_1^*(bx) = e^{bx} - 1$!

For computing the parameters a, b, c we have to consider the following conditions $(f_1^{*'}(b \cdot x) = \frac{d}{dx}f_1^*(b \cdot x)$ and $g_2(f_1(x))' = \frac{d}{dx}g_2(f_1(x)))$:

(I) $a \cdot f_1^*(b \cdot 0) = 0$

(II) $a \cdot f_1^*(b \cdot \lambda) = \pi$

and therefore $a = \frac{\pi}{f_1^*(b \cdot \lambda)}$

$$
\begin{aligned}
(III) \quad (g_2(f_1(0)))' &= c \cdot cos(a \cdot f_1^*(b \cdot 0)) \\
&\quad \cdot a \cdot f_1^{*'}(b \cdot 0) \cdot b \\
&= \frac{c \cdot b \cdot \pi \cdot f_1^{*'}(0)}{f_1^*(b \cdot \lambda)} \\
&= tan(\alpha_1)
\end{aligned}
$$

$$
\begin{aligned}
(IV) \quad (g_2(f_1(\lambda)))' &= c \cdot cos(a \cdot f_1^*(b \cdot \lambda)) \\
&\quad \cdot a \cdot f_1^{*'}(b \cdot \lambda) \cdot b \\
&= \frac{-c \cdot b \cdot \pi \cdot f_1^{*'}(b \cdot \lambda)}{f_1^*(b \cdot \lambda)} \\
&= tan(\alpha_2^*)
\end{aligned}
$$

Dividing (III) by (IV) we get an equation for defining b:

$$\frac{-f^{*'}(0)}{f^{*'}1(b \cdot \lambda)} = \frac{tan(\alpha_1)}{tan(\alpha_2^*)} \tag{7}$$

$$(\alpha_2^* = 180° - \alpha_2)$$

In most cases this equation must be solved by a suitable iteration, if the term $f_1^{*'}(b \cdot c)$ can be determined. Mostly however $f_1^*(b \cdot x)$ and also $f_1^{*'}(b \cdot x)$ must be computed point by point by computing at first $F(t)$. For computing $F(t)$ the migration into x-direction along the meander bend between $L_o = 0$ (starting point) and L_1 (final point) must be known. So we have to measure the length L_1 of the bend. If we have computed $F(t)$ and therefore $F(\frac{L_1}{\delta \cdot u})$, it will be possible to compute b from the quotient

$$b = \frac{F(\frac{L_1}{\delta \cdot u})}{\lambda},$$

in which $\delta \cdot u = a$

a and c can be computed from (II), (III) and (IV).

If $F(0)$ and $f(\frac{L_1}{\delta \cdot u})$ can be computed approximately, we have to check whether the equation (7) is true or not. It would be only necessary to regard one of the angles α_1 or α_2 for deducing the approximation function. The other angle can be computed from equation (7). The difference between the measured angle and the computed angle can be used as an indicator of the quality of the approximation by the approximation function. In order to obtain the term $g_3(g_2(f_1(x)))$ it is necessary to measure the following properties of the meander bend: α_1 or $\alpha_2, A, \lambda, L_1$ and the migration in the x-direction during a certain time for enough points of the bend to approximate the function $f(t)$ sufficiently well. If u is known, values for t can be computed and used for determining the term $F(t)$.

3   COMPUTATION OF $x \cdot b$ FOR A SIMULATION OF $f(t)$ IN THE CASE 2 OF SECTION 2

The function f will be defined now arbitrary for a simulation. But it must be defined in such a way that a realistic situation can be described. The term $f(t)$ of this function will be defined in the following way

$$f(t) = \begin{cases} -k_1 \cdot sin(\frac{\pi}{t_1} \cdot t) - m, \\ \quad \text{if } 0 \leq t < t_1 \\ k_2 \cdot sin(\frac{\pi}{t_2 - t_1} \cdot (t - t_1)) + m, \\ \quad \text{if } t_1 \leq t < t_2 \\ -k_3 \cdot sin(\frac{\pi}{2\pi - t_2} \cdot (t - t_2)) - m, \\ \quad \text{if } t_2 \leq t < 2 \cdot \pi \end{cases}$$

The interval $[0; 2\pi]$, in which the function f is defined, is chosen arbitrarily too. Using a sine function for defining f, it is reasonable to choose the interval in that way. The choice of the interval is only a problem of scale. The symbols t_1 and t_2 define those points of the meander bend where the direction of the migration is changing. If we assume $m \neq 0$, the function f is not continuous at those points. In nature a continuous change of migration cannot be assumed.

For computing the term $F(t)$ the integral constant C_1 for $\int \frac{dt}{f(t)}$ (compare with the right side of equation (6)!) must not equal 0 because $\dot{x}(0)$ is normally $\neq 0$. $|C_I|$ describes a relation between 'the mean flow velocity in the x-direction and the mean migration velocity.

In fig.3 approximated graphs for the curve $b \cdot x = F(t)$ for different sets of the variables $k_1, k_2, k_3, t_1, t_2, m, C_I$ are shown. In the case where the migration direction changes twice for one bend the reverse relation F^{-1} might have two values for the first and the final part of the interval in which the relation is defined. Then, if we compute $y = g_3(g_2(f_1(x)))$, we find that $\alpha_1 > 90°$ and $\alpha_2 > 90°$. In this case the approximation curve describes a meander loop as often found on small rivers which are flowing very slowly in wide valley bottoms.   Not

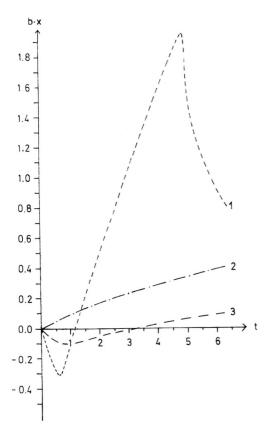

Fig. 3: *Simulations for the curve* $b \cdot x = F(t)$.

curve 1: $k_1 = 0.2$; $k_2 = 10$; $k_3 = 10$; $t_1 = 0.6$; $t_2 = 4.8$; $m = 0.01$; $C_I = 1$
curve 2: $k_1 = -1$; $k_2 = k_3 = 0$; $t_1 = t_2 = 2 \cdot \pi$; $m = 0.01$; $C_I = 1.5$
curve 3: $k_1 = 0.2$; $k_2 = 0.6$ $k_3 = 0$; $t_1 = 0.8$; $t_2 = 2 \cdot \pi$; $m = 0$; $C_I = 3.5$
(Integrals are computed approximately)
Replacing in the equation
$y = g_3(g_2(f_1(x)))$ the term $f_1(x)$ by $F^{-1}(b \cdot x)$ we obtain the equation for an approximation curve of a meander bend in case 2.

all apparently reasonable sets of variables $k_1, k_2, k_3, t_1, t_2, m, C_I$ supply reasonable results; for $x \cdot b = F(t), F(t) \to \pm \infty$ may be possible in the interval $[o; 2 \cdot \pi]$. Therefore, investigations will be necessary to determine in which way migration of the meander bend in x-direction upvalley and downvalley for the deduction of $F(t)$ must be defined. Better results might be possible, if "migration upvalley and downvalley" is defined in relation to a mean migration in the x-direction so that "migration upvalley" is really a migration downvalley but slower than the migration. The "migration downvalley" must be faster than the mean migration.

It must also be regarded that the shape of the meander bend is changing continuously. Thus the parameters of the meander bend, which are determining parameters of the approximation function, also are changing continuously so that we have a special approximation curve only for a moment. If we can assume the same amount of migration for each point of the meander bend not along a straight line but along a special curve, it might be possible to obtain an approximation curve which is valid not only for a moment. Further investigations are necessary to find a solution to that problem.

4   THE PROBLEM OF DEDUCING THE TYPE OF A FUNCTION RESPECTIVELY OF A RELATION FOR f_1^*

If we replace in equation (3) c_o by b and then $b \cdot x$ by $r \cdot h^{-1}(b \cdot x)$ (r constant), in which h^{-1} is the reverse relation of a function h, we obtain after solving that equation to x and regarding the equation (6)

$$h(\frac{1}{r} \cdot ln(t + c_1)) = \int \frac{dt}{\int \frac{dt}{f(t)}}$$

and therefore, differentiating the equation twice and replacing the argument o h by LN

$$f(t) = \frac{h'(LN)^2}{r \cdot h'(LN) - h''(LN)}$$

The function h must be defined in a way that a reasonable term for $f(t)$ can be found. If polynomials are used as approximation for the term of the function h, it can be shown by regarding the right side of the last equation that polynomials of a degree less than 5 do not supply reasonable terms for f(t), because, if the degree is less than 5, there are points where $r \cdot h'(LN) - h''(LN) = 0$ but $h'(LN)^2 \neq 0$. That can be avoided, if the degree of the polynomial is >4. But in those cases it will be impossible, for mathematical reasons, to find the term for the relation h^{-1}.

It is a task for further investigations to find suitable terms or a suitable class of terms for the function h.

5   CONCLUSIONS

In case 1, if the migration of the meander bend in the x-direction is the same at each point, a type of a function has been found which approximates the natural meander bend. By invetigations at natural meanders it has been shown that the quality of the approximation is an indicator for the stability of the meander bend (WIECZOREK 1985). The parameters of the approximation function for a certain bend can be determined from the shape of the bend, which might have been reproduced for example in an aerial photograph (orthophoto).

In case 2, if the migration of the meander bend in the x-direction is not the same at each point, a general type of approximation function could not be found until now. And there is the question, whether this may at all be generally possible because the migration of each meander bend is an individual one. For determining the term of an individual approximation function the parameters of the function cannot be derived from the shape of the natural meander bend only. Also measurements of the amount of the migration of the meander and of the relation between the mean of the x-component of the flow velocity and the mean of the x-component of the migration velocity are needed. The quality of the approximation may be tested by the difference between the position of the summit of the natural meander and that of the approximation curve, as well as by the difference between one of the two angles α_1 or α_2 of the natural meander bend and the approximation curve. For further conslucions, investigations on natural meander bends have to be made and the individual approximation curves have to be computed.

REFERENCES

BRICE, J. (1981): Meandering pattern of the white river in Indiana — an analysis. Morisawa, M. (Ed.): Fluvial Geomorphology, 179–200. London, Boston, Sydney.

DURY, G.H. (1971): Channel characteristics in a meandering channel: Crooked River, Florida. Geogr. Ann. **53 A**, Number 3–4.

DURY, G.H. (1981): Magnitude frequency analysis and channel morphology. Morisawa, M. (Ed.): Fluvial Geomorphology, 91–122. London, Boston, Sydney.

FERGUSON, R.I. (1977): Meander migration, equilibrium and change. Gregory, K.J. (Ed.): River Channel Changes, 236–248.

HJULSTRÖM, F. (1957): Studien über das Mäanderproblem. Bull. No. **51** of the Inst. Hydraulics Royal Inst. of Technology, Stockholm.

LANGBEIN, W.B. & LEOPOLD, L.B. (1966): River meanders — theory of a minimum variance. U.S. Geological Surv. Prof. Pap. **422 H**.

LEOPOLD, L.B. & WOLMAN, M.G. (1960): River meanders. Bull. Geol. Soc. America **71**, 769–794.

SCHEIDEGGER, A.E. (1970): Theoretical Geomorphology. Heidelberg, New York.

SCHELLING, H. v. (1951): Most frequent particle paths in aplane. Transactions Amer. Geophys. Union **22**, No. 2, 222–226.

SCHUMM, S.A. (1963): Sinuosity of alluvial rivers on the Great Plains. Bull. Geol. Soc. America **74**, 1089–1100.

WIECZOREK, U. (1985): Ein mathematisches Modell der Mäanderbogenform für Zentriwinkel unter 180°. Z. Geomorph. N.F. Suppl. Bd. **55**, 57–80, Sept. 1985.

ZELLER, J. (1967): Flußmorphologische Studie zum Mäanderproblem. Geogr. Helvetica, 22. Jg., H. 2, 57–97.

Address of author:
U. Wiezcorek
Lehrstuhl für Didaktik der Geographie der Univ.
Augsburg
Alter Postweg 120
D 8900 Augsburg

CATENA SUPPLEMENT 10   p.121–135   Braunschweig 1987

THE RELATIONSHIP BETWEEN ANNUAL RAINFALL AND SEDIMENT YIELD IN ARID AND SEMI-ARID AREAS. THE CASE OF THE NORTHERN NEGEV.

A. **Yair** and Y. **Enzel**, Jerusalem

SUMMARY

The relationship between the amount of annual rainfall and sediment yield has attracted the attention of many workers. A positive relationship between these two variables up to 300 mm is assumed by most authors. The basic assumption is that in semi-arid and arid areas, the energy available for erosion and transport decreases with decreasing annual rainfall. This assumption encounters serious difficulties when applied to the northern Negev desert (70 to 250 mm) where a converse relationship seems to fit the field conditions better. The explanation proposed for this is that available energy, under the given rainfall conditions, is largely controlled by the efficiency of the transformation of rainfall into runoff. The data clearly show that this efficiency is mainly dependent on the ratio of bare bedrock to soil cover. Soil-covered areas are characterized by a high infiltration rate, and, therefore, by runoff and erosion events of low frequency and magnitude. Rocky areas, which have a low infiltration capacity, are characterized by the high frequency and magnitude of runoff and erosion events. As the extent of soil cover increases (due to weathering and other processes) with increasing annual rainfall, a decrease in the efficiency of runoff and erosion processes can be expected in conjunction with increasing mean annual rainfall, on passing from arid to semi-arid areas. The hypothesis presented is tested for the geological period when loess deposited in the Negev, during the Würm glaciation, led to the nearly complete obliteration and disorganization of the preexisting drainage network, due to the change in the ratio of bare bedrock to soil cover.

ISSN 0722-0723
ISBN 3-923381-10-7
©1987 by CATENA VERLAG,
D–3302 Cremlingen-Destedt, W. Germany
3-923381-10-7/87/5011851/US$ 2.00 + 0.25

1   INTRODUCTION

The relationship between the magnitude of annual sediment yield and annual rainfall has attracted the attention of many researchers. It has been used to explain regional variations in the sediment yield (LANGBEIN & SCHUMM 1958, FOURNIER 1960, WILSON 1969, DOUGLAS 1967, DENDY & BOLTON 1976), to predict sediment yield in ungauged basins (OSTERKAMP 1976), and in discussions on

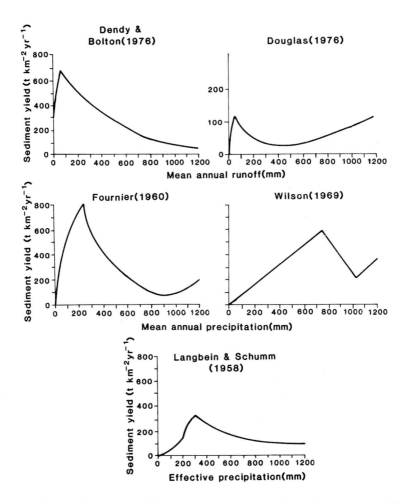

Fig. 1: *The relationship between sediment yield and annual rainfall.*

the effect of climatic changes on sediment yields (e.g. SCHUMM 1965, KNOX 1984).

A positive relationship between annual sediment yield and annual rainfall, at least up to about 300 mm, is assumed by many authors (fig.1). When annual precipitation exceeds 300 mm, it has been suggested that a drop in the sediment yield occurs. LANGBEIN & SCHUMM as well as other authors have proposed that this is due to the fact that the avail-

able energy for erosion and transport increases positively with the amount of annual rainfall up to about 300 mm, at which point the perennial and annual vegetation cover increases surface protection and limits soil erosion.

The increase in the available data on sediment yield all over the world has led several authors to question the validity of the LANGBEIN & SCHUMM rule for areas where annual precipitation exceeds 300 mm. Some authors (see JANSSON

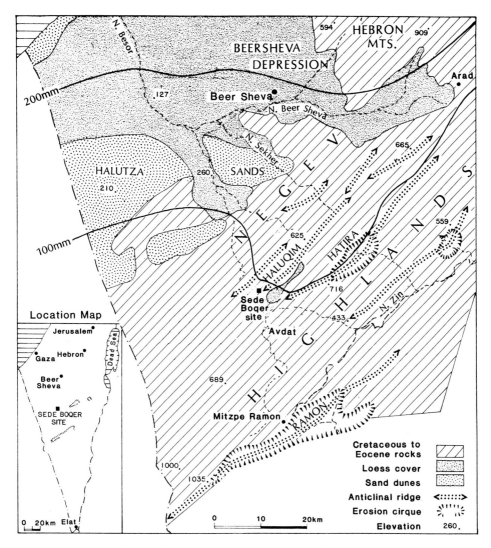

Fig. 2: *Physiographic units in the northern Negev.*

1982, HADLEY et al. 1985, HEUSCH & CAYLA 1986) assume that a positive relationship between sediment yield and annual rainfall exists, suggesting an increase in erosivity which is not offset by the increased protection by the vegetation cover. Other authors (e.g. WILSON 1969, DOUGLAS 1969) locate the peak sediment yield in relatively more humid areas. Finally, TABUTEAU (1960) and WALLING & KLEO (1979) sugget, on the basis of data derived from 1246 stations all over the world, that there is no clear relationship between annual rainfall and sediment yield; they explain this by the influence of factors other than climate and vegetation. Among these are: local relief, lithology, seasonality and hu-

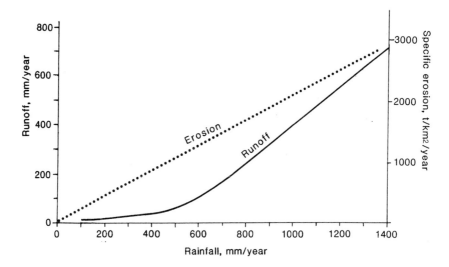

Fig. 3: *The relationship between annual rainfall, runoff and sediment yield (after HEUSCH & CAYLA 1986).*

man activity.

All the papers quoted above deal with the sediment yield in areas where the annual rainfall exceeds 200 mm. On these areas relatively large body of soil erosion data is available. The limited data available on climate, soils and hydrology from arid areas preclude reliable estimates of soil erosion rates and of their variation with annual rainfall. Under such conditions, a positive linear or asymptotic relationship (e.g. KNOX 1984, HEUSCH & CAYLA 1986) is usually assumed (see fig.3). The validity of such an assumption has already been questioned by SCHICK (1977), who pointed out that for a ten-year period, the mean annual sediment yield of the Yael Watershed, which has a mean annual rainfall of 30 mm, was 390 t/km^2 "that considerably exceeds the accepted norm of arid environments".

This paper has two main objectives:

● To examine the relationship between climate and erosion in the case of the northern Negev desert, in the area where annual rainfall ranges from 90 mm to 250 mm.

● To discuss the hypothesis that in the area under consideration, a negative relationship between annual rainfall and sediment yield fits the situation better than the positive relationship usually assumed.

2   DESCRIPTION OF THE STUDY AREA

The study area (fig.2) extends from the semi-arid Beersheba depression in the north to the arid Ramon ridge in the south. The topographic elevation increases southward from 200 m at the central part of the Beersheba depression to 1010 m at the summit of the Ramon ridge. The mean annual rainfall decreases gradually southward – 205 mm at Beersheba and 73 mm at Mitzpe Ramon. There are two major distinct physiographic units in this area.

2.1   THE ROCKY NEGEV HIGHLANDS

The Negev Highlands consist of Cretaceous and Tertiary limestones and chalks. They are characterized by a rugged topography of dissected plateaux and anticlinal ridges with extensive steep rocky slopes.   Bare bedrock outcrops extend over 50–80% of the surface forming the upper to middle part of the hillslopes. A contiguous soil cover occurs on the colluvial stony lower slopes and along the flat alluvial valley bottoms. The vegetation cover is 5–15%, up to one-third of this vegetation consists of Mediterranean Irano-Turanian shrub species (YAIR & DANIN 1980).

2.2   THE LOESS-COVERED AREAS

A contiguous loess cover is characteristic of the Beersheba depression, with a thickness of up to 12 m (BRUINS & YAALON 1979). The topography is gently rolling plains, with the loess cover and thickness increasing in the downslope direction. Loess thickness decreases towards the margins of the depression where rocky outcrops become more common. The vegetation cover is less than 5% and shrubs of the Mediterranean Irano Turanian type are almost completely absent (KADMON 1984).

With respect to runoff and erosion processes the main difference between the two physiographic units described above may be summarized as follows:

- Annual rainfall is twice as high in the northern loess area than in the rocky southern area.

- The extent of rock outcrops increases southward with decreasing annual rainfall while the extent of soil cover increases towards the northern, climatologically more humid, area.

- Slope gradients are higher in the dissected rocky area than in the flat rolling plains.

- Vegetation cover, although limited, is far more extensive in the southern than in the northern area.

3   METHODOLOGY

Soil erosion was recorded at one long-term research station at Sde Boker (YAIR & LAVEE 1981, YAIR & SCHAHAK 1982). Thus far, data collected at this stage was limited to hillslope plots. It is clear that the analysis of the relationship between annual rainfall and sediment yield for the northern Negev area cannot be based on direct measurements of soil erosion. Rather, the analysis will be based on two complementary approaches.

- The first approach relies on the detailed study of present-day runoff and erosion processes and their implications with respect to the spatial variability of soil erosion in the area under consideration.

- The second approach is based on the study of the evolution of the drainage network in the last 100,000 years, during which period wetter climate prevailed in the area until the Holocene period (fig.4).

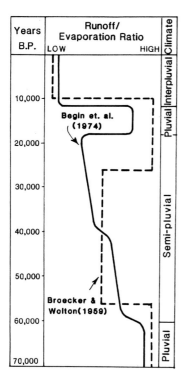

Fig. 4: *Climatic changes in the Middle East since the last glacial period. Rain intensity 36 mm/hr.*

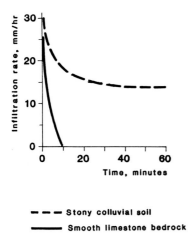

— — — Stony colluvial soil

——— Smooth limestone bedrock

Fig. 5: *The hydrological response of rocky and soil-covered areas to simulated rainfall.*

4 FACTORS AFFECTING PRESENT-DAY RUNOFF AND EROSION PROCESSES

4.1 EFFECT OF SURFACE PROPERTIES ON RUNOFF

Spatial variations in runoff are greatly influenced by spatial differences in the infiltration capacities of the surface material. With respect to surface properties, the study area may be subdivided into two distinct units: the rocky areas, and the soil-covered areas. Fig.5 represents the hydrological response of simulated rainfalls over these two surface units. Rainfall simulations were performed using a sprinkler (MORIN et al. 1970) which accurately reproduces the main features of natural rainfall. The simulated rainstorms represent rather extreme conditions of rain intensity, and, in particular, duration (KUTIEL 1978). The data obtained clearly indicate that the colluvial loess soils are characterized by a high infiltration rate, which remains so (approx. 17 mm/hr) even after one hour of high-intensity rain. On the other hand, a very low infiltration rate, which drops to zero after about ten minutes, is characteristic of the dense, low-porosity, crystalline limestone. These results are fully corroborated by hydrological data collected under natural rainfall conditions at the Sde Boker experiment site (YAIR 1983, YAIR & LAVEE 1985). Available data indicate that the threshold amount of daily rainfall necessary to generate runoff in the rocky areas is very low (1–3 mm). The threshold is greater for the stony colluvial soils (3–5 mm) and higher still (> 10 mm) for the stoneless loess soils of the Beersheba area (STIBBE 1974). As rainshowers below 3 mm represent ap-

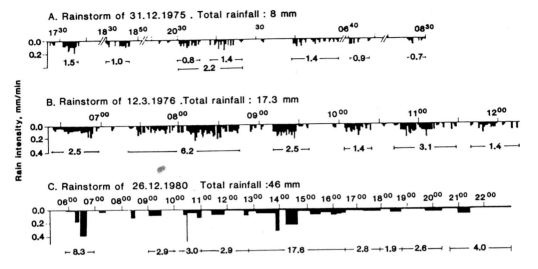

Fig. 6: *Temporal variations in rainfall during rainstorms.*

proximately 60% of rain events in the area, the frequency and magnitude of runoff events are both much higher on rocky than on soil-covered areas (YAIR 1983).

4.2   EFFECT OF RAINFALL PROPERTIES ON RUNOFF

Rainfall in the Negev is limited to the winter season. Most rainstorms belong to the category of frontal storms, known for their low to medium intensity. Rainstorms with an intensity exceeding 30 mm/hr, represent only 5% of the total rainfall, whereas rainstorms with an intensity below 5–10 mm/hr constitute about 77% of the total annual rainfall (KUTIEL 1978). This is well illustrated by fig.6. Even for the high magnitude storm, that occurred in December 1980, the average rainfall intensity for the entire storm did not exceed 3 mm/hr with very short peak intensities of 27 mm/hr, which lasted for a few minutes. The second important characteristic of these

storms is that they consist of several separate showers, each with only a few millimeters of rain. Consecutive showers are separated by time intervals, ranging from a few minutes to more than an hour, during which time the soil can drain and dry. The rainfall characteristics described above greatly accentuate the difference between the hydrological response of rocky and soil-covered areas which have been described above. Due to the prevailing discontinuous low-to-medium intensity rainstorms coupled with the high infiltration capacity, the soil-covered areas are able to absorb all rainwater in most rainstorms, thus no runoff is produced. Furthermore, when runoff does occur, its rate may be expected to be very low and highly discontinuous both in time and in space. A converse situation exists in the rocky areas. In this case, the quick response to rainfall results in runoff generation during most of the low-intensity, short-duration, rainshowers (YAIR & LAVEE

Year	Hillslope minicatchment			Loess microcatchment*		
	Rain (mm)	No. of flows	Runoff (mm)	Rain (mm)	No. of flows	Runoff (mm)
1982–83	136	21	27.0	170.0	4	7.8
1983–84	72	5	6.5	84.5	1	2.0
*EVENARI et al. (1984)						

Tab. 1: *Hydrological data: hillslope mini-catchment and loess microcatchment (1982–84).*

1985). The differential response to rainfall of rocky and soil-covered areas under natural rainfall conditions is well illustrated by the data presented in tab.1.

The microcatchments drain a loess-covered area some 15 km south of Beersheba, whereas data on the rocky slopes is derived from the Sde Boker experiment site.

4.3 EROSION ON ROCKY AND SOIL-COVERED AREAS

The analysis of surface and rainfall properties leads to the conclusion that runoff frequency and magnitude can be expected to be higher in the climatologically dry but rocky southern area than in the northern climatologically wetter loess-covered area. This situation should be reflected in a higher erosion rate and sediment yield in the arid than in the semi-arid areas. However, the discrepancy in the sediment yield is further enhanced by the activity of burrowing and digging animals. Previous studies (YAIR 1974, YAIR & SCHAHAK 1982) drew attention to the intense activity of desert animals in the area studied, and the important consequences of this on soil erosion. Porcupines in search of bulbs for their food, break the soil curst which otherwise, due to its mechanical properties and its cover of soil lichens and algae, inhibits soil erosion. Thus disaggregated soil becomes available for transport by shallow flows. Similarly, burrowing by

isopods delivers small faeces which disintegrate easily under the impact of raindrops. Quantitative measurements show that the amount of loose soil produced through the biological activity is strikingly non-uniform, being much higher over the rocky than over the soil-covered areas. Furthermore, a comparison between the spatial distribution of loose soil and the pattern of soil erosion indicates that these two factors are strongly linked. Erosion and sediment yields are accelerated over the rocky areas, but limited over the soil-covered areas (YAIR 1974, YAIR & SCHAHAK 1982). The explanation proposed was that rocky areas generate a high runoff per unit area, which in conjunction with the extensive mounds of disaggregated material produces a high erosion rate. A converse situation is characteristic of the soil-covered areas where the limited amounts of loose soil, coupled with the low velocities of the limited runoff, result in low sediment yields.

4.4 IMPLICATIONS OF PRESENT-DAY PROCESSES ON THE ISSUE OF SEDIMENT YIELD

As previously indicated, many authors (e.g. KNOX 1984, HEUSCH & CAYLA 1986, HADLEY et al. 1985) assume a decline in sediment yield with increasing aridity (fig.1), on the grounds that lower annual rainfall would mean a lower frequency of rainfall and runoff events and hence less energy available for erosion and transport. Similarly, various investigators (ABRAHAMS 1972, GREGORY 1976, KNOX 1984) have suggested that the densities of drainage channels tend to be maximum in semi-arid regions.

All these assumptions encounter serious difficulties when applied to the northern Negev desert, which extends from an arid to a semi-arid area. Here, detailed study of rainfall, runoff and erosion processes have indicated that under present-day rainfall conditions runoff and erosion are mainly governed by the ratio of bare bedrock to soil cover rather than by the amount of annual rainfall. In areas where this ratio is high, the rocky areas respond quickly to rainfall and generate high runoff yields, which result in a high erosion rate. It is interesting to note that the high erosion is observed over the area in which vegetation cover is relatively high and the zoological activity intense. At the other end of the spectrum, soil-covered areas generate limited runoff and sediment yields due to their high infiltration rate. Once again, it is interesting to note that only a low sediment yield is observed in areas in which the vegetation cover and zoological activity are both extremely limited (YAIR, 1987).

Application of these results on a regional scale suggests that sediment yields should decrease as one passes from an arid to a semi-arid area. This would be due directly to the regional non-random distribution of rocky and soil-covered areas. The extent of bare bedrock outcrops usually increases with decreasing annual rainfall, while the extent of soil cover increases towards the semi-arid areas. The latter trend is especially pronounced where, as in the northern Negev, there is

a contiguous and extensive loess cover.

5 RECENT EVOLUTION OF THE DRAINAGE NETWORK IN THE NORTHERN NEGEV

The positive relationship of runoff and erosion processes to the ratio of bare bedrock to soil cover should also affect the properties of the drainage network. This may be tested in the northern Negev. Large amounts of loess material were deposited in the Negev since the last glacial period. This increased the extent of soil cover considerably. Analysis of a stratigraphic section (fig.7) shows the loess overlies a conglomerate unit of Upper-Middle Palaeolithic age when deposited on former channels (GOLDBERG 1981). On slopes loess is in direct contact with the older marine Eocene or Cretaceous bedrock (phot.1). To date, paleosols derived from weathering of the local bedrock have not been observed underneath the loess cover on the older rocks. Prior to loess deposition the landscape therefore probably consisted of barren rocky hillslopes with very active channels capable of transporting coarse boulders. In other words, limited weathering, intense hillslope erosion processes and high energy channel flows, indicative of arid climatic conditions, prevailed in the area before the loess was deposited. However, with the loess deposition there occured significant change in the hydrological regime. Channels that once were able to transport coarse particles began to deposit fine sandy, silty and clayey particles which require much less transportation energy than coarse particles. The deposition rate of the fine grained materials was so rapid that entire val-

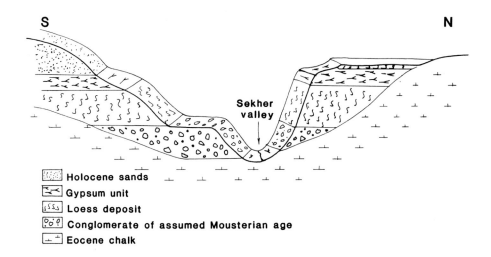

Fig. 7: *Stratigraphic section of the southern part of the Beersheba depression (after ENZEL 1984).*

Photo 1: *Buried valley: sharp contact between the loess covr and older bare bedrock surface.*

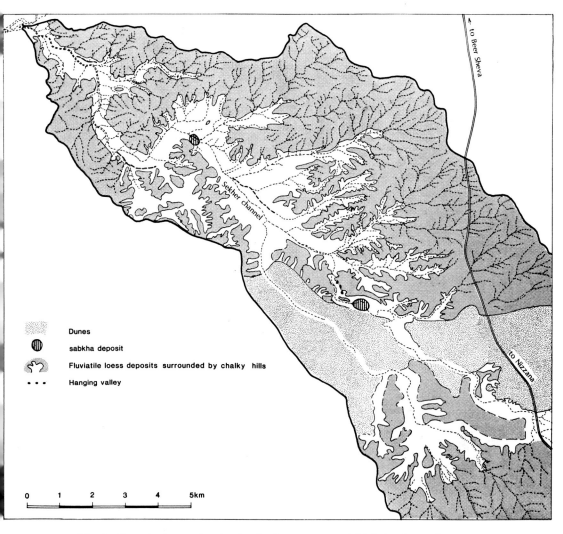

Dunes

sabkha deposit

Fluviatile loess deposits surrounded by chalky hills

Hanging valley

0 1 2 3 4 5km

Fig. 8: *Low drainage density in the loess area and high in the rocky area.*

leys were completely buried under the loess mantle (phot.1). The ensuing drastic decrease in the transporting capacity of the preexisting drainage network led to a considerable decrease in the drainage density (fig.8), and, in some places, to the complete disorganization of the drainage network. Lakes in the loess area, in which gypsum up to 2 m thick was de- posited (figs. 7 and 8), were recently pointed out, by ENZEL (1984). One of these lakes was formed at an elevation of 340 m across the Sekher valley (fig.8), which was once one of the major chan- nels draining the northern Negev. Its drainage area above this saline lake was quite extensive covering 150 km². The very existence of the lake dating from

Photo 2: *A hanging valley at the junction of a tributary, draining a loess-covered area, with the main Sekher channel.*

some 10,000 years B.P. (ENZEL 1984) indicates that at that time the Sekher valley terminated in a swampy area, since the route westward to the Mediteranean sea was obliterated.

A second drastic change in the hydrological regime occurred at the beginning of the Holocene period. The Shekher valley started to deeply incise draining lakes and swamps. During this time occurred interesting differential response of its tributaries. Tributaries that drained

rocky slopes were incised at the same rate as the main valley; their channels join the main valley at the same elevation as the main channel. However, tributaries that drained loess-covered areas were incised at a much slower rate than the main valley, which they join in a dry waterfall (phot.2). The formation of hanging valleys in the loess area and their absence in the rocky areas is an additional indication that runoff, erosion and transportation processes are much lower in the loess than in the rocky areas.

In order to evaluate the significance of the recent evolution (described above) on the relationship between annual sediment yield and climate, one must bear in mind that research in various disciplines: Prehistory (GOLDBERG 1981); Palinology (HOROWITZ 1979); Pedology (BRUINS & YAALON 1979); Paleohydrology (ISSAR & BRUINS 1984) and Sedimentology (COUDE-GAUSSEN et al. 1983), tends to agree that, despite slight climatic fluctuations, most of the loess cover was deposited under climatic conditions that were more humid than those of the present time (fig.3). ISSAR & BRUINS (1983), who studied the isotopic composition of groundwater in the Negev and Sinai as well as the clay content of the loess soils, reach the conclusion that between ca. 100,000 and 10,000 years B.P. "the amount of precipitation was 50–100% more than that of the present, while during the arid spells the precipitation was still somewhat higher than today". HOROWITZ (1979) goes as far as to suggest that during the Mousterian period (80–90,000 years B.P.) the "Climate belts were approximately 200–250 km south of their present positions". In other words, typical Mediterranean conditions existed in the area where the present-day average annual rainfall is less than 100 mm.

6   CONCLUSION

The prevailing idea that the denudation rate increases from zero to about 300 mm average annual rainfall is based on the assumption that surface properties are on the whole uniform within this wide range of climatic conditions and that erosivity is mainly controlled by the amount of annual rainfall. This assumption encounters serious difficulties when applied to the northern Negev, where a converse relationship seems to fit the reality better. The explanation proposed for this converse relationship is based on the study of present-day processes and on the analysis of the drainage network in recent geological history when climatic conditions differed from those that exist today.

The detailed study of present-day processes clearly indicates that surface properties, namely, the ratio of bare bedrock outcrop to soil cover, play a predominant role in runoff generation and in erosion processes. Runoff and erosion are positively related to this ratio; since it is higher in arid than in adjoining semi-arid areas, sediment yields are higher in the former than in the latter areas.

This conclusion is fully corroborated by the processes which governed the recent development of the drainage network in the northern Negev. Loess deposition into the Negev coincided with the transition to a wetter climate. Under such conditions two important factors controlling the rate of geomorphic processes changed simultaneously: first, the amount of annual rainfall, and second, the extent of soil cover, both of which increased. Analysis of the specific influence of each of these factors on landscape evolution clearly indicates that the increase in soil cover, due to a drastic decrease in runoff, resulted in a general obliteration of the preexisting drainage network, predominating over the possible positive effect of rainfall increase on soil erosion.

ACKNOWLEDGEMENT

We would like to express our thanks to Prof. F. Ahnert of the Geographisches Institut, Aachen, Germany, for his fruit-

ful comments and to Mrs. T. Sofer of
the Department of Geography at the Hebrew University for drawing the illustra-
tions.

REFERENCES

ABRAHAMS, A.D. (1972): Drainage densities
and sediment yields in eastern Australia. Australian Geographical Studies, **10**, 19–44.

BRUINS, H.J. & YAALON, D.H. (1979). The
stratigraphy of the Netivot section in the desert
loess of the Negev (Israel). Acta Geologica
Academiae Scientarum Hungaricae. T. **22**, 1–
4, 161–164.

COUDE-GAUSSEN,   G.,   OLIVE,   P.
& ROGNON, P. (1983): Datation de dépôts
loessiques et variations climatiques a la bordure
nord du Sahara Algéro-Tunisien. Revue de Geologie Dynamique et Geographie Physique, **24**,
1, 61–73.

DENDY, F.E. & BOLTON, G.C. (1976): Sediment yield — runoff drainage area relationships
in the United States. Journal of Soil and Water
Conservation, **31**, 264–266.

DOUGLAS, I. (1967): Man, vegetation and the
sediment yield of rivers. Nature, **215**, 925–928.

ENZEL, Y. (1984): The geomorphology of the
lower Sekher Valley. M.Sc. thesis, The Hebrew
University of Jerusalem, 102 pp. (in Hebrew
with English abstract).

EVENARI, M., ROGEL, A., MASIG, D. &
NESSLER, U. (1984): Runoff farming in the
Negev desert of Israel.   8th Progress Re-
port. Dept. of Botany, Hebrew University of
Jerusalem, 36 pp.

FOURNIER, F. (1960): Climat et Erosion. Paris,
Presses Universitaires de France, 203 pp.

GOLDBERG, P. (1981):   Late Quaternary
stratigraphy of Israel: An ecclectic view. Collo-
ques internationaux du C.N.R.S. no. 598. Pre-
histoire du Levant, 58–66.

GREGORY, K.G. (1976):   Drainage networks
and climate. In: Derbyshire, E. (ed.), Geomorphology and Climate. Wiley, N.Y., 289–315.

HADLEY, R.F., LAL, R., ONSTAD, C.A.,
WALLING, D. & YAIR, A. (1985): Recent developments in erosion and sediment yield studies.   International Documents in Hydrology.
UNESCO, Paris, 125 pp.

HEUSCH, B. & CAYLA, O. (1986):   Assess-
ment of sediment discharge measurements in the
Maghreb countries. Journal of Water Resources
(Iraq), **5**, 1, 349–366.

HOROWITZ, A. (1979): The Quaternary of Israel. Acad. Press, 344 pp.

ISSAR, A.S. & BRUINS, H.J. (1983):   Special climatological conditions in the deserts of
Sinai and the Negev during the latest Pleis-
tocene. Palaeogeography Palaeocilmatology and
Palaeoecology, **43**, 63–72.

JANSSON, M.B. (1982): Land erosion by water in different climates. Uppsala University,
Sweden, Report no. **57**, 159 pp.

KADMON, R. (1984): Spatial variations and environmental factors along arid slopes in the Ho-
vav Plateau area. M.Sc. thesis, The Hebrew
University of Jerusalem, 102 pp. (in Hebrew
with an English abstract).

KNOX, J.C. (1984): Fluvial responses to small
scale climate changes.   In: Costa, J.E. &
Flesicher, P.J. (eds.), Developments and Applications of Geomorphology. Springer-Verlag,
Berlin, 318–342.

KUTIEL, H. (1978): The distribution of rain intensities in Israel. M.Sc. thesis, The Hebrew
University of Jerusalem. (in Hebrew with abstract in English).

LANGBEIN, W.B. & SCHUMM, S.A. (1958):
Yield of sediment in relation to mean annual
precipitation.   Transactions of the American
Geophysical Union, **39**, 1076–1084.

MORIN, J., CLUFF, C.B. & POWERS, W.K.
(1970): Realistic rainfall simulation for field testing. Trans. of the Amer. Geophys. Union, **51**,
4, 292.

OSTERKAMP, W.R. (1976):   Variation and
causative factors of sediment yields in the
Arkansas River Basin, Kansas. In: Proceedings
of the 3rd Federal Inter-Agency Sedimentation
Conference. Washington, D.C. Water Resources
Council, 1–59.

SCHICK, A.P. (1977): A tentative sediment budget for an extremely arid watershed in the southern Negev. In: D.O. Doehring (ed.), Geomorphology in arid regions. Binghampton, 139–163.

SCHUMM, S.A. (1965): Quaternary Paleohy-
drology. In: H.E. Wright & D.G. Frey (eds.),
The Quaternary of the United States. Princeton
University press, N.J. 783–794.

STIBBE, E. (1974): Hydrological balance of Li-
mans in the Negev. Volcani Institute for Agricultural Research. Project no. 304, 14 pp.

TABUTEAU, M.M. (1960): Etude graphique pour leç consequences hydro-erosives du climat Mediterraneen. Bulletin de l'Association Geographique Française, **295**, 130–142.

WALLING, D.A & KLEO, A.H.A. (1979): Sediment yields of rivers in areas of low precipitation — a global view. I.A.S.H. Publ. no. **128**, 479–492.

WILSON, L. (1969): Les relations entre les processus geomorphologiques et le climat moderne comme methode de palaeoclimatologie. Revue de Geographie Dynamique. Ser. 2, 11, 303–314.

YAIR, A. (1974): Sources of runoff and sediment supplied by the slopes of a first order drainage basin in an arid environment. Abhandlungen der Akademie der Wissenschaften in Göttingen. Mathematisch-Physikalische Klasse, III. Folge, **29**, 403–417.

YAIR, A. (1983): Hillslope hydrology, water harvesting and areal distribution of some ancient agricultural systems in the northern Negev Desert. Journal of Arid Environments, **6**, 283–301.

YAIR, A. (1987): Environmental effects of loess penetration into the northern Negev Desert. Journal of Arid Environments, **13**, 9–24.

YAIR, A. & DANIN, A. (1980): Spatial variations in vegetation as related to the soil moisture regime over an arid limestone hillside, northern Negev, Israel. Oecologia (Berl.), **4**, 83–88.

YAIR, A. & LAVEE, H. (1981): An investigation of source areas of sediment and sediment transport by overland flow along arid hillslopes. Proceedings of the Symposium on Erosion and Sediment Transport Measurements. Florence, Italy. I.A.H.S. Publ., **133**, 433–446.

YAIR, A. & LAVEE, H. (1985): Runoff generation in arid and semiarid zones. In: Hydrological Forecasting. M.G. Anderson and T.P Burt (eds.), Chap. 8, 183–220. John Wiley & Sons. London.

YAIR, A. & SCHAHAK, M. (1982): A case study of energy water and soil flow chains in an arid ecosystem. Oecologia (Berl), **54**, 389–397.

Addresses of authors:
Prof. A. Yair
Yehuda Enzel
Institute of Earth Sciences, Hebrew University
Jerusalem 91904, Israel

CATENA SUPPLEMENT 10   p.137–146   Braunschweig 1987

A MULTIVARIATE STATISTICAL ANALYSIS OF SEDIMENT YIELD AND PREDICTION IN ROMANIA

I. **Ichim** & M. **Radoane**, Piatra Neamt

SUMMARY

To develop a multiple regression model, we took 99 small catchments (A < 50 km^2) from two lithologically distinct complexes, flysch rocks (n = 36) and Neogene molasse rocks (n = 63). For each drainage basin, we determined 28 independent variables as controlling factors. According to the determination coefficient and significance level we selected three equations for flysch rocks and four equations for Neogene molasse rocks (tab.2). Testing the equations for the catchments revealed that the equations (1) and (4) offered the best estimates of the sediment yields for both lithological areas. The equations were applied to the Putna river basin, upstream of the Prisaca cross-section (A = 1,100 km^2) which lies on flysch and on Neogene molasse. We identified 274 third order drainage basins (Strahler's system), of which 196 were on flysch and 78 were on Neogene molasse. For each basin we determined the sediment yield.

ISSN 0722-0723
ISBN 3-923381-10-7
©1987 by CATENA VERLAG,
D–3302 Cremlingen-Destedt, W. Germany
3-923381-10-7/87/5011851/US$ 2.00 + 0.25

1 BACKGROUND

Despite the progress in sediment yield prediction many problems still remain. The most frequently used predictors are multiple regression models, but in their application to particular regions there are some insurmountable problems. During the last five years several valuable papers have been published which deal with various aspects of this topic (GRIFFITHS 1982, JANSSON 1982, WALLING 1983, WALLING & WEBB 1983, ONSTAD 1984, HADLEY et al. 1985). One problem is the great range, on a regional scale, of some of the variables included in models (e.g. those of a climatic and a hydrologic nature). By contrast, other variables have a specific significance mainly for the region for which the model was developed. In this paper we describe a predictive model for Romanian conditions. It has the following aims:

a) definition of the fluvial sediment system and of the hierarchy of its controlling factors,

b) determination and selection of the prediction equations and

c) application of the models.

F. AHNERT (EDITOR): GEOMORPHOLOGICAL MODELS — THEORETICAL AND EMPIRICAL ASPECTS

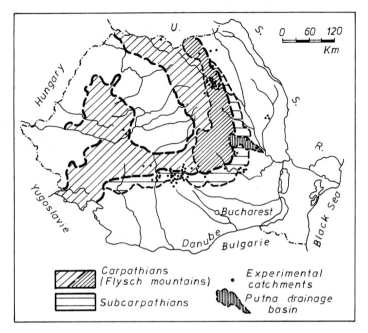

Fig. 1: *Position of the experimental catchments.*

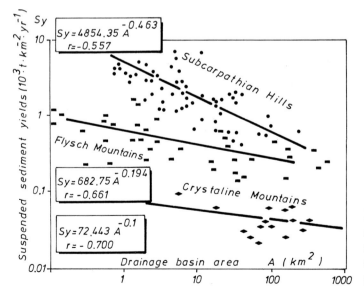

Fig. 2: *Relationship between sediment yield (S_y) and drainage basin area (A) in Romania.*

2   THE SEDIMENT SYSTEM AND THE INPUT VARIABLES

A major part of the fluvial geomorphic system is the **sediment system** which has at least 4 major components:

a) the **controlling factors**;

b) the **geomorphological processes**;

c) the **sediment sources and the sediment sinks**;

d) the **sediment yield.**

This is a general structure; in a systemic approach towards a prediction model one must consider the first three components as inputs and the last component as output. In the study of the inputs we considered variables of the main domains of influence on sediment yield (the climatic, geological, hydrological, geomorphological, vegetational and anthropogenic domains). Special attention was paid to the geomorphological variables because in many other models they do not seem to receive sufficient attention.

The data are from small catchments (usually <50 km^2) in Romania which has a temperate continental climate. Initially, 115 catchments were studied for which measurements of sediment production exist (fig.1). The relation between the catchment surface and the sediment yield is noticeably influenced by the lithology (fig.2). Only very few catchments lie on crystalline rocks; these were therefore not considered. Of the 99 basins included in this study, 36 are from the flysch area and 63 from the molasse hills of the Subcarpathians.

The flysch mountains lie in the Eastern Carpathians and consist of lenses of highly folded sandstone, alternating with marls, clay schists and conglomerates. They are almost exclusively in the forested zone which has an average annual precipitation of 600–1,200 mm.

The Subcarpathians is a region of hills with a fold structure, that lies between the Carpathian and the non-Carpathian zones. The main characteristics are determined by the lithology of the molasse deposits on which landslides and mudflows occur frequently, resulting in the highest erosion rates in Romania.

Initially we determined the hierarchy of all drainage basins (Strahler's system). Then, for each basin, we determined the values of 28 variables considered as possible input variables to the model. The number of variables could be greater, but it was considered that 24 morphometric variables would include most information about the relief of a small catchment. The additional variables represent either long term average controls, such as precipitation, or extreme states of the system (e.g. Qmax and Qs with return period of 100 years) with obvious effects on sediment yield. We also considered the percentage of forest cover which partially reflects land use patterns.

3   THE HIERARCHY OF THE CONTROLLING FACTORS

Three groups of methods were used to form the hierarchy of the sediment yield controls: elementary methods, analytical methods and combined methods.

The elementary methods applied were as follows:

a) bivariate regression analysis and

Subcarpathian hills area (n = 63)				Flysch mountain area (n = 63)			
Correlation coefficient data log$_{10}$		Spearman's coefficient		Correlation coefficient data log$_{10}$		Spearman's coefficient	
Variable	r	Variable	S	Variable	r	Variable	S
Qs	−0.674	Qs	−0.833	d	0.950	Qs	−0.919
A	0.671	A	0.831	A	0.949	L1	0.825
Qmax	0.663	Qmax	0.819	Qs	−0.949	L2	0.819
P	0.643	P	0.781	Qmax	0.948	D	0.813
D	0.615	Lt	0.776	L1	0.942	A	0.807
Lt	0.600	Lint	0.775	N1	0.939	d	0.805
L1	0.588	L1	0.742	L2	0.933	Lt	0.805
Lmed	0.584	D	0.732	D	0.933	N1	0.797
d	0.573	d	0.723	Lint	0.925	P	0.794
L2	0.550	Lmed	0.712	P	0.920	Ω	0.783
Lint	0.535	L2	0.669	N2	0.913	Lmed	0.782
N1	0.525	N1	0.666	Lt	0.910	Pmm	0.781
N2	0.469	N2	0.649	Ω	0.895	N2	0.773
Dt	−0.428	Rb	0.534	Lmed	0.873	Lint	0.772
Emax	0.403	Emax	0.515	Emax	0.790	Qmax	0.766
Rb	0.380	Ω	0.463	RR	−0.787	RR	−0.690
D1	−0.369	Dt	−0.405	Pmm	0.717	Emax	0.653
Ω	0.326	RR	−0.365	Hmed	0.632	Hmed	0.631
Ih	−0.276	D1	−0.355	Rb	0.621	Rb	0.598
RR	−0.255	Ih	−0.299	Lm2	0.550	Lm2	0.397
Lm2	0.245	Sb	−0.123	Cf	0.450	C	−0.329
Sb	−0.115	Lm2	0.096	D1	−0.417	Cf	0.307
Cf	−0.088	Pmm	0.090	Ih	−0.407	D1	−0.282
Hmed	−0.072	Hmed	−0.078	C	−0.352	Ih	−0.258
Lm1	0.061	Lm1	0.072	Dt	−0.087	Sb	−0.210
C	0.039	Af	−0.045	Sb	−0.248	Dt	−0.138
Pmm	0.031	C	0.030	Lm1	−0.238	Af	0.151
Af	−0.026	Cf	−0.021	Af	0.143	Lm1	−0.024

Tab. 1: *Controlling factor hierarchy of the sediment yield (tonne/yr) based on bivariate correlation between Sy(tonne/yr) and each independent variable.*

Symbols:
Geomorphological variables: Ω - basin order (Strahler's system); N1 - basin magnitude (Shreve's system); N2 - number of the second order channels; A - basin area (km^2); Hmed - average elevation of the drainage basin (m); Emax - maximum energy of landscape (m); P - basin drainage perimeter (km); Sb - average inclination of the drainage basin (%); D - diameter of the circumscribed circle of the basin (km); d - diameter of the inscribed circle of the basin (km); Cf - form coefficient of the basin; Ih - hypsometric integrale (%); C - circulatiry of the basin; Rb - bifurcation ratio; L1 - exterior links length (km); L2 - length of the second order channels (km); Lt - total channel networks length (km); Lint - interior links length (km); Lm1 - average length of the first order links (km); Lm2 - average length of the second order links (km); Lmt - average length of the total channel networks (km); D1 - drainage of the 1st order links density (km/km^2); Dt - drainage density of the total channel network (km/km^2); RR - relief ratio (m/km);
Climatic variables: Mean annual precipitations (Pmm, mm);
Hydrologic variables: Qmax - maximum discharge (1%) (m^3/s); Qs - maximum runoff (1%) (m^3/km^2/s);
Land utilise variables: Af - forest area (%).

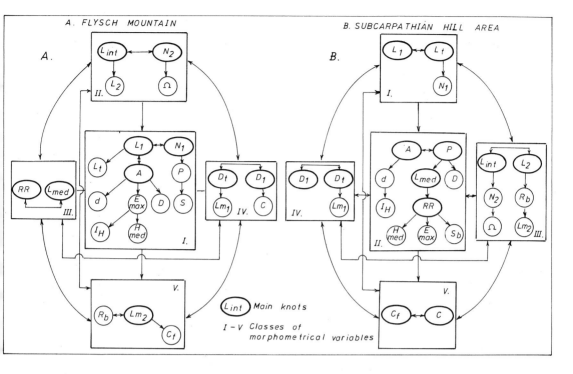

Fig. 3: *Typological classification of the morphometric variables.*

b) analysis of the matrix of both correlation coefficients and rank or Spearman's coefficients.

They produced two results which may be related to the choice of variables: first, there was a visual similarity between the hierarchy resulting from the correlations based on logarithmic values (log 10) and those of the Spearman's cofficients and secondly, that lithology clearly underlies the apparent importance of some variables in determining the sediment yield (tab.1). In the Subcarpathians, lithology, by favouring landslides and mudflows, had a disturbing effect in the sediment transfer regime and reduced the correlation between $Sy(ton/yr^{-1})$ and every variable, and also between the different variables in the study.

The analytical methods consisted of

a) McQUITTY algorithm (1957) for typological classification based on the correlation matrix (logarithmic data) and

b) stepwise multiple linear regression.

The algorithm was applied separately to the two lithologies for the morphometric variables in order to minimize the multicolinearity among the morphometric variables. We also wanted to know if the lithology appreciably influenced the class grouping of the variables. In addition, it was possible to decide which variables included in the main nodes should be included in the model (fig.3). Stepwise multiple linear regression was made for every, separately taken, variable (logarithmic data) to determine the degree to which it took part in the estimation of the dependent varible. This was equivalent to determining the b_k coefficients from the equation:

$$Y = b_o + \sum_{k=1}^{28} b_k \cdot x_k$$

The criterion for including or excluding a variable was the "F" test i.e. the added variable must cause the greatest reduction of the sums of the squares of the estimation errors.

The combined method consisted of applying the previous methods and stressing, in the factor choice, geomorphological knowledge of the relief dynamics of the drainage basin.

4 DETERMINING AND CHOOSING THE EQUATIONS

Using multiple regression, 53 equations were obtained of which three functions for flysch and for Neogene molasse deposits were retained four functions. Retention was based on the following considerations (tab.2.):

(i) the methods used to develop statistically a hierarchy of controls;

(ii) the highest value of the coefficient of determination and a very high or high significance level;

(iii) the number of variables included in the model should be determined relatively easily and inexpensively both in the field and in the laboratory.

The morphometric variables best represented in the models are: the relief ratio (RR), the bifurcation ratio (Rb), the drainage density (Dt) and the drainage basin area (A). Elements that define the

exterior links length (Nl, Ll, Lml) also appear. This may be related to the fact that the first order network is the main area of origin of the sediments in the small catchments. On this basis it may be concluded therefore that the development of a predicting model of sediment yield, at least in small catchments, must be mainly concerned with the analysis of the morphometric characteristics which asserted themselves in the models.

Testing the equations for the 99 drainage basins revealed results that generally conformed with the coefficient of determination of every function. The equations (1) and (4) (tab.2) provided the best estimates of sediment yield, for both lithological areas.

5 APPLYING THE MODELS

The models were applied in the Putna river basin, upstream of the Prisaca cross-section (A = 1,100 km^2), where the building of a dam is expected to form a reservoir of about 100×10^6m^3. Five gauging stations provided data of water and sediment discharge for more than 15 years. Additional data were obtained from 4 small catchments in which field experiments have been made. Flysch rocks occur in 72% and Neogene molasse rocks in 28% of the basin. The regression equations obtained were selected to

(a) investigate the possibilities of generalizing them for another region,

(b) to determine the amount of sediment added to the sediment delivery and

(c) to help solve the probable siltation problems in the Prisaca Reservoir, when completed.

Method of input variables selection		Equations	Determination coefficient ($r^2 \times 100$)
flysch area Correlation matrix (elementary methods) ($n = 36$)	$\log Sy =$	$3.205 - 0.3451 \log Qs^b + 0.7818 \log d^a$ $+ 0.1524 \log L1 + 0.0555 \log Emax + 0.062 \log A$	91^a
Multiple regression step with step algorithm (analytical methods) ($n = 36$)		(the results aren't conclusive)	
Typological methods ($n = 36$)	$\log Sy =$	$12.31 - 0.5094 \log N1 - 0.2306 \log Rb$ $- 0.3765 \log Lint + 0.931 \log DT + 0.2306 \log RR$ $- 4.93 \log Pmm + 4.023 \log Qmax^a$	91^a
Combination methods ($n = 36$)	$\log Sy =$	$7.985 + 0.8138 \log A^a = 0.304 \log Rb$ $+ 0.1486 \log DT - 0.1547 \log RR + 0.089 \log Af^a$ $- 1.571 \log Pmm$	92^a
Subcarpathians region Correlation matrix (elementary methods) ($n = 63$)	$\log Sy =$	$6.5669 - 2.5925 \log Qs^a - 0.7412 \log A$ $- 0.0054 \log N1 - 0.08 \log Lmed + 0.224 \log RR^b$	75^a
Multiple regression step with step algorithm (analytical methods) ($n = 63$)	$\log Sy =$	$5.0827 + 0.3879 \log Rb^b - 0.4267 \log L1^b$ $- 0.2404 \log Lm1^b + 0.3932 \log RR^b$ $- 1.8618 \log Qs^a$	79^a
Typological methods ($n = 63$)	$\log Sy =$	$3.622 + 0.3154 \log Emax^b - 0.5763 \log P^e$ $+ 0.1662 \log Cf + 0.4899 \log Rb^e$ $+ 0.4072 \log Lint^c - 0.6819 \log Dt$ $- 0.4571 \log Qs^a$	76^a
Combination methods ($n = 63$)	$\log Sy =$	$4.5402 - 0.1782 \log + 0.7485 \log A^a$ $+ 0.0365 \log Cf + 0.1042 \log Dt + 0.3318 \log RR^b$ $+ 0.5439 \log Pmm^d$	74^a

a - very highly significant (99.9 percent level); b - highly significant (99.5 percent level);
c - significant (97.5 percent level); d - low significant (95.0 percent level);
e - poorly significant (90.0 percent level)

Tab. 2: *Multiple regression equation for sediment yield prediction in small catchments (A <50 km²) of Romania.*

Catchments	Area (km²)	Basin order	Sediment yield (t km⁻²yr⁻¹)	
			measured (1967–1980)	estimated
Hanganu	3.00	III	3068	4089
Hurjui	1.58	II	4717	4177
Cremenea	2.87	III	3879	3236
Monteoru	4.43	III	4228	3491

Tab. 3: *Sediment yield measured (GASPAR et al. 1982) and sediment yield estimated with Equations (1) and (4) (ICHIM & RADOANE).*

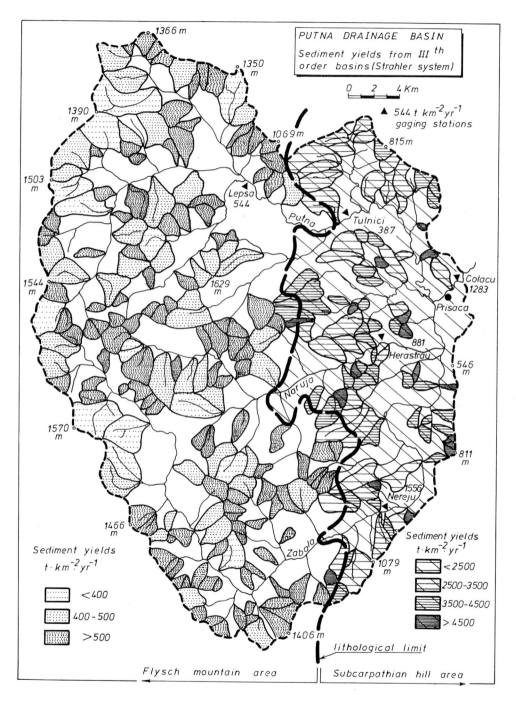

Fig. 4: *Putna drainage basin. Sediment yields from third order basins (Strahler's system).*

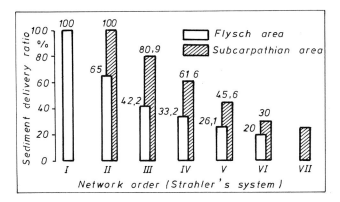

Fig. 5: *Sediment delivery ratio to network channel order (Strahler's system).*

The river network of this basin has the following Strahler hierarchy:
274 third order basins, $\overline{A} = 2.0$ km²;
61 fourth order basins, $\overline{A} = 9.79$ km²;
15 fifth order basins, $\overline{A} = 56.3$ km²;
3 sixth order basins, $\overline{A} = 336.0$ km².

For each basin we determined the 28 variables used in the development of the model and applied them to the prediction functions in tab.2. Each sediment production value (ton/yr) obtained for the 274 third order basins was expressed in ton/km²/yr and shown in fig.4. Sediment yields for some representative catchments of first and second order were also determined. The data were estimated with equations (1) and (4) (tab.2). These are comparable with field measurements in small catchments in Neogene molasse rocks obtained by GASPAR et al. (1982) (tab.3.). Using **gross erosion**[1], sediment yield for second order basins on Neogene molasse deposits produced an average value of 4,538 t km²yr^{-1} and for first order basins on flysch rocks an average value of 1,255 t km²yr^{-1}. In area of Neogene molasse large active landslides and mudflows disturb the elemen-

tary river network and channel processes, being, in fact, the beginning of third order streams. The largest gross erosion in Romania has been measured in the molasse: 10,000–30,000 m³ km^{-2}yr^{-1} in some areas, and in small catchments more 3,000 m³ km^{-2}yr^{-1} has occurred frequently (UNTARU et al. 1986). By contrast, in the flysch area, the erosion rate is smaller and channel processes appear first in second order streams. **Sediment yield** was, therefore, established conventionally for first order basins in flysch and for second order basins in the Neogene molasse area as **gross erosion**.

To determine the sediment delivery ratio (SDR) for each catchment, we used the relation

$$SDR = \frac{S_y(tkm^{-2}yr^{-1})}{E_s(tkm^{-2}yr^{-1})} \cdot 100$$

where S_y is the area unit sediment yield at the basin outlet and E_s is the gross erosion. We related the sediment yield for each order to these values obtaining the sediment delivery ratio according to Strahler's system of ordering of drainage basins. The generalized tendencies of the two lithologies are represented in fig.5. Based on these results, it was concluded that:

---

[1] Gross erosion is defined as "the sum of interrill, rill, gully and channel erosion" (CHANG & WONG 1983, 63, ONSTAD 1984, 74).

(i) The gross erosion is four times greater in the Subcarpathian area than in the flysch mountains;

(ii) The sediment delivery is 1.5 times greater in the Subcarpathian area, but the difference diminishes with the increase in the size of the basins. Therefore, for basins smaller than order five, a high gross erosion results in a large sediment delivery.

(iii) In the flysch region, more than 50% of the sediments originating in small catchments are deposited in third order basins, but in the Subcarpathian area, only 30% of the sediments are deposited in third order basins.

REFERENCES

CHANG, M. & WONG, K. (1983): Effects of land use and watershed topography on sediment delivery ratio in East Texas. Beiträge zur Hydrologie, 9, 1, 55–69.

GASPAR, R., UNTARU, E., ROMAN, F. & CRISTESCU, C. (1982): Cercetari hidrologice in bazinele hidrografice torentiale mici. MFMC, Depart. Silv., ICAS, 65 p.

GRIFFITHS, A.G. (1982): Some suspended sediment yields from South Island Catchments, New Zealand. Water Res. Bull., 662–671,

HADLEY, R., LAL, R., ONSTAD, C., WALLING, D., & YAIR, A. (1985): Resent developments in erosion and sediment yield studies. UNESCO, Paris, 127 P.

ICHIM, I., RADOANE, M., URSU, C. & DUMITRESCU, GH. (1986): in "Hidrotehnica", 31, 10, 296–301. Bucureşti.

JANSSON, B.M. (1982): Land erosion by water in different climates. UNGI Rapport 57, Uppsala Univ., 141 p.

McQUITTY, L.L. (1957): Elementary linkage analysis for isolating orthogonal and oblique types and typal relevances. Educ. Psychol. Measur. 17, 207–229.

ONSTAD, C.A. (1984): Sediment yield modelling, in erosion and sediment yield. Hadley & Walling (ed.), GeoBooks, 71–89.

UNTARU, E., TRACI, C., CALOIAN, Gr. & ROMAN, F. (1986): Valorificarea prin impadurire a terenurilor excesiv degradate prin eroziune si alunecari in zona Vrancea. Terra, 2, 39–43.

WALLING, D.E. (1983): The sediment delivery problem. J. of Hydrology, 65, 209–237.

WALLING, D.E. & WEBB, B.W. (1983): Patterns of sediment yield. In: Background to Paleohydrology, Ed. K.J. Gregory, John Wiley & Sons, 69–100.

Address of authors:
I. Ichim, M. Radoane
Research Station "Stejarul"
Piatra Neamt
5600 Alexandru cel Bun, 6,
Romania

CATENA SUPPLEMENT 10   p.147–159   Braunschweig 1987

MODELLING OF
WATER AND SEDIMENT BUDGET:
CONCEPTS AND STRATEGIES

J.S. **Rawat**, Almora

SUMMARY

A review of current flow models reveals that the use of sediment and water budgets and their routing analysis is in its infancy; sediment storage is an essential but poorly understood and poorly quantified component of the flow models; our ability to conduct field studies of the sediment transport processes and apportionment of rain input is limited. Episodic processes dominate sediment and water flow, but theories and quantification of these processes are not well developed; biota play a variety of essential roles in the production, transport and storage of sediment and water, but knowledge of biological functions is poorly integrated into quantitative analysis of flow models, and the role of tectonism has not yet been satisfactorily included. Keeping in mind these limitations, the present paper includes the basic ingredients of water and sediment budgets and offers a brief discussion on problems related to the concepts and strategies of flow models, namely, what are the parameters of water and sediment budget models, and what is the nature of spatial variations of water and sediment flow models in terms of scale and different environmental conditions (e.g. geological, vegetational, climatic, anthropogenic and technogenic)?

ISSN 0722-0723
ISBN 3-923381-10-7
©1987 by CATENA VERLAG,
D–3302 Cremlingen-Destedt, W. Germany
3-923381-10-7/87/5011851/US$ 2.00 + 0.25

1   INTRODUCTION

1.1   IMPORTANCE

Recently, the study and modelling of water and sediment budgets have increased the understanding of a broad spectrum of current environmental problems. Geomorphological and ecological importance appears from the works of JÄCKLI (1957), RAPP (1960), LEOPOLD et al. (1966), CAIN (1976), DIETRICH & DUNNE (1978), KEISEY (1980), SWANSON et al. (1982), SIMONS et al. (1982), HARVEY (1982), REID (1982) and numerous others. Systematic scientific management of natural and human resources requires knowledge of the interactions among the relevant processes, and their responses to different environmental influences. One important interest of environmental management concerns changes in water and sediment yields. Such changes can be examined through the use of water and sediment budget models. Sediment budget and routing studies have been useful in dealing with a variety of basic and applied problems over a wide range of scales in time and space (cf. SI-

MONS et al. 1982 DIETRICH et al. 1982, LAHRE 1982 and SWANSON et al. 1982a and b).

1.2 DEFINITIONS

1.2.1. A sediment budget is the quantitative expression of various types of movement and storage of sediment within a landscape unit. It includes the eroded material from the land surface by rainsplash, sheetwash, gully erosion, mass-wasting, anthropogenic and technogenic processes, the storage within the landscape unit and the export from the landscape unit through channels in the form of bed-material, suspended and dissolved load.

1.2.2. A water budget is the quantitative expression of the apportionment of the total rainfall on the landscape unit into different pathways. These include interception, evaporation, overland flow, soil infiltration, soil storage, subsurface flow, percolation, ground water and channel flow.

1.3 CURRENT PROBLEMS

Sediment storage is an essential but poorly quantified part of the sediment budget. Episodic events of unusual processes dominate sediment production, transport and deposition as well as the apportionment of rainfall input. Quantification of these processes is not well developed. Biotic processes play an essential role in the water and sediment budget, but knowledge of biological function is poorly integrated into quantitative analysis of water and sediment budgets. Also, the role of tectonism has yet not been satisfactorily included.

1.4 SCOPE OF THE PAPER

This paper examines the basic ingredients of water and sediment budget models and discusses several problems related to the concepts and strategies of flow models, namely, what are the parameters of water and sediment budget models, and what is the nature of spatial variations of water and sediment budgets on the earth surface in terms of scale and different environmental conditions.

2 PARAMETERS OF SEDIMENT AND WATER BUDGET STUDIES

2.1 REVIEW

Early studies of water and sediment flow were concerned with how sediment and water moved through the landscape. DIETRICH & DUNNE (1978) were particularly interested in changes in properties of soil and sediment moving through drainage basins. RAPP (1960) and CAIN (1976) dealt with the relative importance of high magnitude episodic events of low magnitude processes. SWANSON et al. (1982) have introduced sediment budgets to analyse the relative importance of physical processes in the transport of organic and inorganic matter. DIETRICH et al. (1982) have suggested that, to construct a sediment budget, the temporal and spatial variations of transport and storage processes must be integrated and that this requires the recognition and quantification of transport processes and storage elements, and the identification of linkage among transport processes and storage elements. Modelling of water and sediment yields presented by SIMONS et al. (1982) embraced general concepts of mathematical modelling with

Photo 1: *Tectonic landscape along the active and geodynamically sensitive zone (Main Boundary Thrust) in the Kumaon Himalaya, 6 km South West of Nainital (U.P.).*
The tectonically active zone is characterized by huge superficial deposition of landslides and continuous debris flow (central and lower right portion), triangular fault facets (upper part), fault controlled stream, and fault aprons (see photo 3 for close-up view).

emphasis on sediment yield from surface erosion of the sheet-rill type, landslide, gully and channel erosion. The sediment budget of LEHRE (1982) also included physical processes acting upon the earth surface, such as hillslope failures, landslide scarp erosion, gully scarp erosion, bank erosion, bed erosion, suspended load, bedload, dissolved load. Physical processes acting upon the earth surface are therefore the parameters of water and sediment budget studies.

2.2 ROLE OF ENDOGENETIC PROCESSES

However, it is also necessary to identify other parameters of water and sediment budgets. Physical processes acting below the surface of the landscape unit also play a significant role in the control of all processes acting on the earth's surface. For example, there are geodynamically sensitive belts in the central sector of the Himalaya (VALDIYA 1981), related to boundary thrust tear faults, where mass movements and catastrophic landslides occur. The major thrust planes of the Himalaya are still active due to the convergence of the Indian and Eurasian plates at the rate of about 50 mm yr^{-1} (MINSTER & JORDAN 1978). This movement has resulted in new landscapes especially along the tectonic zones (phot.1). Such tectonic landscapes are characterised by whole scale splitting, shearing, shattering and crushing of rocks (phot.2, 3, 4 and 5) which substantially affect sediment yields. Highlighting the interaction between internal and external physical processes VALDIYA (1985, 12) has commented: "The Himalaya is

Photo 2: *Shattered dolomitic rocks on the northern periphery of the tectonic zone, i.e. Main Boundary Thrust zone.*

Owing to recurrent crustal movements, the rocks of the tectonic zones in the Himalaya are crushed, sheared and largely fragmented and are, therefore, susceptible to accelerated erosion and mass-wasting processes. Photo near Hanuman Gari (Nainital U.P.), 5 km North of the Main Boundary Thrust.

Photo 3: *A series of fault aprons on the Main Boundary Thrust zone.*

These fault aprons are still active because they are receiving continuous debris flow from the largely crushed scarp face. A close-up view of Photo 1 (central part of the left half).

Photo 4: *A series of fossil scree cones in the tectonic zone west of Nainital (i.e. Main Boundary Thrust) covered by vegetation.*

The scree cones are incised in the order to 5–50 m indicating recent tectonic uplift. Note upper right, the source region of the scree. This is the zone of crushed, sheared and shattered rocks in the northern periphery of the active tectonic zone (Main Boundary Thrust). See Photo 2 for close-up view.

seismically and tectonically a very sensitive domain. The variety of ecosystems that it supports is therefore fragile, so that even a small disturbance triggers changes that rapidly assume alarming proportions. The boundary thrusts are characterized by multiple splitting and shattring of rocks and are thus particularly vulnerable to extensive erosion and frequent landslides. The transverse faults are responsible for even greater mass movements ...". The geomorphic study of VALDIYA et al. (1984) in the Kumaun Himalaya revealed that:

(I) the Main Boundary Thrust marking the tectonic junction between the Lesser Himalaya and Siwalik molasse represented a zone along which underthrusting still occurred;

(II) depositional terraces have been faulted and displaced vertically as well as horizontally; and

(III) vertical scarps and triangular facets on the hill sides, uplift and dissection by faults of terraces and landslide fans, and presence of abandoned valleys across the Main Boundary Thrust, bore testimony to recent movements that the burden of evidence pointed to uplift of the Siwalik domain by 30 to 80 m relative to the Lesser Himalayan belt.

The geomorphic map of the Dehra Doon area (U.P. Himalaya) prepared by NOSSIN (1971) concluded that uniformity of incision suggested a regional uplift of the area, and that the movement had continued up to the present day.

Photo 5: *Polygenetic landform, i.e. multiple fluvial terraces indicating the successive uplift of the Himalaya.*

Photo at Khairona District Nainital, U.P. India.

From the configuration of terraces and areas of uplifted fan, a total post-Tertiary regional uplift in order of 316–416 m was indicticated (NOSSIN 1971, 19).

2.3 ROLE OF ANTHROPOGENIC AND TECHNOGENIC PROCESSES

The study of exogenic physical processes has dominated most work on water and sediment budgets. But man also plays a significant role.

Important among anthropogenic processes is deforestation. Stripped of the protective vegetal cover, the Himalaya soils lose their capacity to absorb rainwater which instead runs off on the surface resulting in damaging floods in the plains. Since little water percolates, the hillsprings dry up (VALDIYA 1985). A large part of the Indian Himalayas has

been deforested. PATHAK (1983) suggested that in the catchment areas of the central U.P. Himalaya 70% of the total rainwater was used in denudation processes. In the deforested catchments, excluding the evaporation loss, the entire the rain input was available to the soil for denudational processes. It was also evident from thechannel capacity study of a central Himalayan catchment, Jamthara Gad (RAWAT 1986), that the flow capacity of streams was dwindling rapidly where the forest cover was decreasing.

Technogenic processes are also significant. The construction of 44,000 km of roads in the Himalayan region has generated 2.650×10^6 m³ of debris. One kilometer of roads produces 550 m³ of debris from landslides and rockfalls annually. As a result, about 24×10^6 m³ of debris slides down the slopes each

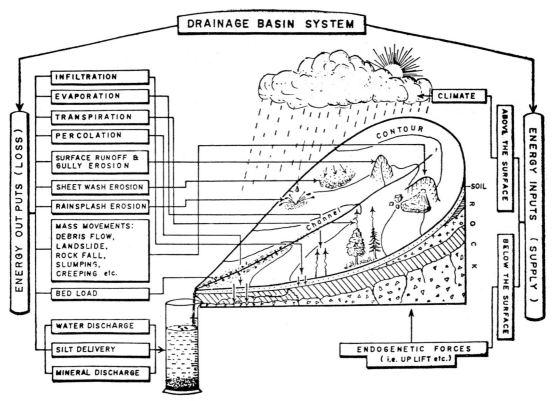

Fig. 1: *The drainage basin is the most practicable unit to monitor the parameters of water and sediment budget. Important parameters are diagrammatically illustrated.*

Energy inputs	Characteristics	Responses (Energy loss)
	Landscape unit: DRAINAGE BASIN	
(A) EXOGENIC	(A) PHYSICAL	(A) HYDROLOGICAL
(i) Precipitation	(i) Landform (with detailed map) Morphometry	Transpiration, through fall, stemflow, overland flow,
(ii) Temperature	(ii) Geology	infiltration, subsurface flow,
(ii) Humidity	(iii) Rocks, intact rock strength, joint density, fractures, bedding, schistosity	percolation, channel flow, evaporation, etc.
	(iv) Soils type, texture, depth	(B) GEOMORPHOLOGICAL
	(v) Climate climatic region, weather characteristics	(i) Hill slope erosion, rainsplash, gully erosion,
	(vi) Vegetation	(ii) Channel erosion, bed load, suspended load, dissolved load;
	(vii) Wild life	(iii) Mass movements, creeping earth flow,
(B) ENDOGENIC	(B) CULTURAL	mudflow, debrisflow,
Tectonic history	(i) Anthropogenic	rockfall, solifluction, snow
Morphotectonics	population distribution density,	avalanche, etc.
Neotectonics	cattle, land use patterns (agricultural, forest, pasture, barren land)	
	(ii) Technogenic, settlements, roads (metalled, unmetalled, cart tracks, foot paths) other construction works, mining, etc.	

Tab. 1: *Synoptic outline of the water and sediment budget studies.*

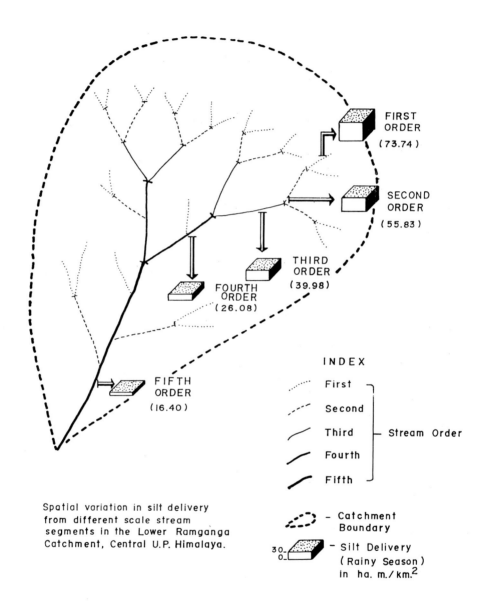

FIRST
ORDER
(73.74)

SECOND
ORDER
(55.83)

THIRD
ORDER
(39.98)

FOURTH
ORDER
(26.08)

FIFTH
ORDER
(16.40)

INDEX

.... First ⎤
---- Second │
/ Third ├ Stream Order
/ Fourth │
/ Fifth ⎦

Spatial variation in silt delivery
from different scale stream
segments in the Lower Ramganga
Catchment, Central U.P. Himalaya.

⌽ – Catchment
      Boundary

30
0   – Silt Delivery
      (Rainy Season)
      in ha. m./km.^{2}

Fig. 2: *Silt-delivery flow model of the Lower Ramganga Catchment (1957 km^2 area) in the central U.P. Himalaya (India) is showing the contribution of Silt-delivery from different order segments.*

The model suggests that the amount of silt contribution has a decreasing tendency as the stream order increases (after RAWAT 1985a).

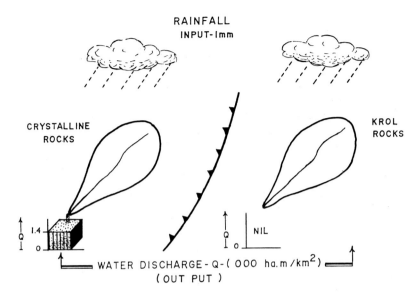

Fig. 3: *A: Spatial variation in water discharge flow in the central Himalayan drainage basins on identical scale and geomorphological conditions and rainfall (i.e. 1 mm) input but different geological conditions.*

The model suggests that on the drainage basin developed on the crystalline rocks (composed of the phyllites and quartzites) of the central Himalaya 1 mm rainfall produces 1.40 thousand m^3/km^2 water discharge, while on the drainage basin developed on the younger and weaker Krol rocks (composed of limestones, sandstones and shales) this amount of rain does not affect the channel discharge because the rainwater percolates below the earth surface (based after RAWAT 1985a).

year, removing vegetation, smothering springs and choking mountain streams (VALDIYA 1985). Mineral exploitation produces similar ecological imbalances in the Himalaya.

The study of water and sediment budget modelling should not, therefore, be restricted to the analysis of exogenic physical processes. Endogenic processes should be taken into account. Among the exogenic processes, anthropogenic, technogenic and biological processes are as important as the physical processes and play a significant role in affecting water and sediment budget of a landscape unit. In conclusion, the components of water and sediment budgets can divided into three groups: energy inputs of water and sediment budgets, their re-

sponses, and the character of landscape unit (fig.1). These three groups contain different parameters (tab.1).

3 CONSIDERATION ON SPATIAL VARIATION

In the early studies of water and sediment dynamics of drainage basins were predominantly based upon the concept of a lumped system in which stream flow was generated uniformly over the watershed, and where the source area was synonymous with the catchment area. The study of a small watershed in Ohio (AMERMAN 1965) revealed that any drainage basin larger than 1.2 to 2.0 hectares must be viewed as physically complex. WALLING (1971) suggested

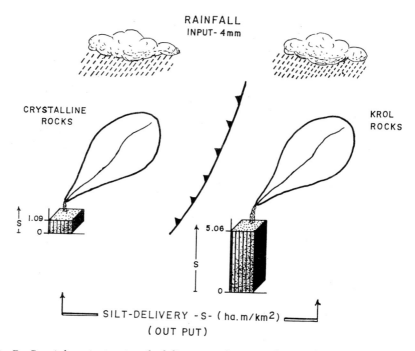

RAINFALL
INPUT- 4mm

CRYSTALLINE
ROCKS

KROL
ROCKS

S

1.09

0

5.06

S

0

SILT-DELIVERY -S- (ha.m/km2)
(OUT PUT)

Fig. 3: *B: Spatial variation in silt-delivery in the central Himalayan drainage basins on identical scale and geomorphological conditions, and rainfall input (4 mm) but different geological character.*
The model suggests that the younger and less resistant Krol rocks (limestones, sandstones and shales) are generating approximately five time higher amount of silt-delivery than that of the older and more resistant crystalline rocks (phyllites and quartzites) (base after RAWAT 1985a).

that contrasts in catchment response within a small area were primarily the result of differences in catchment characteristics rather than climatic inputs.

The water and sediment yields system varies according to scale even within the same environmental region. Therefore, the components of the water and sediment budget identified, quantified and analysed at one scale may not be identical with those recognized at a different scale. For example, silt-delivery from a first order segment was not identical with second, third, fourth and fifth order segments in the Lower Ramganga catchment in central U.P Himalaya (fig.2). Drainage basins consist of many sub-

systems of different scales. The flow model of one sub-system cannot be used to generalize the flow model of another different scale sub-system.

Variations also occurred in the flow systems of drainage basins of identical-size (RAWAT 1985b). For example, in the drainage basins developed on the crystalline rocks of the Central Himalaya, 1 mm rainfall produced 1.40 thousand m^3/km^2 monsoon discharge. In the drainage basins, developed on the weaker and younger Krol rocks of the Central Himalaya, on the other hand, this amount of rainfall did not affect the channel discharge because the rainwater percolated below the earth sur-

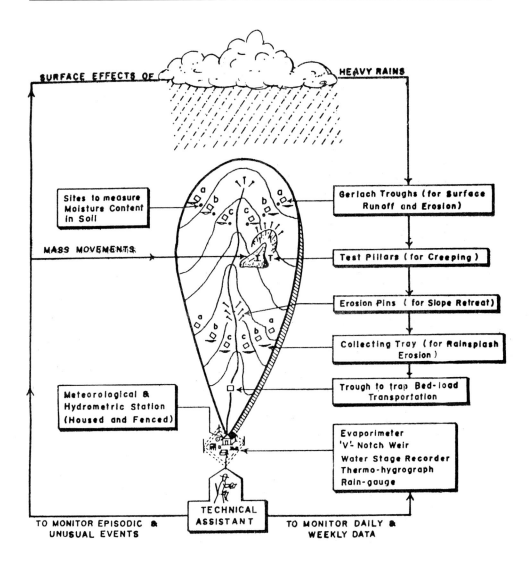

Fig. 4: *Micro catchment instrumentation strategy for flow budgets construction.*

face (fig.3A). As a result, the watersheds of crystalline rocks had 40% more discharge of water than the watershed of identical scale in the Krol formation. Fig.3B shows that on identical scale and rainfall input, the younger and less resistant Krol rocks generated a silt-delivery approximately five times greater than that of the older and more resistant crystalline rocks (RAWAT 1985a).

HAIGH (1982) has suggested that, despite the geomorphic similarities between forested and deforested catchments, the volume of sediment yields differ markedly. For instance the sediment yields from two deforested catchments of the Garwhal Himalaya were 5–7 times larger than those from two comparable forested catchments.

4 CONCLUSIONS

Water and sediment budget study is an interdisciplinary research problem which is in its infancy. Its objective is to identify, quantify and analyse the energy inputs (climate and endogenetic processes) of water and sediment budgets, and their affects (hydrological, geomorphological and biological) on the different characteristics of landscape units. Tab.1 offers a brief synoptic outline. Using this synoptic outline, a watershed in the Central Himalaya, the Nana Kosi, has been used as a natural laboratory since December 1985, to construct the water and sediment budgets for deforested, forested and agricultural lands. The instrumentation within the micro catchments (i.e. forested, deforested, agricultural) is outlined in fig.4. Techniques derived from geological physical, chemical and biological sciences are to be used and it is hoped to present models of flow budgets of the Himalayan watershed within 3 to 4 years.

ACKNOWLEDGEMENT

The generous financial assistance from Department of Science and Technology, Government of India for the project on the Channel Network Capacity and Geochemical Properties of Water of the Nana Kosi Basin is greatfully acknowledged. The author is also thankful to Dr. M.M. Tewari for his cartographic assistance.

REFERENCES

AMERMAN, C.B. (1965): The use of unit source watershed data for runoff prediction. Water Resources Res., **1**, 499–507.

CAIN, N. (1976): A uniform measure of sub aerial erosion. Geol. Soc. Am. Bull., **87**, 137–140.

DIETRICH, W.E. & DUNNE, T. (1978): Sediment budget for a small catchment in mountainous terrain. 2. Geomorph. Suppl., **29**, 191–206.

DIETRICH, W.E. et al. (1982): Construction of sediment budgets for drainage basins. Sediment Budget and Routing in Forested Drainage Basins. U.S. Dept. of Agri. Gen. Techn. Report PNW-141, 5–23.

HAIGH, M.J. (1982): A comparison of sediment accumulation beneath forested and deforsted catchments. Himalaya Research and Development Journal, **1(2)**, 118–120.

HARVEY, M.D. (1982): Use of physical models to determine effects of periodic erosion in steep terrain on sediment characteristics and loads. Sediment Budget and Routing in Forested Drainage Basins, U.S. Dept. Agri., Gen. Tech. Report, PNW-141, 50–58.

JÄCKLI, W.H. (1957): Gegenwartsgeologie des bündnerischen Rheingebietes. Ein Beitrag zur exogenen Dynamik Alpiner Gebirgslandschaften. Beiträge zur Geologie der Schweiz. Geotechnische Serie; Lieferung 36, Bern. 126 p.

KESLEY, H.M. (1980): A sediment budget and an analysis of geomorphic process in the Van Duzen River basin, north coastal California, 1941–1975. Geol. Soc. Am. Bull., Part II, **91**, 1119–1216.

LEHRE, A.K. (1982): Sediment budget of a small coast range drainage basin in North-Central California. Sediment Budget and Routing in Forested Drainage Basins. U.S. Dept. Agri., Gen. Tech. Report. PNW-141, 67–77.

LEOPOLD, L.B., EMMETT, W.W. & MYRIC, R.M. (1966): Channel and hillslope processes in a semiarid area. New Mexico U.S. Dept. Inter. Geol. Surv., Prof. Pap. **352-G**, 193–253.

MINSTER, B. & JORDAN, R. (1978): The present day plate motions. J. Geophys. Res., 83.

MOLNAR, P. (1984): Structure and tectonics of the Himalaya, constraints and implications of geophysical data. Annual Review of Earth and Planetary Sciences, **12**, 484–518.

NOSSIN, J.J. (1971): Outline of the geomorphology of the Doon Valley Northern U.P. India. Z. Geomorph. N.F. Suppl.Bd. **12**, 18–50.

PATHAK, P.C. (1983): Vegetation hydrology and its impact on nutrient cycling in selected forest ecosystems of Kumaon Himalaya. Ph.D. Thesis, Kumaon University, Nainital (India), 250 p.

RAPP, A. (1960): Recent development of mountain in slopes in Kärkevagge and surrounding, northern Scandinavia. Geogr. Ann. **42**, 71–200.

RAWAT, J.S. (1985a): Hydrometric implications of morphometry and geologa, a study of lower Ramganga Catchment. J. Geol. Soc. India, **26(10)**, 734–743.

RAWAT, J.S. (1985b): The drainage basin as a unit for physical environmental studies. In: Environmental Regeneration in Himalaya — Concept and Strategies. (ed. J.S. Singh, Nainital (India), 427–434.

RAWAT, J.S. (1986): A note on the dwindling nature of stream discharge of the central Lesser Himalaya streams, an example from Jamthara Gad drainage networks Dist. Almora (unpublished manuscript).

REID, L.M. (1982): The use of flow charts in sediment routing analysis. Sediment Budget and Routing in Forested Drainage Basins. U.S. Dept. of Agri. Gen. Tech. Report, PNW-141, 154–156.

SIMONS, D.B. et al. (1982): Modelling of water and sediment yields from forested drainage basins. Sediment Budget and Routing in Forested Drainage Basins. U.S. Dept. of Agr., Gen. Tech. Report, PNW-141, 24–38.

SWANSON, F.J. et al. (1982a): Introduction, workshop on Sediment Budget and Routing in Forested Drainage Basins. Sediment Budget and Routing in Forested Drainage Basins. U.S. Dept. of Agri. Gen. Techn. Report, PNW-141, 1–4.

SWANSON, F.J. et al. (1982b): Sediment budget and routing in forested drainage basins. U.S. Dept. of Agri., Gen. Tech. Report, PNW-141.

VALDIYA, K.S. (1981): Tectonics of the central sector of the Himalaya, in Zagros, Hindukush Himalaya. Geodynamic Evolution Series **3**, Amer. Geophy. Union Washington, 87–110.

VALDIYA, K.S. et al. (1984): Geomorphic development across the active main boundary thrust, an example from the Nainital Hills in Kumaon Himalaya. J. Geol. Soc. India, **25(12)**, 761–774.

VALDIYA, K.S. (1985): Accelerated erosion and landslide prone zones in the Central Himalayan Region. In: Environmental Regeneration in Himalaya, Concept and Strategies. (ed. J.S. Singh, Nainital, 12–38.

WALLING, D.E. (1971): Instrumented catchments in South East Devon. Some relationships between catchment charactristics and catchment response. Unpublished Ph.D. Thesis, University of Exeter.

Address of author:
J.S. Rawat
Department of Geography
Kumaun University Campus
Almora 263601 India

SOME PRELIMINARY
LATENT VARIABLE MODELS
OF STREAM SEDIMENT
AND DISCHARGE CHARACTERISTICS

T.K. **Miller**, Bloomington

SUMMARY

Process components of theoretical models often are verified only indirectly by field measurements of indicator variables which are related to, but not identical with, the theoretical constructs. This paper bridges the gap by means of measurement models which link latent theoretical process variables with their respective empirically measured indicator variables. This methodology is exemplified by an analysis of water and sediment discharge characteristics in the Missouri River basin.

1   INTRODUCTION

The process of stream channel development involves a number of mutually interacting endogenous variables, such as channel width, depth and gradient, as well as a set of exogenous variables which are related to water and sediment discharge characteristics for the drainage basin. For this reason, equation (1) is proposed as a general model of the stream channel development process,

$$K = BK + GL + E \qquad (1)$$

where K is a vector of endogenous variables, L is a vector of exogenous variables, B is a square matrix of parameters (with zeros on the main diagonal) for the interactions of the endogenous variables, G is a rectangular matrix of parameters for the effects of the exogenous on the endogenous variables, and E is a vector of random variables representing errors in the equations. In effect, equation (1) is a general system of simultaneous equations with one equation for each endogenous variable. A relatively simple application of such a system is given by MILLER (1984) for the size and shape properties of stream channels.

The specification of any model in terms of the variables involved is, of course, critical to parameter estimation, and therefore to the evaluation of the model as a reflection of an ongoing process. A type of misspecification that has not been given much attention in geomorphology is that of measurement error, where the numerical values analyzed do not perfectly reflect the underlying construct contained in the process theory. Consider the case of water discharge, which is clearly an important factor in the process of channel development. How is this factor incorpo-

ISSN 0722-0723
ISBN 3-923381-10-7
©1987 by CATENA VERLAG,
D–3302 Cremlingen-Destedt, W. Germany
3-923381-10-7/87/5011851/US$ 2.00 + 0.25

rated in the existing models? In general, the approach found in the literature focuses on the use of a particular discharge measurement to represent the theoretical variable. Some researchers have employed the mean discharge for this purpose (e.g. CARLSTON 1976), while others have focused on flood discharge measures (e.g. HARVEY 1969). While it seems reasonable to believe that some discharges are more important than others in the process of channel development, it is not clear that any one discharge measure is predominant. Therefore, if one discharge measure is selected for use as an indicator of the theoretically relevant variable, it is reasonable to view that measure as an indicator containing measurement error. Presumably one might attempt to reduce the amount of measurement error by including a broader set of indicators to represent the theoretical variable. As an example, an array of flood discharges as well as the mean discharge might be jointly taken to represent the water discharge. However, even this broader view would presumably contain some amount of measurement error.

The point of this paper is to illustrate how such a conception of a theoretical variable might be evaluated and accounted for within an overall framework that centers on a system model such as that of (1) above. The principal mechanism for doing this is to associate a "measurement model" with the process model in (1). The measurement model might be focused on the endogenous variables, on the exogenous variables, or separate models may be developed for both sets. The general form of a measurement model is shown in equation (2),

$$X = WL + D \qquad (2)$$

where X is a vector of indicators for a set of "latent" (and theoretically relevant) exogenous variables represented by vector L, W is a rectangular matrix of weights which relate the latent variables to the indicators, and D is a vector of measurement errors accounting for the differences between the latent variables and the indicators. A similar model could be envisioned for the set of endogenous variables in equation (1). Thus, a measurement model may be viewed as an explanatory model for a set of indicators expressed as a function of latent variables and measurement errors.

The principal contribution of general models which include a measurement model component is that within such a context, the process model component may be reasonably interpreted as a **theoretical** model involving relations between constructs that are specified in terms of purely theoretical considerations. An empirical characterization of these theoretical constructs is developed within the framework of the measurement model. Models containing equation elements (1) and (2), therefore, bridge the gap between field measurements and theory in a very explicit way.

Since little has been written on the measurement model concept in geomorphology, the research reported here is focused on that portion of the overall modelling framework. In particular, an effort is made to develop and estimate the parameters of a measurement model for commonly employed indicators of latent variables that are reasonably viewed as exogenous within channel development process. Such indicators are those associated with the processes of water and sediment discharge

(RICHARDS 1982, 13–18).

2 MEASUREMENT MODELS

The purpose of this section is to provide an elaboration of the measurement model concept and to describe one of the ways in which parameters may be estimated (see EVERETT 1984, for an introductory survey). This will be done within the context of a very simple example where there is one latent variable and two indicators. In such a case, equation (2) when written in expanded form contains two equations, one for each of the indicators. These may be written as equations (3) and (4).

$$X_1 = w_1 L_1 + d_1 \qquad (3)$$

$$X_2 = w_2 L_1 + d_2 \qquad (4)$$

Associated with these indicators are two variances and one coverance. If the variables are assumed to be measured as deviations about their means, the variance of X_1 is $E(X_1^2)$, the variance of X_2 is $E(X_2^2)$, and the covariance of X_1 and X_2 is $E(X_1 X_2)$. These expectations, as derived from equations (3) and (4), are presented in equations (5) through (7).

$$E(X_1^2) = w_1^2 E(L_1^2) + E(d_1^2) \qquad (5)$$

$$E(X_2^2) = w_2^2 E(L_1^2) + E(d_2^2) \qquad (6)$$

$$E(X_1^2 X_2) = w_1 w_2 E(L_1^2) + E(d_1 d_2) \qquad (7)$$

It is customary in models of the form of equation (3) and (4) to assume that the random explanatory variable (d) is statistically independent of other explanatory variables (L in this case). Thus, terms involving the covariance of d and L do not qppear in equations (5)–(7), and the variances and covariance of the indicators are functions of the variance of the latent variable, the variances and covariance (although as an initial premise the covariance of measurement errors is often taken to be 0) of the measurement error, and the weights relating the latent variable and the indicators. A similar result holds in general for cases where there are larger numbers of indicators and latent variables. Note that if standardized indicators were employed, equations (5)–(7) would define the elements of a correlation matrix.

The values on the left-hand side of equations (5)–(7) are known quantities within the context of a specific data set, while those on the righthand side are unknown. The estimation problem for a measurement model is to determine the right-hand side values, which are the parametrs of the model. The question of parameter identification is a difficult one in this setting (JÖRESKOG & SÖRBOM 1984,I.20–I.24), but one way of proceeding in the context of an identified model is by way of an iterative unweighted least squares procedure in which the deviations (residuals) of the estimated variance-covariance (or correlation) values of the indicators from the actual values are minimized. The LISREL VI computer program (JÖRESKOG & SÖRBOM 1984) was empolyed in this research as a means by which to estimate parameters using this criterion and to evaluate a variety of measurement models.

3 DATA

The data analyzed in this research was published by OSTERKAMP & HEDMAN (1982) and contains measurements for 252 sites in the Missouri River basin.

Eleven characteristics of water and sediment discharge included in the data set were analyzed here within a measurement model framework. They are: mean discharge; 2, 5, 10, 25, 50, and 100 year flood discharges; bed silt-clay content; bed median particle size; lower bank silt-clay content; and upper bank silt-clay content (OSTERKAMP & HEDMAN 1982, 22–35).

4 EVALUATION METHODOLOGY

One of the unknown parameters of equation (2) is the length of the vector L. That is, for any given set of indicators it is not immediately apparent how many underlying latent variables exist. Given the 11 indicators of water and sediment discharge utilized in this study, it is technically possible for there to be from one through eleven latent variables. One of the objectives of measurement modelling is to determine an appropriate value of this parameter. Theory is used as a guide in this process, as are certain empirical results of the least squares estimation.

In this research, two major empirical results guide the analysis, both of which are reasonably viewed as goodness-of-fit criteria. Recall that the estimation procedure is iterative in nature and attempts to replicate the variance-covariance (or correlation) matrix of the indicators using a least squares criterion. In this case the result is a set of 66 residual values, 11 associated with the main diagonal of the matrix, and 55 with the off-diagonal elements. The root mean square (RMS) of these residuals is one of the evaluation criteria used here. Clearly, a relatively good measurement model will be one with a relatively small RMS value.

A second criterion is based on the "normalized" set of residuals, where each residual is divided by the square root of its asymptotic variance (JÖRESKOG & SÖRBOM 1984, I.42). In this context, residuals larger than two in magnitude indicate a lack of fit, although following normal distribution theory it might be reasonable to expect a roughly .05 occurrence (approximately 3 of the 66 residuals in this case) of such values in a model that fits the data well.

5 ANALYSIS

The modelling strategy employed in this research is guided by the concept of parsimony. That is, the objective is to derive the minimum set of latent variables that accounts for the variation in the indicators of water and sediment discharge. The initial task, therefore, is to evaluate a measurement model for the 11 indicators which incorporates the hypothesis of a single latent variable. Fig.1 presents the causal structure of this model in diagram form. From a theoretical point of view, this model is clearly at variance with prevailing knowledge, since it views both water and sediment characteristics as representative of a single theoretical construct.It is employed here more as a concrete illustration of the approach than as a serious hypothesis to test.

Recall that the measurement model is given by equation (2). In the situation of fig.1, the vectors X, W, L and D would have lengths 11, 11, 1, and 11, respectively. Therefore, the variance-covariance (or correlation) matrix of the indicators would be of dimension 11 by 11. Given the symmetry of the matrix, there would be 11 variances and 55 covariances that could be estimated by specifying values of W, the variance of L, and the vari-

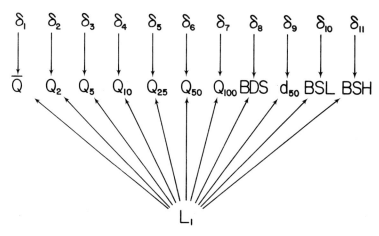

Fig. 1: *The One Latent Variable Model.*

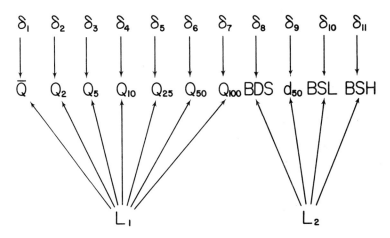

Fig. 2: *The Two Latent Variable Model.*

ances of *D*. As indicated previously, LIS-REL VI is used in this research to find the best fitting values of these parameters using an unweighted least squares criterion. An evaluation of the residuals about this solution for the variance-covariance matrix of the indicators, using the criteria described above, yields an RMS value of .253 and 26 residuals greater than 2 in absolute value. The corresponding values in the case of the correlation matrix of the indicators are .139 and 7. Clearly, the large number of large residuals resulting from this analysis implies that the single latent variable model does not provide a viable explanation for the indicators of water and sediment discharge utilized in this research.

The second model evaluated incorporates two latent variables, L_1 and L_2, as illustrated in fig.2. This model is relatively more satisfying from a theoretical perspective as it associates the water indicators with one theoretical vari-

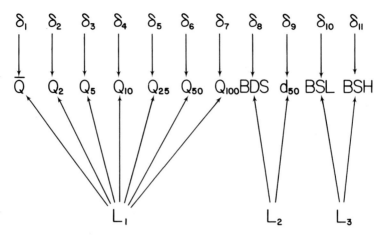

Fig. 3: *The Three Latent Variable Model.*

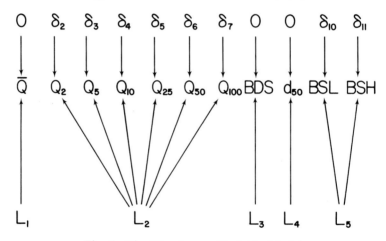

Fig. 4: *The Five Latent Variable Model.*

able and the sediment indicators with another. Note that the thrust of the analysis is to evaluate whether this association of indicators is reasonable, and not to determine the nature of the latent variable itself. As in a traditional factor analysis, the identity of the latent variables would be pursued at a more intuitive level taking into account the specific indicators found to form coherent clusters.

Within the context of equation (2), the second model differs from the first only with regard to the dimensions of W, which in this case are 11 by 2. Column 1 of the W matrix is associated with the latent variable L_1 and column 2, with L_2. The hypothesis stated in fig.2 is implemented within the LISREL framework by **a priori** simply assigning fixed values of 0 for the sediment variables in column 1, and for the water variables in column 2 of the W matrix. Given this specification, the fitted variance-covariance model generates residuals with RMS equal to .163

and a count of large residuals equal to 8. Corresponding values for the correlation model are .077 and 5. The reduction from 26 to 8 in the number of large residuals associated with the variance-covariance model implies that the two latent variable model is a definite improvement over that with one latent variable. At the same time, however, the fact that 8 large residuals (roughly 12% of the total) remain suggests that further improvement of the measurement model may be possible by specifying a third latent variable.

The task of specifying a three latent variable model is most reasonably guided by the matrix of normalized residuals for the two latent variable model just discussed. Since 6 of the 8 large variance-covariance residuals for that model are related to the set of sediment variables, it appears that a change in the specification for the sediment indicators would be a useful step towards a better measurement model. In light of this, the most plausible three latent variable model would be one where the water indicators, the bed sediment indicators and the bank sediment indicators are viewed as functions of separate latent variables. Fig.3 shows such a model in graphical form. The estimation of this model leads to variance-covariance residuals with RMS equal to .160 and a count of large residuals equal to 6. Corresponding values for the correlation residuals are .060 and 2. This represents a slight improvement over the two latent variable model, but the number of large variance-covariance residuals still stands at roughly 10% of the total. This suggests that the model as specified does not provide an adequate explanation for the 11 water and sediment indicators.

An assessment of the normalized resid-

uals for the three latent variable model suggests a further avenue for improvement of the model. Of the six large residuals, that for the covariance of mean discharge and bed silt-clay content is substantially larger than any of the others (its value is -4.6, while the next "largest" is a residual of -2.8). Therefore, these two indicators are not explained well by a model conaining one latent variable for water discharge and one for bed sediments. This leads to a hypothesis that can be expressed in terms of a five latent variable model, shown in graphical form in fig.4. Note that mean discharge and bed silt-clay content have been specified as being equivalent to latent variables, since the measurement error associated with these indicators has been fixed at 0. They are associated with separate latent variables since there is no evidence of high covariance between them. As a consequence, the median grain size indicator is also specified by way of a separate latent variable, while the six flood discharge indicators and the two bank sediment indicators are hypothesized as being associated with two final latent variables. Evaluation of this model leads to an RMS value for variance-covariance normalized residuals of .158 and a count of large residuals equal to 2. Corresponding values for the correlation residuals are 0.028 and 0. Since no more than 5% of the normalized residuals exceed absolute value of 2, these results suggest that the five latent variable model provides an adequate explanation for the 11 water and sediment indicators employed in this research. This in no way proves the model is the only one that might be aceptable, but no more parsimonius model (one with fewer than five latent variables) with equivalent properties was uncovered in the course of this research.

6   DISCUSSION AND CONCLUSION

One important objective of modelling in geomorphology is to develop models that will be useful within the context of landscape management. This implies that the theoretical content of models is of great concern, for if a model is not based on sound theoretical principles, its utility within a management context is questionable. At the same time, it is clear that there is a gap between the theoretical constructs which are recognized as important in geomorphological processes, and the field data which are typically collected, for example, by government agencies. This is well illustrated by the role of sediment variables in the context of the stream channel development process. From a theoretical point of view, various aspects of the sediment load concept are clearly of primary interest. Yet in most situations, the sediment data which are collected simply describe the distribution of sediments at a site. Common indicators are the median grain size and the % of fine sediments by weight. Less frequently encountered is an index of sediment sorting (variance). Just how these indicators relate to theoretical concepts is not clear.

The primary purpose of this paper is to illustrate a methodology which can evaluate hypotheses about relations between latent variables and measurable indicators. As stated previously, the method does not necessarily identify the theoretical construct represented by a latent variable, but it does evaluate whether groups of indicators are reasonably viewed as related to a single theoretical construct. OSTERKAMP & HEDMAN (1982, 3) provide a set of statements about such relationships used in structuring their collection of sediment data, and it is interesting to compare these with the results of this analysis. They write that "... the particle sizes of bank material are indicative of the suspended sediment, whereas the bed material is indicative of the traction-force load". If this is interpreted to mean that an appropriate sediment measurement model should contain two latent variables, one for the bed and one for the bank sediment indicators, then the results stated above indicate that OSTERKAMP & HEDMAN are incorrect in their assertion. The analysis clearly shows that the two bed indicators should not be associated with the same latent variable. On the other hand, an alternative interpretation of OSTERKAMP & HEDMAN's assertion is possible, one which focuses on the concept of "independent" indicators, those which represent substantially different aspects of the theoretical construct. Within this context, the analysis reported here confirms the model with regard to bed sediments, but shows that the bank sediment indicators do not contain independent information about the underlying suspended sediment latent variable.

The implication of this for modelling the stream channel development process is that both bed sediment measures can reasonably be employed as independent explanatory variables, but that both bank sediment measures cannot. Thus, going back to equation (1), the measurement model analysis implies that 3 exogenous sediment variables could reasonably be included in the set L, two representing independent aspects of bed load and one (a composite of two separate bank sediment indicators) representing the suspended load.

The analysis also suggests the reasonableness of including two elements in the set *L* to represent the water discharge indicators. One of these is clearly related to the peak flow concept, and the other to the normal flow regime. Note that the inclusion of both water discharge variables in (1) would be a relatively unusual thing within the tradition of stream channel modelling (although see PICKUP & RIEGER 1979). Workers in this field have generally attempted to rationalize the use of a single explanatory discharge measure related to the "dominant" discharge (RICHARDS 1982, 141–145). Yet it seems perfectly reasonable to view a stream channel as the result of many different discharge stages, one or some of which might well be dominant, but all of which play a role in the development process. A model such as that represented by equations (1) and (2) provides a framework within which such a conception might be implemented and empirical evidence for the dominant discharge concept obtained.

In conclusion, then, the modelling approach utilized in this paper provides capabilities, heretofore not available in geomorphology, which might prove useful in the assessment of various hypotheses, including those pertaining to the stream channel development process. A future step along this research path will involve the integration of the measurement model derived here with a process model of channel cross-section development. Results based on such a modelling procedure should have increased theoretical relevance and illustrate the role that statistical analysis might play in developing the theoretical base of the field.

REFERENCES

CARLSTON, C.W. (1965): The Relation of Free Meander Geometry to Stream Discharge and Its Geomorphic Implications. American Journal of Science **263**, 864–885.

EVEREITT, B.S. (1984): An Introduction to Latent Variable Models. Chapman and Hall, London.

HARVEY, A.M. (1969): Channel Capacity and the Adjustment of Streams to Hydrologic Regime. Journal of Hydrology **8**, 82–98.

JÖRESKOG, K.G. & SÖRBOM, D. (1984): LISREL VI User's Guide. Scientific Software, Inc.; Mooresville, IN 46158 - USA.

MILLER, T.K. (1984): A System Model of Stream Channel Shape and Size. Geological Society of Americ Bulletin **95**, 237–241.

OSTERKAMP, W.R. & HEDMAN, E.R. (1982): Perennial-Streamflow Characteristics Related to Channel Geometry and Sediment in the Missouri River Basin. Geological Survey Professional Paper **1242**; United States Government Printing Office; Washington, D.C.

PICKUP, G. & RIEGER, W.A. (1979): A Conceptual Model of the Relationship between Channel Characteristics and Discharge. Earth Surface Processes **4**, 37–42.

RICHARDS, K. (1982): Rivers — Form and Process in Alluvial Channels. Methuen, London.

Address of author:
T.K. Miller
School of Public and Environmental Affairs,
Indiana University
Bloomington, IN 47405 USA

THE TRANSPORT RESPONSE FUNCTION
AND RELAXATION TIME
IN GEOMORPHIC MODELLING

J. **Hardisty**, London

SUMMARY

A technique is described for the representation of stability in non-linear geomorphic models. The difference between iterative and analytical feedback modelling is emphasised and considered in terms of the mass continuity equation. It is shown that the rate of change of surface elevation, dz/dt, which is predicted by the continuity equation and is here called the transport response function, can be used to depict the stability of a system as a function of the input and the geomorphology. It is suggested that this function may be examined by the use of the relaxation time $R = (z_e - z)/(dz/dt)$ which defines the interval required by the system to change from a state z to the equilibrium state z_e. Furthermore the use of R in this manner produces an immediate and visual representation of the system's stability, allowing stable, transient and unstable landforms to be recognised. Two examples are presented which apply the technique to first an idealised morphology, and then to the form of a beach profile.

ISSN 0722-0723
ISBN 3-923381-10-7
©1987 by CATENA VERLAG,
D–3302 Cremlingen-Destedt, W. Germany
3-923381-10-7/87/5011851/US$ 2.00 + 0.25

1   STATEMENT OF THE PROBLEM

Geomorphologists, in whatever environment they work, aim ultimately to model the evolution of landforms. The form is most simply characterised by the height of the surface above some often arbitrary datum. Choosing the conventional Cartesian co-ordinate axes, x being positive along the horizontal process direction, y also horizontal but normal to x and positive to the right and finally z being the vertical axis which is positive in the upwards sense, then the landform can be defined by:

$$z = f(x, y) \qquad (1)$$

However landforms are rarely static and most workers attempt to understand the dynamic response of the system through time. Again the landform can be defined in this extra dimension as:

$$z = f(x, y, t) \qquad (2)$$

The inclusion of the dependence of the elevation upon time recognises the fact that most modern geomorphologists are not interested in the landform as a static entity but rather they are concerned with the dynamic evolution of the form through time scales which may range from a few seconds to the millions of years of the Quaternary. This step has also led to the development of stability analyses (THORNES 1983) with the search for stabilising negative feedbacks and destabilising positive feedbacks in the relevant systems (see BRUNSDEN & THORNES 1979 and ALLEN 1976 for background references in the geomorphic and geological literature respectively). In general we now develop Eq. (2) and seek to understand the stability of the landform through the mass continuity equation which was originally used by EXNER (1920), but more recently by many workers (see CARSON & KIRKBY 1972 for discussion). The unit width equation represents the relationship between geomorphic change and the spatial and temporal changes in the sediment transport rate (for example ALLEN 1970):

$$\frac{dz}{dt} = -\sigma \left[\frac{\delta j}{\delta x} + \frac{1}{U_g} \frac{\delta j}{\delta t} \right] \qquad (3)$$

where
j is the mass transport rate,
σ is the bulk density of the sediment and
U_g is the speed of the moving grains.

The development of Eq. (2) into Eq. (3) is clarified by consideration of fig.1 which depicts, in the most general terms, the processes involved in the type of subaqueous systems considered here. The independent controls drive local water flows, which in turn move sediment leading to morphological development. The morphodynamic feedback indicates that the form itself can influence both the local flows, a constriction in a river channel for example, and the local transport rate, increasing with increasing bedslope for example. That is $j = f$ (inputs, form) and the inputs themselves are functions of time. The stability is expressed as the rate of change of the surface ele-

vation, dz/dt which will be referred to as the transport response function. The first term on the right-hand side represents the spatial change in the transport rate which, by analogy with the hydraulic nomenclature, may be either uniform or non-uniform. The second term on the right-hand side is the temporal change in the transport rate which may again be steady or unsteady. The bulk density and the negative sign ensure that accretion leads to height increase. The geomorphological problem is then the solution of Eq. (3) and of its integral, Eq. (2).

2   TYPES OF FEEDBACK

These abstractions may be clarified by a simple example. Consider fig.2 which represents the stable form of a geomorphic system in terms of the inputs. The form axis may be any geomorphic descriptor such as the surface height at a point or the slope along a reach; it is only necessary that the form may be represented by a single expression so that a single axis is required for its presentation. The input is a combination of one or more of the independent, but time-dependent, variables which control the system such as basin precipitation, or discharge, and again it is only necessary to reduce this to a one-dimensional expression for the purposes of representation. Fig.2 shows that an equilibrium form is impossible below a certain value of the inputs, and above that value the form expression increases at a decreasing rate until it takes on a maximum at the maximum value of the input in this idealised example.

In practice the theoretical relationship shown in fig.2 is achieved by substituting expressions for the temporal and spatial variations in the sediment transport

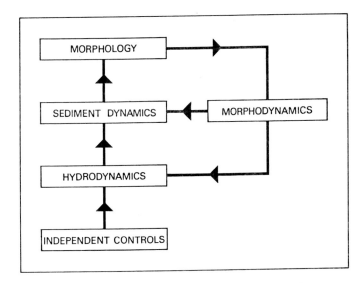

Fig. 1: *General overview of dynamic, subaqueous morphological models with the most common feedback loops.*

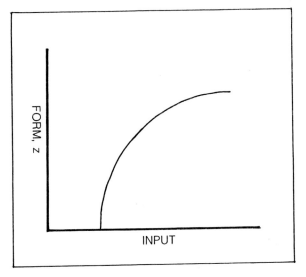

Fig. 2: *Idealised equilibrium form as a function of the input control.*

See text for explanation.

rate into Eq. (3). If non-linearity is present a computer simulation is usually constructed and forced to iterate with a particular input until stability is attained. The input is changed and the sequence is repeated and a new pair of co-ordinates are determined until the expression is defined. I have referred to this as iterative feedback in a previous paper (HARDISTY 1986). Exam-

ples of this type of approach to marine morphological modelling are given by KOMAR (1973) and DAVIDSON-ARNOTT (1981).

An alternative, and potentially more powerful technique is available. It simply involves the definition of the surface response at equilibrium. Typically dz/dt is set to zero, and Eq. (3) may then be solved to define the equilibrium condi-

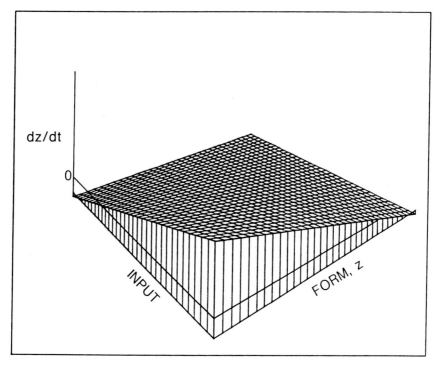

Fig. 3: *The response surface, dz/dt, for the system shown in fig.2.*

tions. I have referred to this as analytical feedback and used it to determine a direct solution for beach gradient as a function of the incident wave parameters in an earlier paper HARDISTY (1986) and in the example described below. The technique is also used by, for example, THORNES (1986) in a hillslope erosion model which is presented elsewhere in this volume.

3   THE TRANSPORT RESPONSE FUNCTION

We may however develop the technique still further. Consider the expression given by Eq. (3) and remove the equilibrium requirement that dz/dt equals zero, plotting instead the full function.

This is shown in fig.3, which is the so-called transport response surface. It is clear that if, as in the diagram, dz/dt passes through the equilibrium value for a given input with dz/dt decreasing as z increases then the system is stable: if z is too large then dz/dt decreases it but if z is too small then dz/dt increases it until equilibrium is established. Alternatively if dz/dt passes through the equilibrium value for a given input with dz/dt increasing as z increases then the system is unstable: if z is too large then dz/dt continues to increase it and if z is too small then dz/dt continues to decrease it. This crucial, and axiomatic, result will be discussed later but we note that the use of the response surface is not teribly illuminating because it only drops below the zero value when erosion occurs and rises above the zero value when the surface is accreting; overall the example merely produces a fairly uniform surface.

4   THE RELAXATION TIME

The usefulness of the transport response function is, however, considerably improved if, instead of simply plotting the response surface as in fig.3, we plot the time it would take for the system to return to equilibrium when disturbed. The idea of quantifying the time a system takes to re-establish equilibrium after disturbance has been discussed by various authors (for example ALLEN 1974, BRUNSDEN & JONES 1984), and tends to indicate a first-order exponential decay toward a characteristic form (BRUNSDEN & THORNES 1979). The total time interval is called the relaxation time, R, which is defined by THORNES & BRUNSDEN (1977, 16) as 'the time taken for a system to achieve a new equilibrium following a change in input or in the internal operation of the system'. We may now use the response function to formalise this definition of R as the ratio of the required change in morphology (from a disequilibrium value z to an equilibrium value z_e) to the rate of change of morphology, dz/dt which is the response function. Thus R becomes:

$$R = \frac{(z_e - z)}{dz/dt} \tag{4}$$

Clearly, as shown in fig.4, the result is far more useful. Instability, whether due to accretion or erosion, is represented by the elevation of the relaxation time, R, above the zero level. Equilibrium, when $R = 0$, is represented by the lowest level, the 'valley'in the relaxation time, which does indeed correspond to the equilib-

rium form shown by the iterative or analytical techniques in fig.2. The diagram represents a stable system with negative feedbacks operating to oppose perturbation. Imagine the system rolling as a marble over this response surface, and finding its way eventually into the equilibrium valley.

Alternatively, however, positive feedbacks may be present and the relaxation time for the inverse of the response function which was shown in fig.3 would then be as shown in fig.5, where any parturbation leads to complete form alteration or destruction. The marble would soon be disturbed from a position on the ridge. Transient stabilities could also be represented in this way, and the relaxation surface would then pass through zero.

Finally it is apparent that the value of R given bx Eq. (4) is strictly only applicable to systems which evidence planar response surfaces, that is for a dz/dt which is linearly related to both the form and the input. This rather severe constaint can be removed by considering the total relaxation time, R_t as the sum of the time taken for each increment of z towards the equilibrium value. Mathematically, we may express this as the integral,

$$R_t = \int_z^{z_e} \frac{z - z_e}{dz/dt}\, dz \tag{5}$$

5   AN EXAMPLE OF BEACH MORPHODYNAMICS

The example described here is an extension of an earlier model which is described in HARDISTY (1986), and the reader is reffered to that paper for a more detailed treatment of the initial stages. The problem addressed was the modelling of beach gradient as a function of the inputs, taken here as the steep-

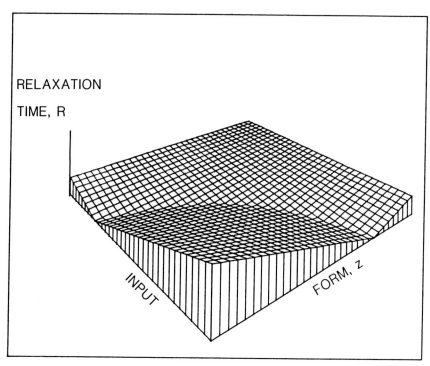

Fig. 4: *The relaxation time, R (Eq. 4), for the system shown in the previous diagrams. Here a stable system is depicted which returns to the equilibrium 'valley'when perturbed.*

ness of the incident waves, H/L, where H is the wave height and L is the wavelength. Second-order Stokes wave theory was used to derive expressions for the nearbed wave-induced flow speeds (the hydrodynamics), U_{in} and U_{ex}, and durations t_{in} and t_{ex}, which in turn drove a slope inclusive Bagnold type of bedload equation (the sediment dynamics) to calculate the nett onshore and offshore transports beneath a single wave, J_{in} and J_{ex}:

$$J_{in} = (k_1 U_{in}^3 t_{in})/(\phi + \beta)$$

$$J_{ex} = (k_1 U_{in}^3 t_{in})/(\phi - \beta)$$

$$U_{in} = B/2(gd(1 + F))^{0.5}$$

$$U_{ex} = B/2(gd(1 - F))^{0.5}$$

where k_1 is an empirical calibration coefficient with a value of about 12.8 kg $m^{-4} s^{-2}$ (HARDISTY et al. 1984) and

$$F = (0.01B^3)/(H/L)^2$$

where B is the ratio of the wave height to the water depth at the breakpoint, g is the acceleration due to gravity, d is the local water depth, ϕ is coefficient of dynamic friction of the sediment and β is the bedslope. These may be combined with the wave period, T, to express the continuity quations for a point as:

$$\frac{dz}{dt} = \frac{J_{in} - J_{ex}}{T} \qquad (6)$$

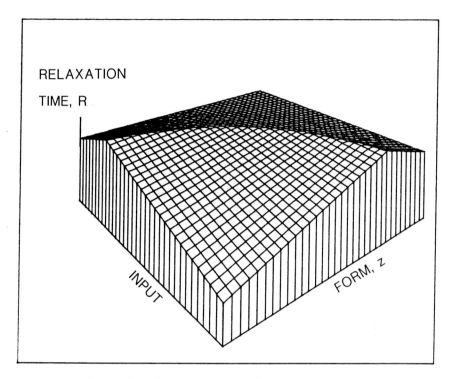

Fig. 5: *The relaxation time, R, for an unstable system.*

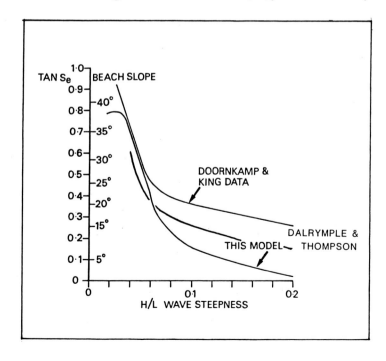

Fig. 6: *Analytical feedback model for beach gradients as a function of the incident wave steepness.*

This diagram is analogous to fig.2.

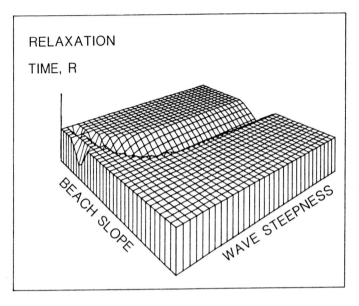

RELAXATION

TIME, R

BEACH SLOPE

WAVE STEEPNESS

Fig. 7: *The relaxation time for the beach model.*

This diagram is analogous to fig.4.

We firstly solve Eq. (5) for geomorphic equilibrium and express the form in terms of the local beach gradient, s_e. The result is plotted in fig.6, which is seen to compare favourably with the empirical data of DOORNKAMP & KING (1972) and DALRYMPLE & THOMPSON (1976) although the model appears to underpredict for higher values of H/L where the data suggests rather high beach slopes. Fig.6 is analogous to Fig.2 for $dz/dt = 0$. We next plot the transport response function for all values of dz/dt as shown in HARDISTY (1986) fig.6. This representation is analogous to fig.3. We finally examine the relaxation time of the system and plot R from Eq. (4) for the beach equations as shown in fig.7. This representation is analogous to fig.4 and shows that the system is indeed stable with negative feedbacks due to the differential influence of the bedlsope on the onshore and offshore sediment transport rates.

6   CONCLUDING REMARKS

This paper has illustrated how the sediment response function, dz/dt and the relaxion time, R, might be used to analyse the behaviour of geomorphic forms. A further development of the technique would be to compare the relaxation time R corresponding to particular inputs with the time over which those inputs operate on the system which may itself be referred to as the duration time D. Clearly if R/D is greater than unity then stability will result though a lag time given by $(R - D)$ will be present. Conversely if the ratio is less than unity then, although stability may be theoretically possible, it cannot in reality be achieved within the available time. It appears that this kind of idea may usefully be applied as a quantifiable alternative to the time scales suggested by DAVIS (1899) or by SCHUMM & LICHTY (1965), or to the transit form ratio of BRUNSDEN & THORNES (1979).

ACKNOWLEDGEMENT

The author thanks John Thornes, Ted Culling, Donald Thompson, John Brew and Richard Whitehouse for the discussions and Robin Davidson-Arnott for the criticism of an earlier paper which necessitated the development of the response surface idea. Thanks are also due to Dr. G. Pagan's Linear Graphics Ltd for assistance with the contouring software.

REFERENCES

ALLEN, J.R.L. (1970): Physical Processes of Sedimentation. Allen & Unwin, London, 248 pp.

ALLEN, J.R.L. (1974): Reaction, relaxation and lag in natural sedimentary systems: general principles, examples and lessons. Earth Sci. Review 10, 263–342.

ALLEN, J.R.L. (1976): Computational models for dune lag-time: general ideas, dificulties, and early results. Sediment. Geol., 15, 1–55.

BRUNSDEN, D. & JONES, D.K.C. (1984): The geomorphology of high magnitude — low frequency events in the Karakoram Mountains. In: International Karakoram Project Vol. I, Cambridge, C.U.P., 383–388.

BRUNSDEN, D. & THORNES, J.B. (1979): Landscape sensitivity and change. Trans. Inst. Brit. Geog., 4, 463–484.

CARSON, M.A. & KIRKBY, M.J. (1972): Hillslope form and process. Univ. Press, Cambridge, 475 pp.

DALRYMPLE, R.A. & THOMPSON, W.W. (1976): Study of equilibrium beach profiles. Proc. 15th Conf. Coastal Eng., Hawaii, 1277–1296.

DAVIDSON-ARNOTT, R.G.D. (1981): Computer simulation of nearshore bar formation. Earth Surface Processes and Landforms, 6, 23–34.

DAVIS, W.M. (1899): Tjhe geographical cycle. Geogr. Jnl., 14, 481–504.

DOORNKAMP, J.C. & KING, C.A.M. (1971): Numerical Analysis in Geomorphology: An Introduction. Arnold, London.

EXNER, F.M. (1920): Sitzungsber. Akad. Wiss. Wein., Math-Naturw. Kl., Abt. 2a, 129, 929–952.

HARDISTY, J., HAMILTON, D. & COLLIER, J. (1984): A alibration of the Bagnold beach equation. Mar. Geol., 61, 95–101.

HARDISTY, J. (1986): A morphodynamic model for beach gradients. Earth Surface Processes and Landforms, 11, 327–333.

KOMAR, P.D. (1973): Computer models of delta growth due to sediment input from rivers and longshore transport. Geol. Soc. Am. Bull., 82, 2217–2226.

SCHUMM, S.A. & LICHTY, R.W. (1965): Time, space, and causality in geomorphology. Am. Jnl. Sci., 263, 110–119.

THORNES, J.B. (1983): Evolutionary geomorphology. Geography, 68, 225–235.

THORNES, J.B. (1986): A competition model for soil erosion. Unpublished paper.

Address of author:

J. Hardisty
Marine Morphodynamics Unit
Department of Geography
Royal Holloway & Bedford New College
London, University
Egham, Surrey, U.K., TW20 OEX

CATENA SUPPLEMENT 10   p.181–192   Braunschweig 1987

THE HOLON:
HIERARCHY THEORY
AND LANDSCAPE RESEARCH

M.J. **Haigh**, Oxford

SUMMARY

Hierarchical structure is a fundamental property of all natural systems. However, the implications of hierarchical synergetics in landscape systems have never been explored. The key concept in modern hierarchy theory is KOESTLER's notion of the holon. A holon is any stable sub-whole in a hierarchy. It is a self-creating, open system, governed by a set of laws which regulate its coherence, stability, structure and functioning. It also possesses the potential of adaptation to the challenge of environmental change. There are two aspects to the operations of a holon. First, there are its relationships to the larger order whole(s) into which it is integrated and by which its activities are constrained. Second, there is the fact that it is a whole in its own right which integrates the operations of lower level subwholes. This paper considers the processes of self-organisation in soil dynamics. It examines interactions between levels in the landscape 'holarchy'. These are evaluated in terms of scale, communication, stability and evolution in a fluctuating energy stream.

ISSN 0722-0723
ISBN 3-923381-10-7
©1987 by CATENA VERLAG,
D–3302 Cremlingen-Destedt, W. Germany
3-923381-10-7/87/5011851/US$ 2.00 + 0.25

1   GENERAL SYSTEM VIEWPOINTS

The core hypothesis of system theory is that it is as valid to study the interactions between objects as it is to study the objects themselves. A system is a structured set of interactions recognised for the purpose of investigation. It has four invariant properties (LASZLO 1972). First, it is a wholeness. Second, it has an identity or persistence which resists disturbances in its environment. Third, it has the capacity to adapt to meet sustained challenges posed by its environment. Finally, it exists as part of a nested hierarchy of systems (SIMON 1962, PATTEE 1973).

General system methodologies require that the researcher examine nature as an energy stream, a 'wholeness in flowing movement' (BOHM 1980). They require the researcher to unfold system structures from an implicately enfolded multidimensional unity and to examine these structures as multi-level, quasi-organic, wholes. The approach has produced some of the more exciting new, transdisciplinary viewpoints in science (cf. synergetics (HAKEN 1977, 1984, 1985), 'Gaia' (LOVELOCK 1979), and the new theory of evolution (JANTSCH 1980)). However, there are great tracts of General System thinking which remain underexplored. Chief among these are the theoretical implications of the fourth invariant property of all systems: hierarchical structure.

2   HIERARCHIES AND HOLONS

Turning the world around to study it as a nested series of systems within systems is a difficult conceptual exercise. Viewed from this angle, every natural system exists both as a wholeness in its own right and as a part within a larger order wholeness. It is a system which integrates the operations of lower order subsystems and which is itself constrained by the operations of the higher level system of which it forms a part. KOESTLER (1967) introduced the term **Holon** to cover the concept of an open system examined as a part of a hierarchical structure (BAHM 1984). The term **Holarchy** was suggested for a hierarchy examined as a series of nested holons (KOESTLER 1967, 1978). A holon is defined by a set of governing principles which KOESTLER (1978, 342) calls the system's canon. The canon of the holon determines its invariant properties, the laws which govern its structure and functioning. Within this rule, most complex holons have an array of options, possible responses to environmental change. KOESTLER (1978, 293) calls these options 'flexible strategies'. The canon, which establishes the holon's identity, tends to be associated with the holon's role as a component part of a larger order wholeness. The holon's options in response represent its capacity for self-assertion as a wholeness in its own right. The behaviour of any holon tends to be reconcilable in terms of stresses between the forces which tend to subordinate the

activities of the holon within a larger organisation and those which assert its independence.

3   HIERARCHY NOTIONS IN GEOGRAPHY

Hierarchy theory is employed in three areas of landscape geography. First, it is employed for landscape classification and terrain synthesis (ISACHENKO 1973, NAVEH & LIEBERMAN 1984, MAZUR 1985, FRENCH 1986). Second, it is employed for studies of drainage networks which usually (HORTON 1945, JARVIS 1976) involve the technique of stream ordering. WOLDENBERG (1969, 1979) has attempted to expand these notions towards the recognition of a periodic table of spatial hierarchies. However, both of these approaches deal with their spatial systems in terms which recognise system dynamics but which do not encompass hierarchical change or systems evolution. In both cases, the system is treated as a fixed object like a building, not a dynamic entity like a vortex in a stream. However, landscape geocomplexes and river systems are definitively open systems.

The third approach to hierarchical structures in landscape systems has been indicated by SCHUMM & LICHTY (1965), followed by JACKSON (1975), CAMBERS (1976) and PENNING-ROWSELL & TOWNSEND (1978). SCHUMM & LICHTY examined landscape evolution as a nested hierarchy of timescales (fig.1). Their purpose was to examine the relationships between what they considered to be the three levels of research then current in the discipline. The paper establishes the canon of each

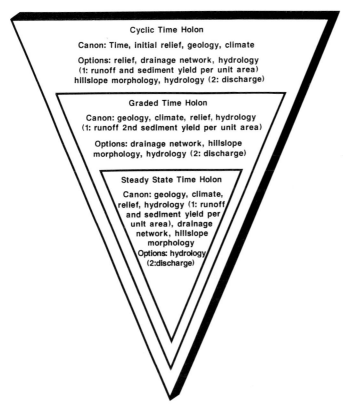

Cyclic Time Holon

Canon: Time, initial relief, geology, climate

Options: relief, drainage network, hydrology
(1: runoff and sediment yield per unit area)
hillslope morphology, hydrology (2: discharge)

Graded Time Holon

Canon: geology, climate, relief, hydrology
(1: runoff 2nd sediment yield per unit area)

Options: drainage network, hillslope
morphology, hydrology (2: discharge)

Steady State Time Holon

Canon: geology, climate,
relief, hydrology (1: runoff
and sediment yield per
unit area), drainage
network, hillslope
morphology
Options: hydrology
(2:discharge)

Fig. 1: *Cyclic time
holarchy.*

research holon as a timescale and series of independent variables. It also considers the dependent variables, or flexible options, available to each holonic level in the context of the system's canon. The array of dependent and independent variables differ from holon to holon even though these holons are clearly arbitrary divisions of a single continuum. Both in terms of operating time scale and evolutionary sequence, the agenda for research at each level differs.

The same is true if this holarchy is unfolded in a slightly different fashion to encompass both space and time (fig.2). This holarchy expands the scheme of SCHUMM & LICHTY (1965) to include some additional levels of research in the

drainage basin. At each level, the topic for research is governed by the scale and time span and, at each level, the criteria involved in research projects will differ. However, once again, the levels are linked as a causal sequence that can be projected in terms of partness and wholeness from any given level to all others.

Fig.3 transfers this ideology to the soil system. The soil system holarchy is founded in the atoms and then the molecules that build up the primary particles of the soil. The primary particles of the soil become assembled into soil aggregates and peds. Differentiation of such structures creates the horizons of the soil and they in turn define the pedon and polypedon. Sequences of polype-

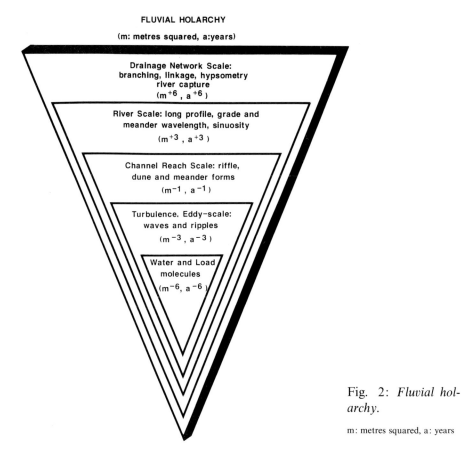

FLUVIAL HOLARCHY

(m: metres squared, a:years)

Drainage Network Scale:
branching, linkage, hypsometry
river capture
(m^{+6}, a^{+6})

River Scale: long profile, grade and
meander wavelength, sinuosity
(m^{+3}, a^{+3})

Channel Reach Scale: riffle,
dune and meander forms
(m^{-1}, a^{-1})

Turbulence. Eddy–scale:
waves and ripples
(m^{-3}, a^{-3})

Water and Load
molecules
(m^{-6}, a^{-6})

Fig. 2: *Fluvial hol-
archy.*

m: metres squared, a: years

dons define the soil association. Conversely, the soil association includes the polypedons. This in turn constrains the distribution of pedons, the disposition of soil horizons, the character of soil aggregates, the behaviour of soil primary particles, the molecular and the atomic constituents of the soil.

4 SELF-ORGANISATION

In geomorphology, the theory of thresholds has become well established (SCHUMM 1978) and workers have begun to model system bifurcations by catastrophe theory (GRAF 1979, THOR-

NES 1983). However, relatively little attention has yet been paid to the phenomena of self-organisation (JANTSCH 1980), strange attractors (CULLINGS 1985) and the emergence of dissipative structures. In fact, even this terminology remains unfamiliar to many geomorphologists.

PRIGOGINE (NICOLIS & PRIGOGINE 1977) conceives of open systems as dynamic structures which extract energy from their system environment and dissipate entropy back into the environment. In other words, open systems use an external source of energy as fuel and, by the construction and repair of their

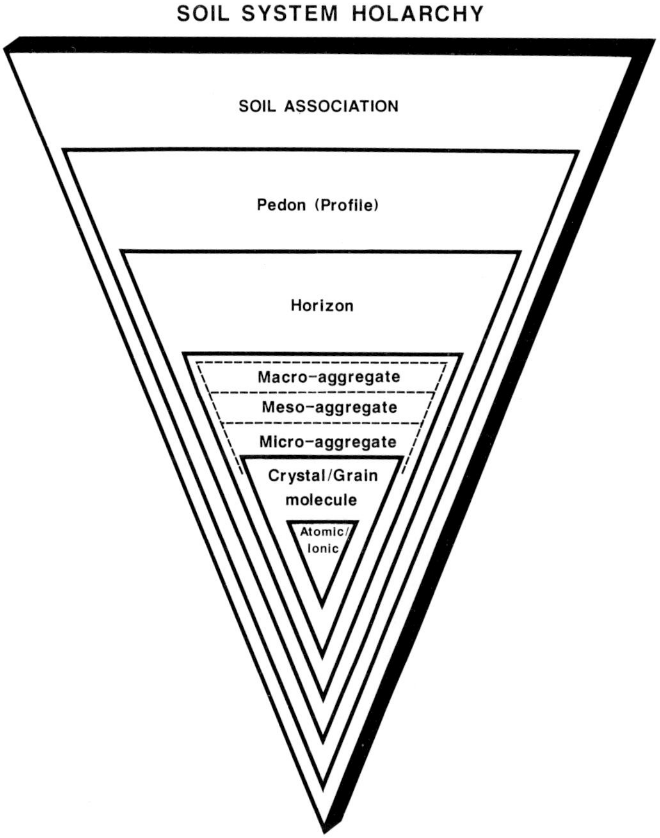

SOIL SYSTEM HOLARCHY

Fig. 3: *Soil system holarchy.*

internal structures, prevent the natural processes of breakdown, exhaustion and decay. By these processes, the structures are able to counteract thermodynamic decay and decomposition caused by the normal conversion of energy to entropy during the operation of the system. So, such a system has the capacity to preserve itself and perhaps also to reduce its internal entropy by storing energy captured from outside its boundaries.

Any system which takes energy from the environment and uses it to selfcreate at a lower entropic level can be said to evolve. Evolution, then, is a process which runs against the dictat of the Second Law of Thermodynamics. In this scheme, energy is dissipated and entropy

accumulated progressively through the operations of the system. In evolution, the system dissipates entropy and accumulates energy through its operations. An increase in energy within a system is capable of causing the system to reorganise as a lower entropy structure.

PRIGOGINE recognises that the process is not a smooth transition. Complex open systems tend to include sophisticated feedback regulators which function to preserve the system from fluctuations in the environment and so conserve the systems identity. However, many systems have several identities, that is conditions around which they may stabilise. These multiple system equilibrium states are called systems attractors (NICOLIS

& NICOLIS 1984). As energy accumulates within a system, the system is forced towards its bounds of metastability. In this vulnerable state, a power surge can force the system beyond the control of its current attractor and towards a new one, perhaps at a radically lower entropic state.

So, in classical geomorphology, an addition of relief energy causes a featureless landscape to become reorganised as a drainage system. This system evolves from a relatively inefficient condition towards greater organisation by a series of restructurings called river capture. In the evolution of a soil profile, the differentiation of different horizons marking different process thresholds, and the stages of vegetative colonisation and their reorganisations of the soil system, can all be charted in similar terms. The rule remains throughout, energy is accumulated so that entropy is dissipated.

BEREZIN et al. (1984), however, describe a process of soil shrinkage where the reverse is true. Water is normally considered as the major energetic agency in soil dynamics. As water is withdrawn from a single soil aggregate, shrinkage occurs, the particles move closer together, and volume decreases smoothly. In a larger soil mass, however, there is adhesion between the soil aggregate and the surrounding soil, so shrinkage can only occur with the formation of cracks, the development of interaggregate fractures. This occurs when the suction pressure in the separating ped exceeds the resistance of structural bonds in the soil. Further desiccation of the soil causes further increases in suction pressure and new instability leading to the formation of a new order of cracks and still smaller peds. The process involves a series of threshold suction pressure levels and a

series of jumps as the soil abruptly restructures into increasingly complex networks of soil cracks. Again, water vapour is a very high entropy structure. The molecules dart about in a state of near total disorder. Remove energy from this system and molecular attraction draws the molecules together as water droplets. Remove still more energy and the molecules become restructured as the highly organised rigid matrix of an ice crystal. Restore energy to this system and the organisation is lost.

The emergence of such 'equilibrium structures' (BLUMENFELD 1981) does not contradict the general theory of systems evolution (JANTSCH 1980). However, it does illustrate one consequence of hierarchical structure and of the character of the relationships between holonic levels in a holarchic system. The addition of energy to a holarchy can cause system breakdown because that energy does not make the same impact on all levels of the holarchy. It may work more upon one level than another and so cause one or more holons to become more organised. A general feature of systems evolution is that it permits the system to distance itself from its environment. This ('autopoiesis' (JANTSCH 1980)) can be damaging to a hierarchical structure if it reinforces a holon's self-assertive tendencies against that holarchy's constraints of integration.

In sum, an over-evolved or "over-excited" (KOESTLER 1979) holon will tend to break away from the controls of the higher holarchic levels and so disrupt the holarchy. So a social group invested with sufficient power or information can destroy the hierarchy of a nation state, so a cancer cell can subvert an organism, so heated water molecules can break up an ice crystal.

The problem is fundamental. A holarchy consists of layers of holons each of which is governed by a distinct and individual set of rules (canon: KOESTLER 1979). The challenges of the environment (LASZLO 1972) which encourage evolutionary adaptation, must have a different impact on each level of the holarchy. There can be no expectation that the adaptational options exercised by a particular holon will be to the benefit of the whole hierarchy.

In the soil holarchy, the reorganisation of surface soil aggregates as a soil crust is caused by exposure to the disruptive forces of rainsplash impact. It is an adaptive response to the local environmental challenge. However, it is maladaptive as far as higher levels of the soil holarchy are concerned. The presence of the soil crust impedes the infiltration of water and so retards pedogenesis and the differentiation of soil horizons. At the surface, crusting permits the accumulation of surface waters, the generation of sheet wash and eventually gully erosion, which may destroy the whole soil profile and drastically modify the arrangement of soils in the geocomplex.

ROSEN (1985, 392) notes 'a notion of fitness defined for the system as a whole, with respect to which behaviour can be characterised as adaptive or not includes a corresponding notion of adaptation on the behaviour of its subsystems'. As a higher level holon evolves towards the condition which creates least stress within its own environment, so it imposes altered constraints upon its subsystems. As a lower level holon evolves, it requires different forces to integrate it within the body of a larger order whole.

Since the canon of each holon differs, so the forces of selection invoke different stresses and responses at each level. Just

as the holon's functional options differ, so must the holon's definition of fitness. The dynamics of selection at each level inevitably build up stresses within the holarchy. If the holarchy is to survive, and clearly most do because hierarchical structuring is ubiquitous (cf. SIMON 1962, PATTEE 1973), the hierarchy must have a way of accommodating to this disruption. It must be able to respond to destructive adaptations developing at different levels.

Two options are available. The hierarchy may break down to the level of the largest stable sub-whole, or it may restructure.

5 HIERARCHICAL RESTRUCTURING

Evolving holarchies adapt to change by restructuration rather than by disintegration. PLATT (1970) calls these restructurings 'hierarchical jumps' but the phenomenon is essentially the same as that described for the emergence of a dissipative structure (PRIGOGINE & STENGERS 1984) or for synergetic self-organisation (HAKEN 1977). First, there is a build up of stress, dissonance, or conflict at the affected level (cf. KUHN 1962, YABLONSKY 1984). In KOESTLER (1979) terms, there develop significant inefficiencies in the canon of the restructuring holon. Eventually, at an instant which is unpredictable 'like the quantum leap for the electron' (BOHM 1970), and which may occur at any point in the normal cycle of the system, the system transforms. The transformation is usually complete and it creates a radically different, usually more efficient, structure. Significantly, the change comes about in a time span which is usually far shorter than the system's normal relaxation time (PLATT 1970).

The reason is that this kind of reorganisation is a process of a lower level holon. As one proceeds upwards through a holarchy the holons become more general, more readily decomposible, and slower in operation. Soil aggregates break up and reform over a timescale which may be measured in weeks, but it takes decades for a soil horizon to form, centuries for a mature soil pedon to evolve, and rather longer for a full blown geocomplex. A hierarchical restructuring is a process that jumps across two levels in the hierarchy. It cannot take place at the level undergoing breakdown. In fact, 'in any intellectual system, or living organism, or a self-stabilising flow system, any buildup of already conflicting elements generally calls forth a response that simply makes the stress greater' (PLATT 1970, 52). The instability generally has its roots in the over-excited holons of the 'i-1' hierarchical level, and their reaction times are too fast for the 'i' level holon's self-regulating system. Instead, the 'i' level system tends to be forced into a pattern of self-destructive overcompensations often manifested as an increasing pattern of oscillation or irregularity in its behaviour. However, the 'i' level holon is not usually at the apex of the holarchy. It is also a part of a larger i+1 holon which constrains its operation and which requires its operations for its own larger integrative needs. Restructuring, therefore, occurs at the level of the 'i-1' holon, which is the level of the largest stable subwhole and the level where the holons are becoming most independent of the constraints imposed by the higher system levels. However, if the holarchy is to survive the crisis, then it is necessary that the new structure is also capable of functioning as a component in the 'i+1' holon. PLATT (1970, 52) gives this everyday illustration of the process in operation in a business hierarchy. The office 'boss' is ineffective (i level), in desperation his junior executives (i-1) begin to 'go over his/her head' to higher management (i+1) because they identify the boss's actions as their problem. Often, the last complaint of the boss before resignation is that central office (i+1) is not backing him/her up (i) and is undercutting his/her authority (i-1).

In ecology, there is the concept of the ecological niche: a resource area or functional space in the ecosystem which is occupied by a particular species holon. This niche is occupied in defiance of the competitive pressure from species in neighbouring resource areas. If the niche occupier is destroyed, perhaps by a lower level disturbance such as a virus, the niche may not remain vacant indefinitely, and the larger ecosystem will tend to survive the disturbance. Australian ecosystems, grassland and forest, are similar to those in the rest of the world. However, niches occupied by placental mammals elsewhere are occupied by more primitive marsupial forms. In many cases, the placental mammal and marsupial equivalent are surprisingly similar in form.

So what rules determine whether or not a hierarchical jump has positive or negative impact on the holarchy? The issue resolves as a matter of inter-holonic communication. The key is the degree to which a particular holon may be constrained within the holarchy. ALLEN & STARR (1982, 17–20) analyse this relationship in terms of scale.

A scale is a period of time or space over which signals are integrated to give a message. A signal is a string of energy, matter or information in transit between communicating entities. A signal has no space or time implications. However, a message is affected by the way in which the signal is transmitted, the loss of information in transit and the way in which it is accepted by the receiver. All three of these processes are affected by time, space, and the efficiency and sensitivity of both transmitter and receiver. The communication between holons, then, has scale (ALLEN & STARR 1982, 17–18).

ALLEN & STARR (1982, 20) consider the scale of a holon to be a fundamental property and that the scale of both the integrating and integrated holons within the holarchy is determined by their information handling attributes. 'The way a holon converts unscaled signal into scaled messages determines its functional environment' and position in the hierarchy. The relationship between the scale and the signal they express as an equation which in electronics describes a filter. In the holarchy, both the transmitting holon and receiving holon filter the signals they send and receive (cf. KOESTLER 1967). In physical geography these kinds of inter-holon communication are mixed into our notions of thresholds (BRUNET 1968, SCHUMM 1978). In many cases, a threshold trigger does not reflect the operation of processes included within a particular holon, but is rather a response to a signal moving vertically through the natural holarchy. So, the destruction of a plantation agro-ecosystem may be due to the evolution of a particular viral strain or to a global economic crisis. Equally, the initiation of erosion by rilling may be caused by the interaction between a particular turbulence and a particular group of soil particles or it may be the result of scour due to a chance obstruction. Collapse of

the plantation agro-ecosystem was not predictable in terms of the normal operations of that system and the onset of concentrated wash was not predictable in terms of thin flows of water across a particular soil.

6 PERTURBATIONS AND HOLON EVOLUTION

As ALLEN & STARR (1982, 104) note, significant fluctuations often occur at a single scale. A disturbance can only affect a holon if it is of an appropriate scale. A small and ephemeral fluctuation can pass unnoticed. However, if the disturbance is long and large, it becomes just part of the system's operational rules. Problems occur, however, if the holon and the disturbance operate at the same scale. The tendency then is for the disturbance and the holon to assume a common identity. The perturbation becomes incorporated as part of the system and from that point on it is the removal of the fluctuation which constitutes the system disturbance. Grassland geocomplexes, like the North American prairie, require regular perturbation by fire. When this disturbance is removed, the prairie system degrades. Vertisol development requires the regular perturbation of desiccation crack formation. Deprived of this pedoturbation the soil is quickly transformed.

It requires a special type of fluctuation to facilitate systems evolution. A disturbance can affect only those holons which are close to it in scale. However, its impact, if it does not destroy the holon, will be to cause that holon to transform to incorporate the disturbance. A regular disturbance becomes part of a system's operating instructions (ALLEN &

STARR 1982, 108). So, system perturbations which effect evolutionary change
must be rare and transient phenomena
occuring at a scale close enough to that
of the afflicted holon(s) to allow comu-
nication, but far enough away to resist
incorporation.

PRIGOGINE (PRIGOGINE &
STENGERS 1984) confirms that the
emergence of a new dissipative structure
requires a dynamic open system operating near the limits of its metastability
in an environment which supplies system
perturbations. In such a restructuring,
vulnerability to that perturbation can be
established from within. The evolution of
a meander loop predisposes it to restructuring by truncation during a flood. Its
truncation then can be named a reasser-
tion of the meander's partness within the
river system holarchy. In other cases, the
disturbances can grow until they saturate
the environment as might be the case
with an evolving gully network, a developing illuvial soil horizon, or a series of
expanding karst depressions (SCHEID-
EGGER 1983). The phenomenon of 'saturation' represents the completion of a
hierarchical restructuring.

7   CONCLUSION

Ludwig von BERTALANFFY (1967,
27–28) has written: 'A general theory
of hierarchic order, obviously, will be a
mainstay of general systems theory ... the
question of hierarchic order is intimately
connected with those of differentiation,
evolution and organisation ... In the last
[instance], hierarchic order and [system]
dynamics may be the same'. However,
hierarchy theory remains the Cinderella
of General Systems Theory and is only
lately receiving serious attention. Physical geographers have long been aware

that they are dealing with a landscape
which is a nested hierarchy of systems
and subsystems at all scales. Hierarchy theory lies near the heart of two
of geomorphology's most cited classics
(SCHUMM & LICHTY 1965, HOR-
TON 1945).

Despite this, physical geographers
have been slow to recognise hierarchy
theory as a legitimate area for research
and present approaches to natural hierarchical structures tend to ignore system
dynamics. However, as the phenomena
of self-organisation come to feature more
strongly in research agenda, so an appre-
ciation of hierarchical dynamics becomes
more essential.

The holon, an open system viewed as
a level within a hierarchical structure,
may be the key to understanding the
multi-layered dynamics of natural systems. Hierarchies are synergetic open
systems whose critical aspects are in the
balance between the self-assertive and
integrative tendencies of their member
holons. The differential impacts of evolutionary and adaptational changes on different holon levels create stresses within
the holarchy. Beyond a certain threshold,
stimulated by an environmental fluctuation of appropriate scale, these stresses
can result in either the disruption of the
holarchy or its transformation through
hierarchical restructuring.

Understanding and recognising hierarchical restructuring is a sophistication
of today's crude conceptualisation of system thresholds. It indicates a new agenda
for research in which considerations of
the communication between levels in natural systems and the controls of the phenomena of self-organisation become the
primary focus.

REFERENCES

ALLEN, T.F.H. & STARR, T.B. (1982): Hierarchy: perspectives for ecological complexity. University of Chicago Press, Chicago.

BAHM, A.J. (1984): Holon: three conceptions. Systems Research **1(2)**, 145–150.

BECK, L.W. (1952): Philosophic inquiry. Prentice Hall, New Jersey.

BEREZIN, P.N., VORONIN, A.D. & SHEIN, YE V. (1984): An energetic approach to the quantitative evaluation of soil structure. Soviet Soil Science **15(5)**, 103–109.

BLUMENFELD, L.A. (1981): Problems of Biological Physics. Springer-Verlag, Berlin.

BOHM, D. (1980): Wholeness and the implicate order. Routledge and Kegan Paul plc, London.

BOHM, D. (1970): cited in PLATT (1970).

BRUNET, R. (1968): Les phénomènes de discontinuité en géographie. Centre de Recherches et Documentation Cartographiques et Géographiques (CNRS Paris), Mémoires et Documents, N.S. **7**, 9–107.

CAMBERS, G. (1976): Temporal scales in coastal erosion. Institute of British Geographers, Transactions, N.S. **1(2)**, 246–256.

CULLINGS, W.E.H. (1985): Equifinality: chaos, dimension and pattern. London School of Economics, Graduate School of Geography, Geography Discussion Papers, **19**, 1–83.

FRENCH, N.R. (1986): Hierarchical conceptual model of the alpine geosystem. Arctic and Alpine Research, **18(2)**, 133–146.

GRAF, W.L. (1979): Catastrophe theory as a model for change in fluvial systems. In: Rhodes, D.D. & Williams, G.P. (eds), Adjustments of the fluvial system. Proceedings, Tenth Annual Geomorphology Symposium Series, Binghamton, New York, 13–32. Kendall-Hunt Publishing Co., Dubuque, Iowa.

HAKEN, H. (1985): Synergetics — an interdisciplinary approach to phenomena of self-organisation. Geoforum, **16(2)**, 205–212.

HAKEN, H. (1984): The science of structure: synergetics. Van Nostrand Reinhold, New York.

HAKEN, H. (1977): Synergetics: an introduction. (2nd edition), Springer-Verlag, Berlin.

HORTON, R.E. (1945): Erosional development of streams and their drainage basins: hydrophysical approach to quantitative morphology. Geological Society of America, Bulletin, **56**, 275–370.

ISACHENKO, A.G. (1973): Principles of landscape science and physical-geographic regionalisation. Melbourne University Press, Carlton.

JACKSON, R.G. (1975): Hierarchical attributes and a unifying model of bedforms composed of cohesionless material and produced by shearing flow. Geological Society of America, Bulletin, **86**, 1523–1553.

JANTSCH, E. (1980): The Self-Organizing Universe: Scientific and Human Implications of the Emerging Paradigm of Evolution. Pergamon Press, Oxford.

JARVIS, R.S. (1977): Drainage network analysis. Progress in Physical Geography, 1, 271–295.

KANEKO, K. (1986): Collapse of Tori and Genesis of Chaos in Dissipative Systems. World Scientific, Singapore.

KOESTLER, A. (1967): The ghost in the machine. Hutchinson and Co., London.

KOESTLER, A. (1978): Janus: a summing up. Hutchinson and Co., London.

KUHN, T.S. (1962): The structure of scientific revolutions. University of Chicago Press, Chicago.

LASZLO, E. (1972): The systems view of the world. G. Braziller Inc., New York.

LOVELOCK, J.E. (1979): Gaia: a new look at life on Earth. Oxford University Press, Oxford.

MAZUR, E. (1985): Special Issue. Geografický Časopis, 37 **(2–3)**, 121–376.

NAVEH, Z. & LIEBERMAN, A.S. (1984): Landscape ecology: theory and application. Springer-Verlag, New York.

NICOLIS, C. & NICOLIS, G. (1984): Is there a climatic attractor? Nature, **311**, 529–532.

NICOLIS, G. & PRIGOGINE, I. (1977): Self-organisation in non-equilibrium systems: from dissipative structures to order through fluctuations. Wiley Interscience, New York.

PATTEE, H.H. (1973): Unsolved problems and potential applications of hierarchy theory. In: Pattee, H.H. (ed.), Hierarchy theory: the challenge of complex systems. 130–156, G. Braziller Inc., New York.

PENNING-ROWSELL, E. & TOWNSEND, J.R.G. (1978): The influence of scale on the factors affecting stream channel slope. Institute of British Geographers, Transactions N.S. **3(4)**, 395–415.

PLATT, J. (1970): Hierarchical restructuring. General Systems, **15**, 49–54.

PRIGOGINE, I. & STENGERS, I. (1984): Order out of chaos: man's new dialogue with nature. Bantam, New York and W. Heinemann, London.

ROSEN, R. (1985): Anticipatory systems: philosophical, mathematical and methodological foundations. Pergamon Press, Oxford.

SCHEIDEGGER, A.E. (1983): Instability principle in geomorphology. Zeitschrift für Geomorphologie, N.F. **27(1)**, 1–19.

SCHUMM, S.A. (1979): Geomorphic thresholds: the concept and its application. Institute of British Geographers, Transactions N.S. **4(4)**, 485–515.

SCHUMM, S.A. (1977): The fluvial system. Wiley Interscience, New York.

SCHUMM, S.A. & LICHTY, R.W. (1965): Time, space and causality in geomorphology. American Journal of Science, **263**, 110–119.

SIMON, H.A. (1962): The architecture of complexity. American Philosophical Society, Proceedings **106(6)**, 467–482 (and) General Systems, **10** (1965), 63–76.

THORNES, J.B. (1983): Evolutionary geomorphology. Geography, **68(3)**, 225–235.

WOLDENBERG, M.J. (1969): Spatial order in fluvial systems: Horton's laws derived from mixed hexagonal hierarchies of drainage basin area. General Systems **14**, 23–35.

WOLDENBERG, M.J. (1979): A periodic table of spatial hierarchies. In: Gale, S. & Olsson, G. (eds.), Philosophy in geography. D. Reidel Publishing Co., Dordrecht, NL, 429–456.

YABLONSKY, A.I. (1984): Science as an open system. In: Gvishiani, J.M. (editor-in-chief), Systems research: methodological problems. USSR Academy of Sciences, Institute for System Studies. Pergamon Press, Oxford, 211–228.

Address of author:
Martin J. Haigh
Geography Unit
Oxford Polytechnic
Oxford OX3 0BP, UK

ON THE PROBLEM OF
GEOMORPHOLOGICAL PREDICTION

A.M. **Trofimov**, Kazan

SUMMARY

Geomorphological forecasts based on observation series do not always produce satisfactory results. A new approach to forecasting is introduced, based on the concept of process development, i.e. a functional gemorphological forecast which presents in essence a search and analysis of combinations of geographic situations and their evaluation and coding in special prognostic heuristic maps. The functional forecast is based on conceptual models. The construction and subsequent analysis of the model permits a search for spatial and temporal regularities as well as for "local inhomogenities" which are sites of new geographic spatial-temporal structures.

Investigations carried out over a series of years have shown that human components sometimes play a significant role in the formation and development of relief. Moreover, man's influence is sufficiently important to change the space and time frameworks within which geomorphological processes should be examined. In this connection it is quite natural that there has been a growing use of

ISSN 0722-0723
ISBN 3-923381-10-7
©1987 by CATENA VERLAG,
D–3302 Cremlingen-Destedt, W. Germany
3-923381-10-7/87/5011851/US$ 2.00 + 0.25

short- and long-term geomorphological forecasting, with the help of which it is possible to develop a common strategy to prevent undesirable outcomes.

Geomorphological prediction is now an established research tool: its general tactical and strategical foundations have been established; its aims and problems have been postulated and, finally, geomorphological prediction methods have been united into a single system (ZEIDIS et al. 1981, PROBLEMI ... 1982).

Prediction theory in geomorphology is based on the general geomorphological principle which expresses some consistency of exogenic processes which have developed, and are developing, relief forms and waste cover. The relationships between the relief form, the regolith cover and the waste transport yield the notion of compound integrated geomorphological systems. This type of problem can be approached by systems analysis, using a group of methods called mathematical-geographical modelling (MGM). To make use of MGM, the object of prediction is first defined by a set of informations which are chosen according to the aim. This procedure is part of an iterative sequence. Both the aim and the initial information set are respecified many times in the process of prediction. Secondly, the aim defines the duration over which a prediction is required, and in consequence its required precision. These parameters in turn define the likelihood that prediction will be successful.

This dialogue between aims and information finally requires particular prediction methods, which are classified in the work of I.M. ZEIDIS et al. (1981).

Relevant methods include all available formal approaches to prediction in geomorphology. They are generally based on observed data series over time and relevant spatial data sets. The latter rely on an ergodic property of geomorphological processes. The bases of these approaches have been quantitative, descriptive, logical and logical-mathematical models, more recently also of mathematical-geomorphological models.

Having studied the process and its system dependences on many factors one can obtain a model which allows one to follow the evolution of a landform and the associated process development for various combinations of natural factors. With the help of various analogues the same model can be used in a range of physical-geographical and geomorphological contents.

Of primary importance in these models is the time factor. The development process is artificially divided into a series of sequential stages. A change from one stage to the next involves a change of quality which can be interpreted as a change of state. Some changes occur in response to external effects. Generally this response is completed with some delay — the system's "relaxation time". This time needed by a system to approach a stable state is considered to be a characteristic time. In geomorphological prediction it is very important to define for how long a particular geomorphological system "remembers" its past

state, or how long it takes to "forget" it. There is a very wide range of characteristic relaxation times: they are significant targets for research.

In geomorphology at present one of the most valuable forecasting methods is that based on the qualitative theory of dynamic systems (AHNERT 1973, TROFIMOV & MOSKOVKIN 1980). Negative feedbacks in the system with a constant external environment give a tendency of convergence towards some dynamic steady state (dynamic homeostasis). It follows from this that one target for efficient control of geomorphological systems is to define these steady states and to encourage transference of the system to them as soon as possible (a problem in time minimization). This transfer time is equivalent to a relaxation time, and can be defined within dynamic system theory by introducing an a priori time lag into the initial set of equations.

For example TROFIMOV & MOSKOVKIN (1980) analyse the steady state for an abrasion slope using the following dynamic system

$$
\left\{
\begin{array}{l}
\frac{dm}{dt} = v_{und} + v_{acc} - v_{rem} \\
v_{und}\alpha = V(1 - [m/m_o]) \\
v_{rem} + v_{und}\alpha = V = const, \alpha = const >
\end{array}
\right.
$$

The first equation of the system is the equation for material balance (m) at the base of an abrasion slope, where $v_{und}, v_{rem}, v_{acc}$ are respectively rates of bedrock undercutting, removal and accumulation of waste at the slope base; m_o is the value of waste cover above which there is no further erosion of the bedrock (i.e. $v_{und} = 0$); and V is an effective intensity influence on bedrock and waste.

The solution of the given system with

initial condition is as follows:

$$m(o) = M$$

$$m(t) = \frac{(v_{acc} + \frac{V}{\alpha})(1 - exp(-\frac{V}{m_o}(\frac{1+\alpha}{\alpha})t)}{\frac{V}{m_o}(\frac{1+\alpha}{\alpha})}$$
$$+ \frac{\frac{V}{m_o}(\frac{1+\alpha}{\alpha})M\,exp(\frac{V}{m_o}(\frac{1+\alpha}{\alpha})t)}{\frac{V}{m_o}(\frac{1+\alpha}{\alpha})}$$

From the latter one can see that a limiting quantity of waste is developed

$$\lim_{t \to \infty} m(t) = \frac{m_o(v_{acc}\alpha + V)}{V(1 + \alpha)}$$

Further, by modifying the relation $\lim m(t) = ; < ; > m_o$ one can obtain various variants of a cliff development and of accumulation (or removal) of waste over bedrock. According to the limit expression the relaxation time equals infinity. However, due to the rapid exponential tendency towards a steady state one can take a finite relaxation time $\alpha m_o/[V(1 + \alpha)]$ at which $m(t)$ becomes sufficiently close to m_o. By changing model parameters we can change this relaxation time.

The example given illustrates a significant step forward towards functional geomorphological prediction, based on the rates of processes, and away from the widespread use of time series analysis of system behaviour, for geomorphological forecasting. Rhythms of natural processes cause variations in the rates of system development. Consequently, system interactions give rise to a complicated network of changes in dominant processes and states, which have been formulated by MAKKAVEEV (1976) in the law of factor relativity. He states that combinations of natural conditions and of processes depending on them, together with internal and external properties, respond to some definite effects ambiguously. They give rise to definite combinations of interactions which characterize the course of development of particular processes. For instance, in order to predict karst collapse in a particular area one must take into consideration, first that the process can take place only where there are karst rocks, second that conditions are not identical everywhere even within the karst rock area, because specific conditions are required for a collapse: one then may delimit zones of territory in which collapse is probable. As a result, prediction maps may be constructed on an essentially functional basis. The principal strategy of geomorphological predictions is thus a search for significant functional combinations, with evaluation and coding in the form of special purpose maps.

Thus, we come to a conclusion that prediction in geomorphology should be based on an understanding of function, based on a knowledge of process types; rates in time and space should be built into a predictive model. To determine parameter values, initial and boundary conditions, control of statistical hypotheses etc., one needs statistical time or space series. That is why conceptual notions formalized into a standard conceptual model should be the base of geormorphological prediction (TIMOFEEV & TROFIMOV, 1983).

Conceptual models are accumulations of knowledge and notions on structures, functions and interactions of geosituations among themselves and with the environment. They are described by a great number of models: some of them descriptive, others in mathematical notation (TROFIMOV & PANASYUK 1984). As has been said above, formalization could reach any level: from "real" geography models, for instance, cartographical ones, to entirely mathematical-geographical ones.

Conceptual models are the basis for functional prediction. To construct them one should solve a number of problems. For instance, in what environment do the processes under consideration take place? Are these environments stable at particular points in space and time? How do they change and develop in time? Do they have orientation in development and are characterized by the elements of retrospection? Do they possess a "structural memory" (ZEIDIS & SIMONOV 1980) and how much time is needed "to forget" past states? Can they be characterized by a "characteristic time" and how long does their "relaxation time" last? How do fluctuations of geosituations correlate with resulting changes in basic processes? Can fluctuations in basic processes change geosituations and vice versa? The list of problems can be extended still further.

The analysis of these problems has shown that a geographical prediction deals with a search for steady conformities of a space and time character. SAUSHKIN (1976) called this a "search for rudiments of the future in the present". It involves a search for places of "local heterogeneities" which may be invisible in initial stages but have a sufficiently constant concentration of substance and energy occurring in a particular geographical environment.

There are two aspects of this search for local heterogeneities: the aspect of space and the aspect of time. The first may be called a statistical one. It suggests that when processes are defined at every point then there appear definite conformities. For instance, on a map of the environment made with the help of isolines one can define a "response surface". It is the result of the actions of a great number of factors, the combination of which is different and changes from one point of space to the other. It is difficult to define a "norm" for factor interactions. One therefore uses a statistic smoothing procedure to draw attention to the "background" (or trend) surface by removal of high frequency fluctuations. A regression trend surface depicts a basic factor in one way. A procedure of space smoothing may also be carried out by different means. The most widely used methods are the methods of a "slip window", FIORTOFT's method and the method of space smoothing (PANOFSKY & BRIER 1958). The last function is proportional to the departures of the bidimensional normal distribution and is used for the smoothing of data defined in regular grid cells. The difference between initial and smoothed "relief" (surface) is a residual surface (or residual map). This surface is the result of process development at particular sites. Usually the residual surface shows influence zones, "nuclei" of concentration, typology zones, etc. It helps to predict the operation of processes in space. Thus, the spatial aspect of a search for areas of local heterogenity leads to making special-purpose maps for both background levels and residuals.

The time aspect of a search for local heterogenities deals with a contextual analysis of geosituations on the base of time series. An ergodic property of geomorphological systems favours a connection between time and space notions. Research methods of this aspect have been widely published (ZEIDIS et al. 1981, PROBLEMI ... 1982, and others).

ACKNOWLEDGEMENT

The author is very grateful to Professor F. Ahnert for his valuable comments, which improved the work a great deal.

(Please note: these comments were based on the critical assessment of the paper by two referees. F.A.)

REFERENCES

AHNERT, F. (1973): COSLOP-2: A comprehensive model program for simulating slope profile development. Geocom Programs, **8**, 99–122.

MAKKAVEEV, N.I. (1976): Obschi zakonomernosti erosionno-ruslovih protzezov. - Ruslovic protzezi. T. 10, Leningrad: Gidrometeoizdat (in Russian).

PANOFSKY, H.A. & BRIER, G.W. (1958): Some applications of statistics to meteorology. Univ. Park. Pennsylvania.

PROBLEMI REGIONALNOGO GEO-MORPHOLOGITCHESKOGO PROGNOSA (1982): Moskva: Nauka (in Russian).

SAUSHKIN, J.G. (1976): Istoria i metodologia geographitcheskich nauk. Moskva: MGU (in Russian).

TROFIMOV, A.M. & MOSKOVKIN, V.M. (1980): theoretical preconditions of the control over the exogenic processes. In: 24th IGC. Main session. Vol. **1**, 30–31, Tokyo.

TROFIMOV, A.M. (1983): Geosituatzionnaya conceptsia v geographi. Isvestia VGO, t. 115, N 6, 509–514 (in Russian).

TROFIMOV, A.M. & PANASYUK, M.V. (1984): Geosituation conception and environment control problems. In: 25th IGC. Abstracts of papers. Caen, Paris, T. **1**, 17–29.

ZEIDIS, I.M., SIMONOV, J.G. (1980): Effect structurnoi pamiati v dinamice geographicheskin javleni. Vestnik MGU. Ser. geogr., N 4 (in Russian).

ZEIDIS, I.M., SIMONOV, J.G. & TROFIMOV, A.M. (1981): Teoria i method prognozirovania eksogennih processov. In: Klimat, relief i dejatelnost cheloveka. Moskva: 260–266 (in Russian).

Address of author:
Prof. Dr. A.M. Trofimov
Head of the Economical-Geography Department
of Kazan State University
Leninstr. 18
Kazan, USSR

| CATENA SUPPLEMENT 10 | p.199–210 | Braunschweig 1987 |

THE FUNDAMENTAL PRINCIPLES
OF LANDSCAPE EVOLUTION

A.E. **Scheidegger**, Vienna

SUMMARY

The analysis of landscapes as dynamic "systems" was probably started by DAVIS who proposed a theory of cyclic evolution. Starting with a tectonic uplift (an endogenic process), a landscape would proceed from a stage of youth to one of maturity and of old age by constant degradation (exogenic process). Unfortunately, the theory of DAVIS contains a misinterpretation inasmuch as the landscape evolution has never been observed in the supposed fashion on a single object. It rather appears that landscapes are the instantaneous result of concurrently active uplift (endogenic process) and degradation (exogenic process), which view has been taken as the result of a fundamental **"principle of antagonism"** of landscape evolution. It turns out that the endogenically caused features are statistically systematic, the exogenically caused features statistically random. This fact can be demonstrated on typical examples.

A further **principle** active in landscape evolution is that **of instability**: deviations from uniformity generally tend to increase. This fact is expressed e.g. in the growth of meander loops, erosion

ISSN 0722-0723
ISBN 3-923381-10-7
©1987 by CATENA VERLAG,
D–3302 Cremlingen-Destedt, W. Germany
3-923381-10-7/87/5011851/US$ 2.00 + 0.25

cirques, karst holes, etc.: Many examples can be given.

A consequence of the instability principle is the formation of characteristic chains of features: Thus, a slope always has a flat eluvial section at the top, a steep colluvial section in the middle and a flat alluvial section at the toe. This fact has been termed the **"catena (chain) principle"**, which states that the entire landscape is composed of chains as referred to above.

In addition to the above principles, one notes a certain directivity in the evolution of landscapes: Erosion and degradation occur in sich a fashion that statically stable forms are prefeentially selected. This has been termed the **"selection principle"** which explains the formation of such features as triangular peaks or circular towers.

Finally, there is the **principle of tectonic predesign** which states that although exogenic phenomena occur in a random fashion, systematic features may be created which are the result of tectonic predesign. Such instances can be traced, for instance, in the development of drainage patterns.

The interplay of the above principles can be shown to be fundamental in the evolution of landscapes as **systems**.

1   INTRODUCTION

Landscapes present pictures of a bewildering complexity. They contain various types of features and elements such as mountains, river valleys, coastal inlets, glaciers and many others. The literature describing individual types of features and establishing their taxonomy is extremely large. Much has been learned about the mechanics of the genesis of such features and of their decay. However, in addition to a study of individual features, the study of their interplay is of interest. A "landscape" consists of a great number of single features. In this instance, it may be considered as a "system" containing many "elements". What is to be studied, then, is the evolution of the "system" as a whole, and not necessarily the exact evolution of each individual component-feature thereof.

Thus, the aim of the present paper is to bring some order into the great variety of landscapes and to explain their genesis. In order to achieve this aim, it is first of all necessary to establish a taxonomic classification of the different landscapes and then to search for the fundamental principles which govern their evolution.

2   PHENOMENOLOGY OF LANDSCAPE TYPES

The great variety of landscape types has let it appear as desirable to attempt a descriptive natural history of their genesis. Thus, it has been postulated long ago that each landscape represents a certain stage of an evolutionary development. It was noted that erosion and degradation by water, ice and wind ("exogenic" agents, i.e. agents originating outside the solid Earth) represent powerful forces that affect a landscape. Since there has to be something **present** before it can be **degraded**, it was an obvious suggestion to postulate that the evolution of landscapes is cyclical: first there would be a build-up by tectonic forces ("endogenic" agents, i.e. agents originating inside the solid Earth); then the relief would pass (by erosion and degradation) from a "youth"-stage through a "maturity" to an "old age"-stage, the end of the cycle (DAVIS 1924).

Typical characteristics were postulated for these stages: in youth, steep and narrow valleys, pointed peaks; in maturity, rounded peaks and broad valleys; in old age, peneplanation to a base level of erosion. Thus, each particular landscape would be classified according to the stage of its development: youth, maturity or old age (SCHEIDEGGER 1987).

However, it is to be severely doubted that the cycle theory of DAVIS has any base in reality: The supposed landscape evolution has never been seen on a single object; rather it has been **assumed** that e.g. the Vosges or the Appalachians represent the later, "mature" stage of an erstwhile "young" mountain range of the aspect of the Alps. More recent investigations (cf. SCHEIDEGGER 1979) indicate, in fact, that landscape evolution is not cyclical at all, but that a landscape represents simply the instantaneous state in the interaction between the endogenic and exogenic processes, which act antagonistically. Nevertheless, the "youthful", "mature" and "old" landscapes represent taxonomic types which can still be used for classification purposes. Thus far, the terms "youth", "maturity" and "old age" as applied to a landscape are entirely qualitative. Evidently, an exact quantitative definition is required. In order to obtain this, it is evidently necessary to have a single parameter that character-

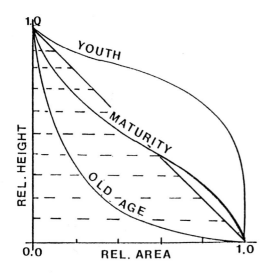

REL. HEIGHT

REL. AREA

YOUTH

MATURITY

OLD-AGE

Fig. 1: *Typical hypsometric curves (after STRAHLER 1957): The isosceles triangle is stipled.*

izes the "stage" of a landscape. Such a parameter can be based on the idea of a "hypsometric curve". The hypsometric curve of a region is obtained by calculating the percentage area above a certain height level. In geomorphology it is customary to divide the heights and areas by the total height difference (measured from the lowest to the highest point in the area) and the total area, so that one is dealing with "relative" quantities. Then, the "age stage" of a landscape may be identified from the observation of STRAHLER (1957) that the **hypsometric** curve of a "youthful" landscape is convex, that of a "mature" landscape is more or less straight, and that of an "old" landscape is concave (fig.1). This observation can be expressed by the introduction of a **stage-index**, which is obtained by dividing the area under the hypsometric curve by the area of the isosceles rectangular triangle with vertex at the origin of the graph. The age index thus defined can vary from 0 to 2. If it is a > 1, one has a youthful landscape, if it is a < 1, an old-age one. Mature landscapes have an index a ~ 1, where

a range of maybe ±0.1 may be taken. One thus defines the following stages of a landscape:

$$2 \geq a \geq 0.6 \quad \text{youth}$$
$$0.6 > a \geq 0.4 \quad \text{maturity}$$
$$0.4 > a \geq 0 \quad \text{old age.}$$

Sometimes it is convenient to have a "stage index" which varies between 0 and ∞ instead of between 0 and 2. The easiest way to obtain such a quantity is to introduce a "modified" stage index, denoted by a', connected with a by the relation

$$a' = tan(\frac{\pi}{4}a) = tan(a \cdot 45°)$$

Either index, a or a', can be used to characterize a landscape stage.

3 THE PRINCIPLE OF ANTAGONISM

We have noted above that a landscape, — any landscape —, represents the instantaneous equilibrium in the interaction of two antagonistic processes: The endogenetic and the exogenetic processes.

Photo 1: *Random (top)* **versus** *nonrandom (bottom) gullying (top: mine tailing, Danville, Illinois; bottom: Piz Ot, Samnaun, GR, Switzerland).*

The two types of processes have a fundamentally different stochastic nature: Exogenic processes are essentially random, endogenic ones essentially non-random (SCHEIDEGGER 1979; photo 1). The recognition of this fact is based on induction from a vast amount of observational data. Thus, it has been possible in general to explain "exogenic" features by stochastic models, an approach which had probably first been attempted by LEOPOLD & LANGBEIN (1962). It was later extended to many exogenic surface features (cf. SCHEIDEGGER 1970). From all these facts, the conclusion is indicated by induction that there is a general randomness principle at work in exogenic processes and correspondingly a non-randomness principle in endogenic processes. Indeed, the characterization of landscape processes by their stochastic nature (random or non-random) has been used successfully for the identification of the origin of geomorphic feature. It has been shown for instance that the orientation structure of the river trends in the Helvetian Alps is of neotectonic origin, and not the print of a previous random drainage pattern on a plane (SCHEIDEGGER 1979).

The reason for the different statistical nature of the two types of processes must be sought in their mechanical origin: exogenic processes are mainly connected with the turbulence in the air and in the water; turbulence is best described by a stochastic theory. On the other hand, endogenic processes act mainly through the plate tectonic stresses; these are homogeneous and therefore systematic over regions comparable with the dimensions of the lithospheric plates.

After the existence of a principle of antagonistic action of two types of processes has been recognized in the evolution of the Earth's surface features, the necessity arises of characterizing the **strength** of this antagonism. Thus, **intensity parameters** have to be defined. The most natural way of introducing such parameters is evidently by taking the velocities of uplift and of denudation: In a stationary state, these two velocities must be identical. It is therefore possible to determine these parameters either by geodetic measurements (repeated precise levellings) or by measurements of total sediment transport in a river and dividing the volume transported per unit time by the area drained by the river. The dimensions of the intensity parameters of the antagonism are evidently those of a velocity. Their value is in orogenetically very "active" regions of the order of 1 or more millimeters per year; less in other areas.

The "age stage" of a landscape is determined by the intensity of the antagonism: "youth" if the velocities are 1 mm/yr, "old age" if they are 0.1 mm/yr, "maturity" if they are in between.

If the uplift velocity v_u is not equal to the denudation velocity v_d, one has non-stationary conditions. One can thus determine a stationarity index S by taking the ratio

$$S = v_u/v_d$$

This index is equal to **1** under stationary conditions. If it is less than **1**, the landscape decays, if it is larger than **1**, the lansdcape is being built up. There are phenomenological indications for stationarity: In stationary landscapes, the relief follows the STRAHLER curves. In cases of nonstationarity, if the uplift is greater than the denudation, the stage is shifted to "greater" age. Thus, ADAMS (1980) has shown that the New Zealand Alpine peaks are flattopped when the uplift exceeds the denudation, but spiky (the normal youth-form) when uplift is equal to denudation.

As a final remark it should be added that "buildup" may not always be **entirely** of endogenic origin. Evidently, in the lower parts of a relief, exogenically induced **deposition** may also cause an increase in local altitudes, albeit not of relief, inasmuch as differences in height tend to become smoothened out.

4 THE PRINCIPLE OF INSTABILITY

The principle of antagonism has to be modified to include the proposition that the "dynamic equilibrium" in a landscape is generally **unstable** (SCHEIDEGGER 1983). By this proposition we mean two things: First of all, we note that individual landscape features tend to be non-permanent, although their overall appearance may seem to be constant: Thus, individual landscape features change. Second, the direction of the change is such that the features move away from the aspect of uniformity: the dynamic equilibrium is **unstable**. Any deviation from uniformity tends to grow.

Phenomenologically, the operation of the instability principle is seen in many features: Valleys are stepped, river courses are composed of a sequence of riffles and pools (photo 2), erosion cirques tend to grow, karst holes increase. The writer has given a documentation of many such cases in the paper cited above (SCHEIDEGGER 1983).

The reason for the existence of the instability principle has to be sought in the operation of some feed-back mechanism. In all the instances mentioned earlier, the non-uniformity becomes ac-centuated because the rate of growth of a deviation from uniformity increases with the amount of deviation that has already been reached.

This thought can be expressed mathematically: The initiation of the instability can be described as an exponential growth process (positive linear feedback). For any parameter $x(t)$ describing a particular landscape feature, the growth-equation at the initial instances is therefore of the form

$$x(t) = const.exp(\lambda t)$$

where λ (dimension: 1/time) is a measure of the intensity of the instability.

Naturally, such a description is only valid for the very beginning of the phenomenon ("Taylor analysis"). Eventually, a saturation stage is reached beyond which the instabilities can no longer grow. Thus, in the **very** long run, one is again justified to treat geomorphic systems as statistically stationary. For each type of feature under consideration, one can establish a characteristic time T, at which the "microscopic" instability can be replaced by "macroscopic" uniformity considerations.

The above model is evidently correct for many geomorphic features: Erosion rates increase with size of a hole or steepness of a slope, accumulation rates (on mounds, riffles, pools) increase with the **size** of the mound already created etc.: Any deviation from uniformity must therefore become larger at an increasing rate, until some "saturation stage" is reached. In this, the model is entirely independent of the mechanics of the formation of the instability, and it is seen that the "instability principle" is a **general** characteristic of such features.

Photo 2: *Operation of instability principle: Sequence of riffles and pools in the Rosenbach, Vienna, Austria.*

5   THE CATENA PRINCIPLE

A principle related to the instability principle is the "catena principle" (SCHEIDEGGER 1986).

The concept of a catena was originally invented in connection with soil physics: It was noted that certain definite sequences (Latin: catenae) of soil types recur again and again on slopes. These types are connected with their topographic location on the slope (MILNE 1935, 1947). In geomorphology, it is the latter fact which is of interest: the sequences do not only rfer to soil types, but to morphological elements. Thus one has the principle that on slopes and in catchment areas, certain definite sequences (catenas) of morphological elements occur repeatedly.

Fundamentally, on a slope a catena

Photo 3: *Catena prin-
ciple: Eluvial catchment
area (top). and collu-
vial gorge section with
alluvial opening (bot-
tom) of Bighorn River,
Wyoming*

Photo 4: *Selection principle: Towers and bastions (left: Three Sisters near Katoomba, N.S.W.) are selected as statically corresponding to the Eiffel Tower in Paris (right).*

consists of an **eluvial** region at the top (of flat topography with a lip), a **colluvial** region in the middle (of steep topography with large mass flow rates) and an **alluvial** region at the bottom (again of flat topography: deposition represents the main phenomenon). Then, the "catena principle" states that the whole landscape is composed of catenas each of which consists of a flat (top) - steep (middle) - flat (bottom) sequence.

Examples in nature of such catenas can be found in the structuring of Alpine creeks (flat catchment area — gorge section — alluvial cone, photo 3), valley steps (sequences of flat-steep-flat reaches) and even scree slopes. Many examples have been discussed in the cited article of this writer (SCHEIDEGGER 1986).

The mechanical explanation for a fundamental catena scheme lies in similar considerations as that for the instability principle: If one assumes that the erosion rate increases with the topographic gradient, the catena principle follows from this: The steeper the slope, the faster it recedes; the flat regions above and below remain longer.

6   THE SELECTION PRINCIPLE

In addition to the purely stochastic nature of the exogenic processes it may be noted that a certain "directedness" occurs in their action. This is accounted for by the selection principle.

This selection principle was first enounced by GERBER (1969). It states that the degradational and erosional processes occur in such a fashion that statically stable forms (with reference to the prevailing stresses) are preferentially "selected". These prevailing stresses are

primarily self-gravitational streses, i.e. stresses that are induced by the weight of the forms themselves, — with the tectonic stresses playing only a minor role. Thus the natural forms and configurations in a landscape are primarily those that are most stable under their own weight.

Phenomenological confirmations of the operation of the selection principle are seen in the existence of various types of "pillars", "bastions" or "towers" in many mountainous regions (GERBER & SCHEIDEGGER 1969, 1973, 1975).

From the mechanical standpoint, the selection principle can be explained by an analysis of the statics of the forms in question. The form of a "tower" corresponds to the design of, for instance, the Eiffel tower (photo 4). The latter was constructed as a statically most stable form: The mean vertical pressure (weight of the mass of the superjacent structure divided by the cross sectional area) is constant in every cross section if the vertical profile is given by an exponential curve. Similar considerations can also be deduced by finite element calculations; the selection principle is then confirmed in every case (SCHEIDEGGER & KOHLBECK 1985).

7   PRINCIPLE OF STRUCTURAL CONTROL

Finally there is the **principle of structural control** which states that many landscape features are designed by deep-seated tectonic ("structural") processes.

The operation of this principle is rather obvious in connection with the genesis of mountain chains and volcanoes, — i.e. with the genesis of features that are manifestly of endogenetic origin.

However, even in case of exogenically affected features, there may be some tectonic or structural control: Erosion and other exogenic processes tend to act in a fashion which is concordant with lithospheric plate theory. The orientation of the erosional features tends to align itself with the preferential (in a statistical sense) shear directions of the neotectonic stress field.

Thus, it can be shown that the orientation patterns inherent in fluvial and glacial valleys are affected to a large extent by neotectonic processes. Naturally, these features are not caused **directly** by the stress field, but the erosion **occurs preferentially** along the shear directions of the stress field. Similar statements can be made with regard to the orientation of mass movements on slopes. Although landslides are evidently **triggered** by meteorological (or seismic) events, their orientation pattern has been found to be **pre-designed** by tectonic processes (SCHEIDEGGER & AI 1986).

The mechanical explanation of the preferential erosion along shear trajectories must be sought along similar lines as the explanation of the selection principle. The shear directions of the neotectonic stress field are obviously those directions in which the material is nearest to the fracture limit. The exogenic processes act as an additional stress generator and hence failure occurs in the preexisting shear direction. Thus, the preference of the exogenic agents to be effective in this direction is understandable.

8 CONCLUSION

The argument given in this paper has shown that landscapes as systems are subject to a relatively small number of fundamental principles which govern their evolution.

The first fundamental principle is that of the **antagonistic** action of endogenic and exogenic processes. Furthermore, the exogenetic processes are inherently **unstable**, so that non-uniformities develop in the form of riffles and pools in rivers, erosion cirques, karst holes, etc. A special type of unstable features are the **catenas** found in drainage areas. The erosion of prominent relief forms occurs according to a **selection** principle, so that statically stable structures result. Finally, the overall predesign even of erosion features is of **tectonic or structural origin**.

The above principles allow one to interpret landscapes as systems. The various landforms encountered in nature are instantaneous development stages in the interplay of the fundamental endogenic and exogenic geomorphic processes, which occur according to the well-defined basic principles described in this paper.

REFERENCES

ADAMS, J. (1980): Contemporary uplift and erosion of the Southern Alps. Bull. Geol. Soc. Am. Pt. II, **91(1):** 1–114.

DAVIS, W.N. (1924): Die erklärende Beschreibung der Landformen. 2nd ed. Leipzig, Teubner, 565 pp.

GERBER, E. (1969): Bildung von Gratgipfeln und Felswänden in den Alpen. Z. Geomorph. Suppl. **8**, 94–118.

GERBER, E. & SCHEIDEGGER, A.E. (1969): Stress-induced weathring of rock masses. Ecl. Geol. Helv. **62(2)**, 401–415.

GERBER, E. & SCHEIDEGGER, A.E. (1973): Erosional and sress-induced features on steep slopes. Z. Geomorph. Suppl. **18**, 38–49.

GERBER, E. & SCHEIDEGGER, A.E. (1975): Geomorphological evidence for the geophysical stress field in mountain massifs. Riv. Ital. Geofis. e Sci. Aff. **2(1)**, 47–52.

LEOPOLD, L.B. & LANGBEIN, W.B. (1962): The concept of entropy in landscape evolution. U.S. Geol. Surv. Prof. Pap. **500A**, 1–20.

MILNE, G. (1935): Some suggested units of classification and mapping, particularly for East African soils. Soil Research **4**, 183–189.

MILNE, G. (1947): A soil reconnaissance journey through parts of Tanganyika Territory. J. Ecology **27**, 192–265.

SCHEIDEGGER, A.E. (1970): Theoretical Geomorphology. 2nd ed. Berlin, Springer, 435 pp.

SCHEIDEGGER, A.E. (1979): The principle of antagonism in the Earth's evolution. Tectonophys. **55**, 7–10.

SCHEIDEGGER, A.E. (1983): Instability principle in geomorphic equilibrium. Z. Geomorphol. **27(1)**, 1–19.

SCHEIDEGGER, A.E. (1986): The catena principle in geomorphology. Z. Geomorphol. **30(3)**, 257–273.

SCHEIDEGGER, A.E. (1987): Systematic Geomorphology. Vienna, Springer, 285 p.

SCHEIDEGGER, A.E. & AI, N.S. (1986): Deep processes and geomorphological design. Tectonophys. **126**, 285–300.

SCHEIDEGGER, A.E. & KOHLBECK, F. (1985): The selection principle in surface erosion. Proc. Internat. Symp. Erosion, Debris Flow and Disaster Prevention Tsukuba, Japan, 285–290.

STRAHLER, A.N. (1957): Quantitative analysis of watershed geomorphology. Trans. Am. Geophys. Un. **38**, 913–920.

Address of author:
Adrian E. Scheidegger
Geophysics Section, Technical University
Gusshaus St. 27–29
A-1040 Vienna, Austria

F. Ahnert, H. Rohdenburg & A. Semmel:

BEITRÄGE ZUR GEOMORPHOLOGIE DER TROPEN (OSTAFRIKA, BRASILIEN, ZENTRAL- UND WESTAFRIKA) CONTRIBUTIONS TO TROPICAL GEOMORPHOLOGY

CATENA SUPPLEMENT 2, 1982
Price: DM 120,–/US $ 69,–
ISSN 0722–0723 / ISBN 3–923381–01–8

JAN DE PLOEY (ED.)

RAINFALL SIMULATION RUNOFF AND SOIL EROSION

CATENA SUPPLEMENT 4

Jan de Ploey (Ed.)

RAINFALL SIMULATION, RUNOFF and SOIL EROSION

CATENA SUPPLEMENT 4, 1983

Price: DM 120,–/US $ 75,–

ISSN 0722–0723 ISBN 3–923381–03–4

This CATENA–Supplement may be an illustration of present-day efforts made by geomorphologists to promote soil erosion studies by refined methods and new conceptual approaches. On one side it is clear that we still need much more information about erosion systems which are characteristic for specific geographical areas and ecological units. With respect to this objective the reader will find in this volume an important contribution to the knowledge of active soil erosion, especially in typical sites in the Mediterranean belt, where soil degradation is very acute. On the other hand a set of papers is presented which enlighten the important role of laboratory research in the fundamental parametric investigation of processes, i.e. erosion by rain. This is in line with the progressing integration of field and laboratory studies, which is stimulated by more frequent feed-back operations. Finally we want to draw attention to the work of a restricted number of authors who are engaged in the difficult elaboration of pure theoretical models which may pollinate empirical research, by providing new concepts to be tested. Therefore, the fairly extensive publication of two papers by CULLING on soil creep mechanisms, whereby the basic force-resistance problem of erosion is discussed at the level of the individual particles.

All the other contributions are focused mainly on the processes of erosion by rain. The use of rainfall simulators is very common nowadays. But investigators are not always able to produce full fall velocity of waterdrops. EPEMA & RIEZEBOS give complementary information on the erosivity of simulators with restricted fall heights. MOEYERSONS discusses splash erosion under oblique rain, produced with his newly-built S.T.O.R.M–1 simulator This important contribution may stimulate further investigations on the nearly unknown effects of oblique rain. BRYAN & DE PLOEY examined the comparability of erodibility measurements in two laboratories with different experimental set-ups They obtained a similar gross ranking of Canadian and Belgian topsoils

Both saturation overland flow and subsurface flow are important runoff sources under the rainforests of northeastern Queensland. Interesting, there, is the correlation between soil colour and hydraulic conductivity observed by BONELL, GILMOUR & CASSELLS. Runoff generation was also a main topic of IMESON's research in northern Morocco, stressing the mechanisms of surface crusting on clayish topsoils.

For southeastern Spain THORNES & GILMAN discuss the applicability of erosion models based on fairly simple equations of the "Musgrave-type" After Richter (Germany) and Vogt (France) it is TROPEANO who completes the image of erosion hazards in European vineyards. He shows that denudation is at the minimum in old vineyards, cultivated with manual tools only. Also in Italy VAN ASCH collected important data about splash erosion and rainwash on Calabrian soils. He points out a fundamental distinction between transport limited and detachment-limited erosion rates on cultivated fields and fallow land. For a representative first order catchment in Central–Java VAN DER LINDEN comments contrasting denudation rates derived from erosion plot data and river load measurements. Here too, on some slopes, detachment-limited erosion seems to occur

The effects of oblique rain, time-dependent phenomena such as crusting and runoff generation, detachment-limited and transport-limited erosion including colluvial deposition, are all aspects of single rainstorms and short rainy periods for which particular, predictive models have to be built. Moreover, it is argued that flume experiments may be an economic way to establish gross erodibility classifications. The present volume may give an impetus to further investigations and to the evaluation of the proposed conclusions and suggestions

Jan de Ploey

R. B. Bryan (Editor)

RILL EROSION

Processes and Significance

CATENA SUPPLEMENT 8
192 pages / hardcover / price DM 149,— / US $ 88.—
Special rate for subscriptions until
December 15, 1987: DM 119,— / US $ 70.40

Date of publication: July 15, 1987   ORDER NO. 499/00107
ISSN 0722-0723/ISBN 3-923381-07-7

CONTENTS

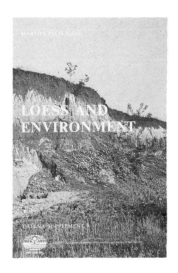

M. Pécsi(Editor)

LOESS AND ENVIRONMENT

SPECIAL ISSUE ON THE OCCASION OF THE XII th International Congress of the INTERNATIONAL UNION OF QUATERNARY RESEARCH (INQUA) Ottawa 1987

CATENA SUPPLEMENT 9
160 pages / hardcover / price DM 128,— / US $ 75.—
Special rate for subscriptions until
December 15, 1987: DM 102,40 / US $ 60.—

Date of publication: July 15, 1987   ORDER NO. 499/00108

ISSN 0722-0723/ISBN 3-923381-08-5

CONTENTS

N E W

CATENA paperback

Joerg Richter

THE SOIL AS A REACTOR

Modelling Processes in the Soil

If we are to solve the pressing economic and ecological problems in agriculture, horticulture and forestry, and also with "waste" land and industrial emmissions, we must understand the processes that are going on in the soil. Ideally, we should be able to treat these processes quantitatively, using the same methods the civil engineer needs to get the optimum yield out of his plant. However, it seems very questionable, whether we would use our soils properly by trying to obtain the highest profit through maximum yield. It is vital to remember that soils are vulnerable or even destructible although or even because our western industrialized agriculture produces much more food on a smaller area than some ten years ago.

This book is primarily oriented on methodology. Starting with the phenomena of the different components of the soils, it describes their physical parameter functions and the mathematical models for transport and transformation processes in the soil. To treat the processes operationally, simple simulation models for practical applications are included in each chapter.

After dealing in the principal sections of each chapter with heat conduction and the soil regimes of material components like gases, water and ions, simple models of the behaviour of nutrients, herbicides and heavy metals in the soil are presented. These show how modelling may help to solve problems of environmental protection. In the concluding chapter, the problem of modelling salt transport in heterogeneous soils is discussed.

The book is intended for all scientists and students who are interested in applied soil science, especially in using soils effectively and carefully for growing plants: applied pedologists, land reclamation and improvement specialists, ecologists and environmentalists, agriculturalists, horticulturists, foresters, biologists (especially microbiologists), landscape planers and all kinds of geoscientists.

Prof.Dr. Joerg Richter
Institute of Soil Science
University of Hannover, FRG

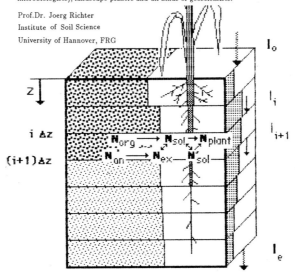

ISBN 3–923381–09–3   Price: DM 38,50 / US $ 24.—

SOIL
TECHNOLOGY

A Cooperating Journal of CATENA

SOIL TECHNOLOGY

This quarterly journal is concerned with applied research and field applications on

- soil physics,
- soil mechanics,
- soil erosion and conservation,
- soil pollution,
- soil restoration.

The majority of the articles will be published in English but original contributions in French, German or Spanish, with extended summaries in English will occasionally be considered according to the basic principles of the publisher CATENA whose name not only represents the link between different disciplines of soil science but also symbolizes the connection between scientists and technologists of different nations, different thoughts and different languages.

The coordinator of SOIL TECHNOLOGY:

Donald Gabriels,
Faculty of Agricultural Sciences, State University of Gent,
Coupure links 653,
B-9000 Gent, Belgium (tel 32-91-236961).

Editorial Office
SOIL TECHNOLOGY

Dr. D. Gabriels
Department of Soil Physics
Faculty of Agriculture
State University Gent
Coupure Links 653
B-9000 Gent
Belgium
tel. 32-91-236961

Papers published in
Vol. 1, No. 1, March 1988

S. A. El Swaify, A. Lo, R. Jay, L. Shinshiro, R. S. Yost: Achieving conservation-effectiveness in the tropics using legume intercrops.

I. Pla Sentis: Riego y desarollo de suelos afectados por sales en condiciones tropicales. / Irrigation and development of salt affected soils under tropical conditions.

K. H. Hartge: Erfassung des Verdichtungszustandes eines Bodens und seiner Veränderung mit der Zeit. / Techniques to evaluate the compaction of a soil and to follow its changes with time.

M. Kutilek, M. Krejča, R. Haverkamp, L. P. Rendon, J. Y. Parlange: On extrapolation of algebraic infiltration equations.

M. Šir, M. Kutilek, V. Kuráž, M. Krejča, F. Kubík: Field estimation of the soil hydraulic characteristics.

J. Albaladejo Montoro, R. Ortiz Silla, M. Martinez-Mena Garcia: Evaluation and mapping of erosion risks; an example from S. E. Spain.

SHORT COMMUNICATIONS

D. Gabriels: Use of organic waste materials for soil structurization and crop production; initial field experiment.

K. Reichardt: Aspects of soil physics in Brazil.

P. Bielek et al.: Internal nitrogen cycle processes and plant responses to the band application of nitrogen fertilizers.

V. Chour: An actual demand for improved soil technology in irrigation and drainage design in Czechoslovakia.

BOOK REVIEWS

ORDER FORM:

Please, send your orders to your usual supplier or to: USA/CANADA: CATENA VERLAG
P.O.BOX 368
Lawrence, KS 66044
USA
phone (913) 843-1234

Other countries: CATENA VERLAG
Brockenblick 8
D-3302 Cremlingen
West Germany
phone 05306/1530
fax 05306/1560

SOIL TECHNOLOGY 1988: Volume 1 (4 issues)

☐ please, enter a subscription 1988
  at US $ 120.— / DM 198,—
  incl. postage and handling
☐ please, send a free sample copy of **SOIL TECHNOLOGY**
☐ please, send guide for authors
☐ please, enter a personal subscription 1988 at 50 % reduction
  (available from the publisher only)
☐ I enclose | check | bank draft | unesco coupons |
☐ charge my credit card (only for orders USA/CANADA)
  ☐ Master Card   ☐ **Visa**

Card No. _____

Expir. Date _____

Signature _____

☐ please, send invoice

Name _____

Address _____

Date/Signature _____